STUDY GUIDE & STUDENT SOLUTIONS MANUAL

BASIC BUSINESS STATISTICS

STUDY GUIDE & STUDENT SOLUTIONS MANUAL

Pin T. Ng *Northern Arizona State University*

BASIC BUSINESS STATISTICS

Ninth Edition

Mark L. Berenson
David M. Levine
Timothy C. Krehbiel

PEARSON
Prentice
Hall

Upper Saddle River, New Jersey 07458

Editor-in-Chief: PJ Boardman
Acquisitions Editor: Tom Tucker
Project Manager: Erika Rusnak
Manager, Print Production: Christy Mahon
Production Editor & Buyer: Carol O'Rourke
Printer/Binder: Courier, Bookmart Press

10 9 8 7 6 5 4 3 2 1
ISBN 0-13-141981-1

Contents

Preface

The ***Study Guide and Student's Solutions Manual*** consists of three major sections. The ***Objective*** section summarizes what is expected of a student after reading a chapter. The ***Overview and Key Concepts*** section provides an overview of the major topics covered in a chapter and lists the important key concepts. The overview and listing of the key concepts are meant not to replace but to supplement the textbook and to reinforce understanding. The ***Solutions to End of Section and Chapter Review Even Problems*** section provides extra detail in the problem solutions.

CHAPTER 1

OBJECTIVES
- To understand how statistics can be used in business
- To be able to identify sources of data
- To be able to distinguish between different sampling methods
- To understand the different measurement scales
- To be familiar with the fundamentals of Windows and Microsoft Excel, Minitab, or SPSS

OVERVIEW AND KEY CONCEPTS
Why a Manager Needs to Know about Statistics
- To know how to properly present information
- To know how to draw conclusions about populations based on sample information
- To know how to improve processes
- To know how to obtain reliable forecasts

The Growth and Development of Modern Statistics

Needs of government to collect data on its citizens

⇩

The development of the mathematics of probability theory

⇩

The advent of the computer

Key Definitions
- **Population (universe):** The whole collection of things under consideration, e.g., all the students enrolled at a university.
- **Sample:** A portion of the population selected for analysis, e.g., all the freshmen at a university.
- **Parameter:** A summary measure computed to describe a characteristic of the population, e.g., the population average weight of all the students enrolled at a university.
- **Statistic:** A summary measure computed to describe a characteristic of the sample, e.g., the average weight of sample of freshmen at a university.

Relationship between Population and Sample

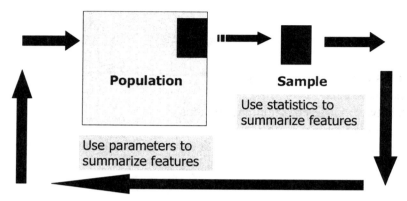

Inference on the population from the sample

The Difference between Descriptive Statistics and Inferential Statistics

- **Descriptive statistics:** Deal with collecting, presenting, summarizing, and analyzing data.
- **Inferential statistics:** Deal with drawing conclusions and/or making decisions concerning a population based only on sample data.

Why We Need Data

- To provide input to survey
- To provide input to study
- To measure performance of ongoing service or production process
- To evaluate conformance to standards
- To assist in formulating alternative courses of action
- To satisfy curiosity

The Different Types of Data Sources

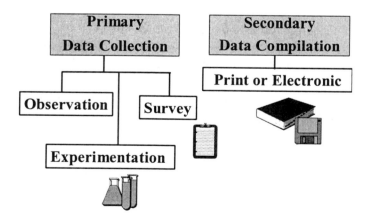

The Different Types of Data

- **Qualitative variable**: A nonnumeric variable, e.g., male or female.
- **Quantitative variable:** A numeric variable, e.g., weight, exam score.
- **Discrete variable:** A variable with only certain values, there are usually gaps between values, e.g., the number of cars a company owns.
- **Continuous variable:** A variable that can have any value within a specified range, e.g., atmospheric temperature.

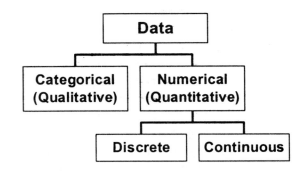

Reasons for Drawing Sample

- Less time consuming than a census
- Less costly to administer than a census
- Less cumbersome and more practical to administer than a census of the targeted population

The Different Methods of Sample Selection

- **A nonprobability sample:** Items or individuals are chosen without regard to their probability of occurrence.
- **A probability sample:** The subjects of the sample are chosen on the basis of known probability.
- **A simple random sample:** Every individual or item from the frame has an equal chance of being selected. Selection may be with replacement or without replacement.
- **A systematic sample:** Decide on a sample size, n; divide frame of N individuals into groups of k individuals, k = N/n; randomly select one individual from the first group; select every k^{th} individual thereafter.
- **A stratified sample:** The population is divided into two or more groups according to some common characteristic, e.g., whether an employee is full-time or part-time; simple random sample is selected from each group; the two or more samples are combined into one.
- **A cluster sample:** The population is divided into several "clusters", e.g., counties or election districts, in which each is representative of the population; a simple random sample is selected from each cluster; the samples are combined into one.

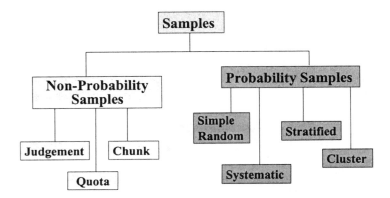

Evaluating Survey Worthiness

- What is the purpose of the survey?
- Is the survey based on a probability sample?
- **Coverage error:** Certain groups of subjects are excluded from the frame and have no chance of being selected in the sample.
- **Nonresponse error:** Failure to collect data on all subjects in the sample.
- **Measurement error:** Inaccuracies in the recorded responses that occur because of a weakness in question wording, an interviewer's effect on the respondent, or the effort made by the respondent.
- **Sampling error:** The chance differences from sample to sample based on the probability of particular individuals or items being selected in the particular samples. Sampling error always exists in a survey.

SOLUTIONS TO END OF SECTION
AND CHAPTER REVIEW EVEN PROBLEMS

1.2   (1)   Place an X in the circle corresponding to your personal income last year.
                ○ Under $20,000   ○ $20,000 – $39,999   ○ $40,000 or more

      (2)   To the nearest thousand dollars, what was your household
            income last year?   _____

      (3)   What Adjusted Gross Income did you report on your
            federal income tax last year?   _____

1.4   (a)   A person who receives a score of 8 or above on a 10-point ordinal scaling.
      (b)   A class that receives an average evaluation score of below 2.0 on a 5-point ordinal
            scaling.
      (c)   A book that receives an average evaluation score of above 8 on a 10-point ordinal
            scaling.
      (d)   A performance that has received a score of above 9 on a 10-point ordinal scaling.
      (e)   A person who is responsible for the performance of a certain number of
            subordinates.
      (f)   A plane that arrives within 2 minutes of the schedule arrival time.
      (g)   The average amount of time measured to the closest minute spent on class related
            activities outside the lectures.

1.6   (a) 001   (b) 040   (c) 902

1.8   (a)   Row 29: 12 47 83 76 22 ~~99~~ 65 93 10 ~~65~~ ~~83~~ 61 36 ~~98~~ 89 58 86 92 71
            Note: All sequences above 93 and all repeating sequences are discarded.
      (b)   Row 29: 12 47 83 76 22 ~~99~~ 65 93 10 65 83 61 36 ~~98~~ 89 58 86
            Note: All sequences above 93 are discarded. Elements 65 and 83 are repeated.

1.10   This is a random sample because the selection is based on chance. It is not a simple random
      sample because *A* is more likely to be selected than *B* or *C*.

1.12   (a)   Since a complete roster of full-time students exists, a simple random sample of 200
            students could be taken. If student satisfaction with the quality of campus life
            randomly fluctuates across the student body, a systematic 1-in-20 sample could also
            be taken from the population frame. If student satisfaction with the quality of life
            may differ by gender and by experience/class level, a stratified sample using eight
            strata, female freshmen through female seniors and male freshmen through male
            seniors, could be selected. If student satisfaction with the quality of life is thought to
            fluctuate as much within clusters as between them, a cluster sample could be taken.
      (b)   A simple random sample is one of the simplest to select. The population frame is the
            registrar's file of 4,000 student names.
      (c)   A systematic sample is easier to select by hand from the registrar's records than a
            simple random sample, since an initial person at random is selected and then every
            20th person thereafter would be sampled. The systematic sample would have the
            additional benefit that the alphabetic distribution of sampled students' names would
            be more comparable to the alphabetic distribution of student names in the campus
            population.

1.12   (d)   If rosters by gender and class designations are readily available, a stratified sample
cont.   should be taken. Since student satisfaction with the quality of life may indeed differ
               by gender and class level, the use of a stratified sampling design will not only ensure
               all strata are represented in the sample, it will generate a more representative sample
               and produce estimates of the population parameter that have greater precision.
        (e)   If all 4,000 full-time students reside in one of 20 on-campus residence halls which
               fully integrate students by gender and by class, a cluster sample should be taken. A
               cluster could be defined as an entire residence hall, and the students of a single
               randomly selected residence hall could be sampled. Since the dormitories are fully
               integrated by floor, a cluster could alternatively be defined as one floor of one of the
               20 dormitories. Four floors could be randomly sampled to produce the required 200
               student sample. Selection of an entire dormitory may make distribution and
               collection of the survey easier to accomplish. In contrast, if there is some variable
               other than gender or class that differs across dormitories, sampling by floor may
               produce a more representative sample.

1.14   (a)   A stratified sample should be taken.
        (b)   Since the stratum may differ in the invoice amount, it may be more important to sample
               a larger percentage of invoices in stratum 1 and stratum 2, and smaller percentages in
               stratum 3 and stratum 4.
        (c)   It is not simple random sampling since not all individual items in the population have an
               equal chance of being selected.

1.16   Three sizes of soft drink are classified into distinct categories—small, medium, and large—
        in which order is implied.

For Problems 1.18 – 1.22, money may be considered discrete by some, since it can be counted to the
nearest penny.

1.18   (a)   numerical, discrete, ratio scale   (g)   categorical, nominal scale
        (b)   categorical, nominal scale   (h)   numerical, discrete, ratio scale
        (c)   numerical, discrete, ratio scale   (i)   numerical, continuous, ratio scale
        (d)   numerical, continuous, ratio scale   (j)   categorical, nominal scale
        (e)   categorical, nominal scale   (k)   categorical, nominal scale
        (f)   numerical, continuous, ratio scale

1.20   (a)   categorical, nominal scale   (e)   numerical, discrete, ratio scale
        (b)   numerical, continuous, ratio scale   (f)   numerical, discrete, ratio scale
        (c)   numerical, continuous, ratio scale   (g)   numerical, continuous, ratio scale
        (d)   categorical, nominal scale   (h)   categorical, nominal scale

1.22   (a)   categorical, nominal scale   (i)   numerical, continuous, ratio scale *
        (b)   categorical, nominal scale   (j)   numerical, continuous, ratio scale *
        (c)   numerical, continuous, interval scale   (k)   categorical, nominal
        (d)   numerical, continuous, ratio scale *   (l)   numerical, discrete, ratio scale
        (e)   categorical, nominal scale   (m)   numerical, continuous, ratio scale *
        (f)   categorical, nominal scale   (n)   numerical, continuous, ratio scale
        (g)   numerical, discrete, ratio scale **   (o)   categorical, nominal scale
        (h)   numerical, discrete, ratio scale   (p)   numerical, continuous, ratio scale*

1.22 *Some researchers consider money as a discrete numerical variable because it can be "counted."
cont. **Some researchers would "measure" the time since starting the job and consider this a continuous numerical variable.

1.24 While it is theoretically true that ties cannot occur with continuous data, the grossness of the measuring instruments used often leads to the reporting of ties in practical applications. Hence two students may both score 90 on an exam—not because they possess identical ability but rather because the grossness of the scoring method used failed to detect a difference between them.

1.26 Before accepting the results of the survey on the effect of gender on online purchases, you might want to know, for example:

Who funded the survey? Why was it conducted?
What was the population from which the sample was selected?
What sampling design was used?
What mode of response was used: a personal interview, a telephone interview, or a mail survey? Were interviewers trained? Were survey questions field-tested?
What type of online purchases were being considered?
What questions were asked? Were they clear, accurate, unbiased, valid?
What results indicate that males were more likely to make purchases online than females?
What was the response rate?
What was the sample size?

1.28 (a)   Possible coverage error: Only employees in a specific division of the company were sampled.
(b)   Possible nonresponse error: No attempt is made to contact nonrespondents to urge them to complete the evaluation of job satisfaction.
(c)   Possible sampling error: The sample statistics obtained from the sample will never be equal to the parameters of interest in the population.
(d)   Possible measurement error: Ambiguous wording in questions asked on the questionnaire.

1.30 Before accepting the results of the consumer expenditure survey, you might want to know, for example:

Who funded the study? Why was it conducted?
What was the population from which the sample was selected?
What was the sample size?
What sampling design was used?
What mode of response was used: a personal interview, a telephone interview, or a mail survey? Were interviewers trained? Were survey questions field-tested?
What operational definition of "spending on eating away from home" was used?
What questions were asked? Were they clear, accurate, unbiased, valid?
What was the response rate?

1.32   Before accepting the results of the survey conducted by Opinion Research Corporation, you might want to know, for example:

         Why was the study conducted?

         What was the population from which the sample was selected?

         What was the sample size?

         What sampling design was used?

         What mode of response was used: a personal interview, a telephone interview, or a mail survey? Were interviewers trained? Were survey questions field-tested?

         What other questions were asked? Were they clear, accurate, unbiased, valid?

         What was the response rate?

     Cingular Wireless can use the information gained from analyzing this survey to educate their consumers on phone etiquette in public places to promote goodwill to the company.

1.34   A population contains all the items whereas a sample contains only a portion of the items in the population.

1.36   Descriptive methods deal with the collection, presentation, summarization, and analysis of data whereas inferential methods deal with decisions arising from the projection of sample information to the characteristics of a population.

1.38   Discrete random variables produce numerical responses that arise from a counting process. Continuous random variables produce numerical responses that arise from a measuring process.

1.40   An interval scale is an ordered scale in which the difference between measurements is a meaningful quantity that does not involve a true zero point. A ratio scale is an ordered scale in which the difference between the measurements is a meaningful quantity that does involve a true zero point.

1.42   Data are needed to provide the input to a study or survey, to measure performance of a process, to evaluate conformance to standards, to assist in deciding among alternative courses of action, and to satisfy our curiosity.

1.44   Fishbowl methods of sampling do not allow for a thorough mixing of items.

1.46   In a simple random sample, each individual item is selected randomly. In a systematic sample, the N individuals or items in the population frame are partitioned into k groups by dividing the size of the population frame N by the desired sample size n. The first individual or item to be selected is chosen at random from the k individuals or items in the first partitioned group in the population frame, and the rest of the sample is obtained by selecting every kth individual or item thereafter from the entire population frame listing.

1.48   In a stratified sample, the N individuals or items in the population are first subdivided into separate subpopulations, or strata, according to some common characteristic. In a cluster sample, the N individuals or items in the population are divided into several *clusters* so that each cluster is representative of the entire population. A random sampling of clusters is then taken and all individuals or items in each selected cluster are then studied.

1.56   Even though Internet polling is less expensive, faster and offers higher response rates than telephone surveys, it is a self-selection response method. Because respondents who choose to participate in the survey do not usually represent the view of the public, the data collected is not appropriate for making inference about the general population.

1.58   (a)   Population for the Goldman Sachs survey is all the U.S. households.
        (b)   Population for Cyber Dialogue survey is all the people who have tried and quit online banking.
        (c)   Cyber Dialogue could have constructed a frame for their survey from the combined list of customers, who tried online banking, of the banks that offered them.
        (d)   They could have drawn a simple random sample or systematic sample from the frame if the characteristics of the customers were randomly distributed across the various banks that offered online banking. If customer characteristics were randomly distributed within and across banks, a cluster sample would be easier to collect. But if different bank attracted different types of customers, a stratified sample would be a better representation of the population.
        (e)   The response will be categorical.
        (f)   This is a statistic.

1.60   (a)   Given the low response rate, the researchers should be especially concerned with nonresponse bias. The low response rate will also increase the sampling error.
        (b)   Researchers can follow up on the nonresponses by mail or telephone to encourage or remind those who have not returned the survey to complete the survey.
        (c)   The researchers can enlist the Chief of Police and the President of the Fraternal Order of Police to mobilize the supervisors of various units to convey to their subordinates the importance of completing the survey. Reminder memos can also be sent from the supervisors. Verbal reminders from the supervisors during weekly meeting will also serve the same purpose.

1.62   (a)   Before accepting the results of this survey, one would like to know (i) what is the purpose of the survey, (ii) what sampling method is being used, (iii) what is the response rate, (iv) what is the frame used in the survey, and (v) how are the questions being phrased.
        (b)   The population will be all the working women which includes those who take advantage of family-friendly schedules and those who do not in the geographic region. The frame can be compiled from the list of the women who file income tax returns in the region. Since there are two natural strata, those who take advantage of family-friendly schedules and those who do not, in the population, a stratified sampling method should be used to better represent the population.

1.64   (a)   Before accepting the results of this survey, one would like to know (i) what is the purpose of the survey, (ii) what sampling method is being used, (iii) what is the response rate, (iv) what is the frame used in the survey, and (v) how are the questions being phrased.
        (b)   An example of categorical variable: "Do you blame the economy?"
        (c)   An example of numerical variable: starting salaries. Level of measurement: ratio.
        (d)   This is a statistic because it summarizes the feature in the sample.

(e)   A stratified sampling method should be used. The employers should be divided into strata according to the different industries. Students should be divided into strata according to their genders and graduating status.

1.66   (a)   The population to which we want to generalize is citizens who are registered to vote and who will actually vote in the election of interest.

(b)   We could take a random sample of voters as they exit the polls.

(c)   Some of the problems might be that it may not be possible to sample all counties so there may be coverage error, there could be nonresponse bias if people who voted a particular way tend to not respond, it does not help predict the outcome of an election prior to the election.

1.68   (a)   Population: Cat owners   (b) Sample frame: Households in the United States

(d)   (1)   categorical   (3) numerical
       (2)   categorical   (4) categorical

CHAPTER 2

OBJECTIVES

- To know how to organize numerical data
- To be able to develop tables and charts for numerical data
- To be able to develop tables and charts for categorical data
- To understand the principles of proper graphical presentation

OVERVIEW AND KEY CONCEPTS
Organizing Numerical Data

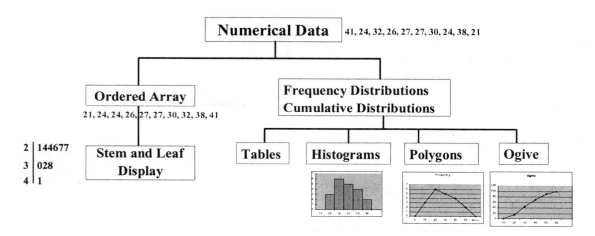

- **Ordered array:** Ordered sequence of raw data.
  - Ordered array makes it easier to pick out extremes, typical values, and concentrations of values.
- **Stem-and-leaf display:** Data are separated into leading digits (stems) and trailing digits (leaves).
  - Allows easy understanding of how the values distribute and cluster over the range of the observations in the data set.
- **Frequency distribution:** A summary table in which the data are arranged into numerically ordered class groupings or categories.
  - Makes the process of data analysis and interpretation much more manageable and meaningful
  - **Selecting the number of classes**: At least 5 but no more than 15 groupings
  - **Obtaining the class intervals:** $\text{width of interval} = \dfrac{\text{range}}{\text{number of desired class groupings}}$.
  - **Establishing the boundaries of the classes**: Non-overlapping classes must include the entire range of observations
  - **Class midpoint:** The point halfway between the boundaries of each class and is representative of the data within that class

- **Relative frequency distribution**: Formed by dividing the frequencies in each class of the frequency distribution by the total number of observations
    - Essential whenever one set of data is being compared with other sets of data if the number of observations in each set differs
- **Percentage distribution:** Formed by multiplying the relative frequencies by 100%
- **Cumulative distribution:** Formed from the frequency distribution, relative frequency distribution or percentage distribution by accumulating the frequencies, relative frequencies or percentages
    - It shows the number of observations below given values (lower boundaries)
- **Histogram:** Vertical bar chart in which the rectangular bars are constructed at the boundaries of each class
- **Percentage polygon:** Formed by having the midpoint of each class represent the data in that class and then connecting the sequence of midpoints at their respective class percentages
    - Useful when comparing two or more sets of data
- **Cumulative polygon (Ogive):** Formed by plotting cumulative percentages against the lower boundaries of the classes and connecting the cumulative percentages
    - It is useful when comparing two or more sets of data

Graphing Bivariate Numerical Data

- **Scatter diagram (scatter plot):** Two-dimensional graph depicting how two numerical variables relate to each other
- **Time-series plot:** Two-dimensional graph that illustrates how a series of numerical data changes over time

Table and Charts for Categorical Data

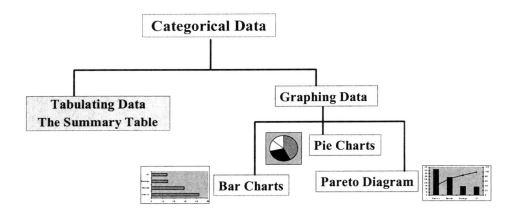

- **Summary table:** Similar to frequency distribution table for numerical data except there is no natural order of the classes
- **Bar chart:** Each category is depicted by a bar, the length of which represents the frequency or percentage of observations falling into a category
- **Pie chart:** The circle of 360^0 is divided into slices according to the percentage in each category
- **Pareto diagram**: A special type of vertical bar chart in which the categorized responses are plotted in the descending rank order of their frequencies and combined with a cumulative polygon on the same scale
    - Useful when the number of classification increases. Enables the separation of the "vital few" from the "trivial many"

Tabulating and Graphing Bivariate Categorical Data
- Contingency table (cross-classification table): Two-way table of cross-classification
- Side-by-side bar chart: Bar charts arranged side-by-side according to the different categories or the two categorical variables; useful when looking for patterns or relationship

Principles of Graphical Excellence
- Well-designed presentation of data that provides substance, statistics and design
- Communicates complex ideas with clarity, precision and efficiency
- Gives the viewer the largest number of ideas in the shortest time with the least ink
- Almost always involves several dimensions
- Requires telling the truth about the data

Common Errors in Presenting Data
- Using "chart junk"
- No relative basis in comparing data between groups
- Compressing the vertical axis
- No zero point on the vertical axis

SOLUTIONS TO END OF SECTION
AND CHAPTER REVIEW EVEN PROBLEMS

2.2   Stem-and-leaf of Finance Scores

5	34
6	9
7	4
8	0
9	38

$n = 7$

2.4   Ordered array: 50 74 74 76 81 89 92

2.6   (a)   Ordered array: 3, 12, 13, 13, 14, 15, 16, 16, 16, 17, 17, 17, 18, 18, 18, 18, 18, 19, 19, 20, 22, 24, 24, 26, 28, 29, 30, 30, 40, 52

       (b)   **PHStat output:**

       Stem-and-Leaf Display
       for PE Ratio
       Stem unit: 10

```
0|3
1|2 3 3 4 5 6 6 6 7 7 7 8 8 8 8 8 9 9
2|0 2 4 4 6 8 9
3|0 0
4|0
5|2
```

       (c)   The stem-and-leaf display provides more information because it not only orders observations from the smallest to the largest into stems and leaves, it also conveys information on how the values distribute and cluster over the range of the observations in the data set.

       (d)   No, there do not seem to be more undervalued stocks than overvalued stocks because there is 1 stock with a P/E ratio below 10 and 2 stocks with P/E ratios above 30.

2.8   (a)   0 0 5 5 5 5 5 5 6 6 6 7 7 7 8 8 9 9 9 10 10 10 10 10 12 12

    (b)   **Excel output:**

```
 0|0 0
 1|
 2|
 3|
 4|
 5|0 0 0 0 0 0
 6|0 0 0
 7|0 0 0
 8|0 0
 9|0 0 0
10|0 0 0 0 0
11|
12|0 0
```

    (c)   The stem-and-leaf display provides more information because it not only orders observations from the smallest to the largest into stems and leaves, it also conveys information on how the values distribute and cluster over the range of the observations in the data set.

    (d)   The monthly service fees seem to be concentrated around 7 dollars since 22 banks have service fees between 5 and 10 dollars.

2.10   (a)   The class boundaries of the 9 classes can be "10 to less than 20", "20 to less than 30", "30 to less than 40", "40 to less than 50", "50 to less than 60", "60 to less than 70", "70 to less than 80", "80 to less than 90", and "90 to less than 100".

    (b)   The class-interval width is $= \dfrac{97.8 - 11.6}{9} = 9.58 \cong 10$.

    (c)   The nine class midpoints are: 15, 25, 35, 45, 55, 65, 75, 85, and 95.

2.12   (a)   (1)   Width of interval $\cong \dfrac{213 - 82}{5} = 26.2 \cong 30$

Electricity Costs	Frequency
$80 up to $110	7
$110 up to $140	13
$140 up to $170	18
$170 up to $200	9
$200 up to $230	3

        (2)   Width of interval $\cong \dfrac{213 - 82}{6} = 21.8\overline{3} \cong 25$

Electricity Costs	Frequency
$75 up to $100	4
$100 up to $125	7
$125 up to $150	17
$150 up to $175	13
$175 up to $200	6
$200 up to $225	3

2.12   (a)   (3)   Width of interval $\cong \dfrac{213-82}{7} = 18.71 \cong 20$

cont.

Electricity Costs	Frequency
$80 up to $100	4
$100 up to $120	7
$120 up to $140	9
$140 up to $160	13
$160 up to $180	9
$180 up to $200	5
$200 up to $220	3

(b)

Electricity Costs	Frequency
$80 up to $100	4
$100 up to $120	7
$120 up to $140	9
$140 up to $160	13
$160 up to $180	9
$180 up to $200	5
$200 up to $220	3

(c)

Electricity Costs	Frequency	Percentage
$80 up to $100	4	8%
$100 up to $120	7	14
$120 up to $140	9	18
$140 up to $160	13	26
$160 up to $180	9	18
$180 up to $200	5	10
$200 up to $220	3	6

(d)   Percentage   The Percentage Histogram
       of Costs

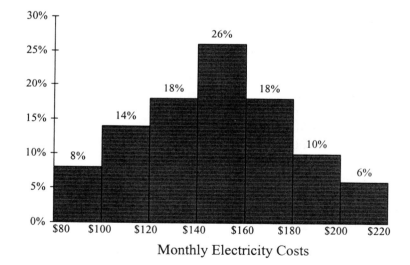

Monthly Electricity Costs

2.12   (e)
cont.

Percentage
of Costs

The Percentage Polygon

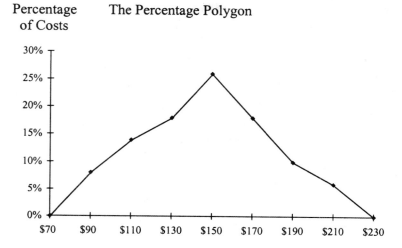

Monthly Electricity Costs

Electricity Costs	(f) Cumulative Frequency Less Than	(g) Cumulative Percentage Less Than
$100	4	8%
$120	11	22
$140	20	40
$160	33	66
$180	42	84
$200	47	94
$220	50	100

(h)

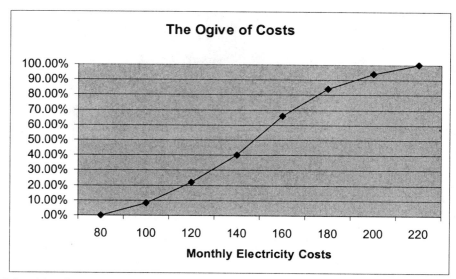

(i)   Monthly electricity costs are most concentrated between $140 and $160 a month, with better than one-fourth of the costs falling in that interval.

2.12   (j)   The percentage histogram displayed in part (d) above clearly shows the upper and
cont.   lower bounds of the seven intervals as well as the percentage of the 50 electricity
               bills sampled that fall in each interval. In comparison, the percentage polygon
               displayed in part (e) above more clearly shows the typical value for each interval (the
               midpoint), but, because the individual points are not labeled on this graph, only
               approximates the percentage of the 50 electricity bills sampled that fall in each
               interval. Both graphs visually depict the distribution of monthly electricity bills
               clearly. The ogive displayed in part (h) above enables us to focus on the cumulative
               distribution, but, because it accrues the numbers of bills up to and including each
               interval, is not as clear in depicting the distribution of individual monthly electricity
               bills.

2.14   (a)

Gasoline Purchases (gals)	Frequency	Percentage
9.0 – 9.9	3	12%
10.0 – 10.9	5	20
11.0 – 11.9	9	36
12.0 – 12.9	6	24
13.0 – 13.9	2	8

        (b)

Gasoline Purchases (gals)	Frequency Less Than	Percentage Less Than
9.0 – 9.9	3	12
10.0 – 10.9	8	32
11.0 – 11.9	17	68
12.0 – 12.9	23	92
13.0 – 13.9	25	100

        (c)

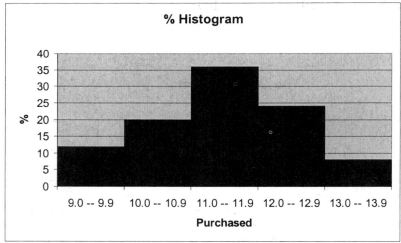

2.14   (d)
cont.

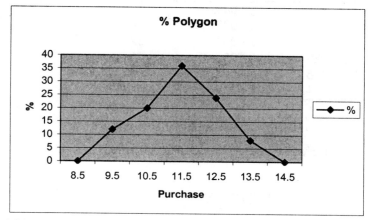

(e)

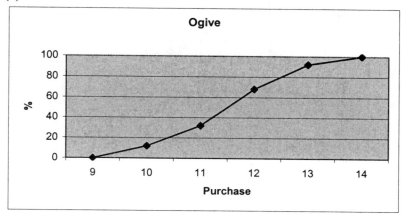

(f)   Most gasoline purchases seem to be concentrated between 11 and 11.9 gallons.

2.16 (a)

Error	Frequency	Cumulative %	Percentage
-0.00350 -- -0.00201	13	13.00%	13
-0.00200 -- -0.00051	26	39.00%	26
-0.00050 -- 0.00099	32	71.00%	32
0.00100 -- 0.00249	20	91.00%	20
0.00250 -- 0.00399	8	99.00%	8
0.00400 -- 0.00549	1	100.00%	1

(b)

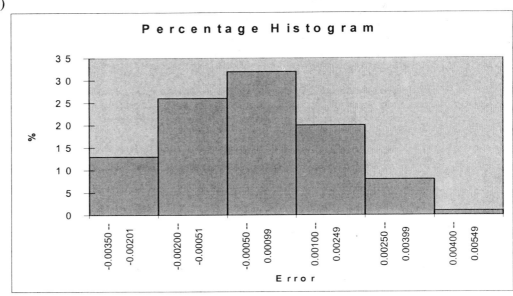

(c)

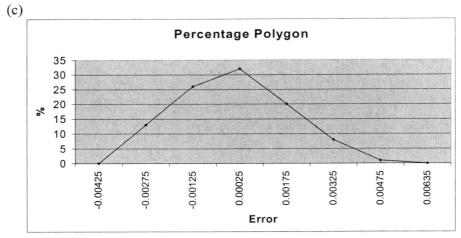

2.16   (d)
cont.

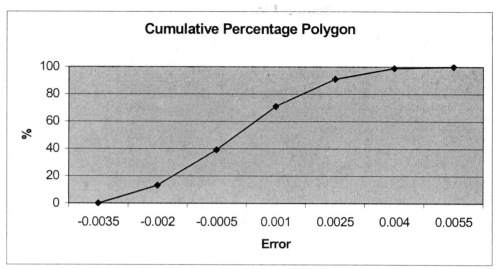

(e)   Yes, the steel mill is doing a good job at meeting the requirement as there is only one steel part out of a sample of 100 that is as much as 0.005 inches longer than the specified requirement.

2.18   (a)

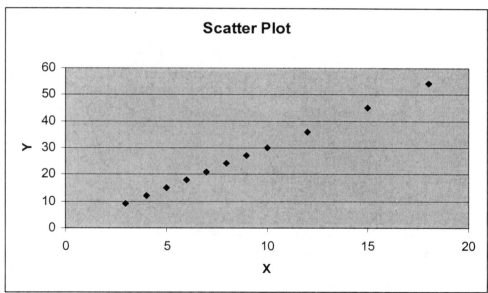

(b)   Yes, there appears to be a positive relationship between X and Y.

2.20   (a)

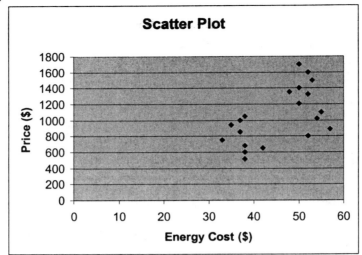

(b)   There appears to be a positive relationship between price and energy cost.

(c)   The data does not seem to indicate that high-priced refrigerators have greater energy efficiency.

2.22   (a)

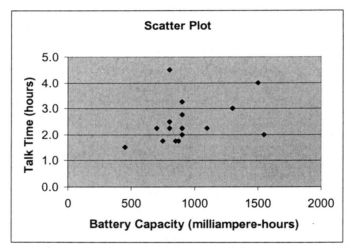

(b)   There does not appear to be any relationship between the battery capacity and the digital-mode talk time.

(c)   No, the data does not support the expectation that higher battery capacity is associated with higher talk time.

2.24   (a)

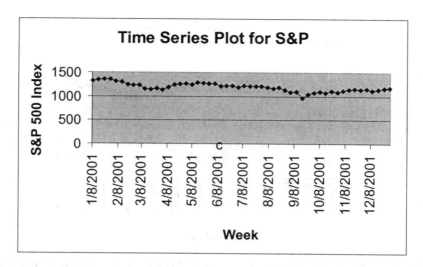

(b)   There seems to be a general downward trend for the S&P 500 Index since February of 2001. It lost about 17% of its value between January 22, 2001 and April 2, 2001. It rebounded back to around 1300 points in May 14, 2001 but immediately followed by another downward trend that culminated on the day of the terrorist attack on the United States on September 11, 2001. A gradual recovery occurred in October 2001.

(c)

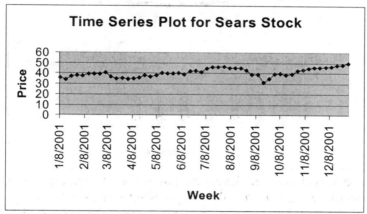

(d)   There seems to be a general upward trend in Sears, Roebuck and Company's stock prices before the terrorist attack in September 2001 in contrast to the downward trend of the S&P 500 Index. There also appears to be a stronger recovery after the attack.

2.24   (e)
cont.

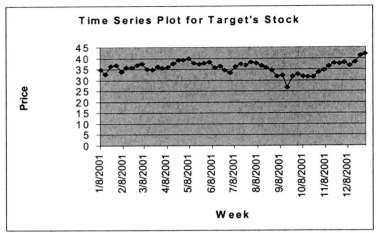

(f)   The stock prices of Target Corporation did not have any apparent patterns before the terrorist attack in September but showed sign of strong recovery after the attack.

(g)

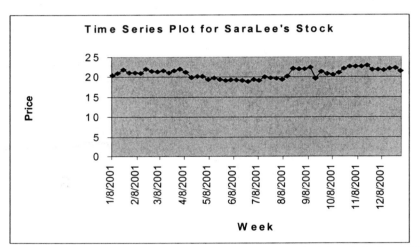

(h)   The stock prices of SaraLee fluctuated around the $20 level during 2001. The terrorist attack seems to have only a slight effect on its stock prices.

(i)   In general, the S&P 500 index had a slight downward trend during 2001 while the stock prices for Sears showed a slight upward trend. The stock prices of Target and SaraLee did not show significant changes during 2001. The terrorist attack in September 2001 had a negative impact on the S&P index and the prices of the stocks. All of them showed sign of recovery after the attack.

2.26   (a)

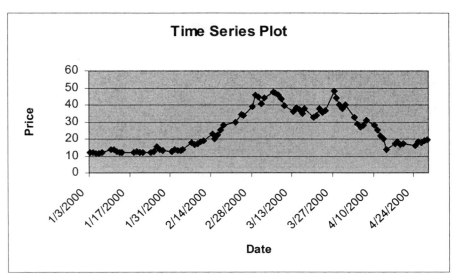

(b)   The volatility of the stock price for WAVX was exemplified by its phenomenal growth rate since February of 2000 and reached its peak at $47.68 on March 6, 2000. It suffered a significant downward adjustment in early March of 2000 but regained its upward momentum around March 21, 2000 to reach $47.93 on March 27, 2000. Another significant drop occurred on March 28, 2000 and stock price had only managed to rebound back to around $20 since.

2.28   (a)

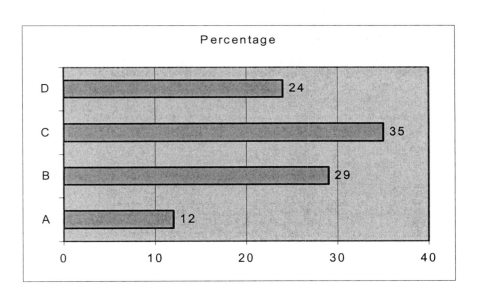

2.28   (b)
cont.

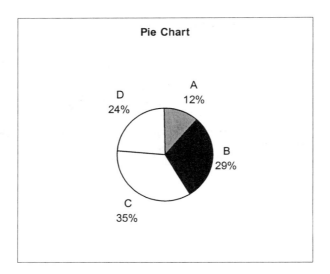

(c)

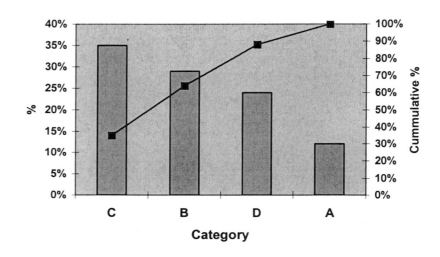

2.30   The various reasons given are denoted as "Reason A", "Reason B", etc., in the following charts.

(a)

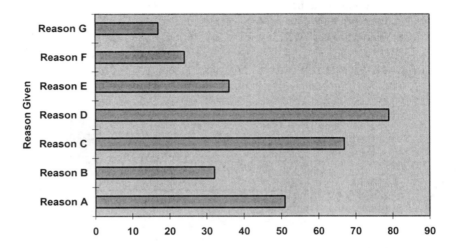

(b)

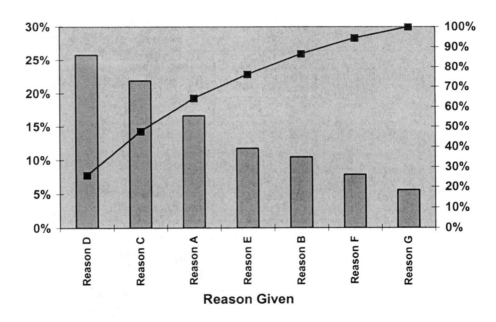

(c)   The Pareto diagram is better than frequency bar chart to portray these data because it not only sorts the frequencies in descending order, it also provides the cumulative polygon on the same scale. From the Pareto diagram, it is obvious that "I do not have time to respond currently", "I do respond to surveys selectively but was unable to respond to this survey" and "It is our firm's policy not to respond to surveys" are the reasons given by more than half of the respondents.

2.32 (a)

ANSWER GIVEN	FREQUENCY	PERCENTAGE
Yes, if the price is right	8183	62%
Yes, but only for a dream job	2772	21%
No, there are good jobs here	792	6%
No, relocation isn't an option	1452	11%
Total	**13199**	**100%**

(b)

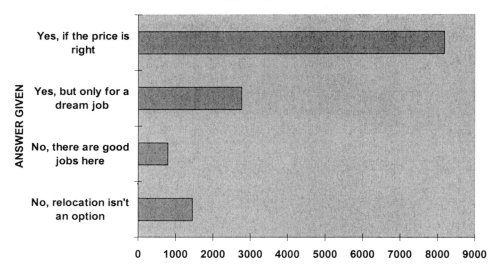

(c)

(d) The bar chart is most suitable if the purpose is to compare the categories. The pie chart is most suitable if the main objective is to investigate the portion of the whole that is in a particular category.

2.34   (a)

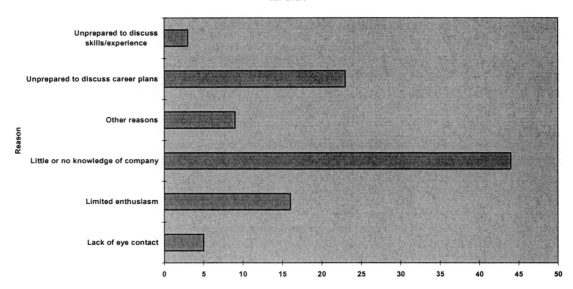

(b)

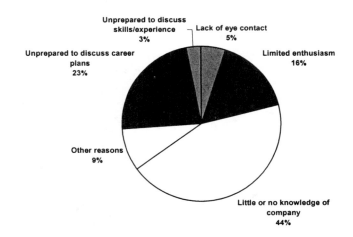

2.34   (c)
cont.

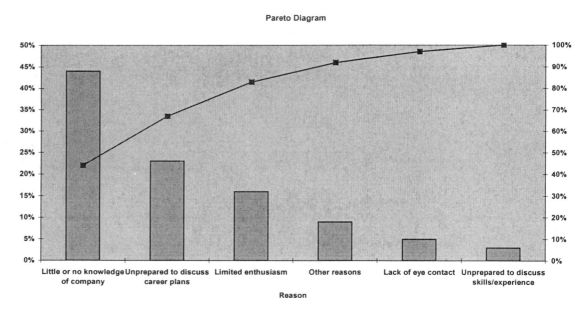

(d)   The Pareto diagram is better than pie chart to portray these data because it not only sorts the frequencies in descending order, it also provides the cumulative polygon on the same scale. From the Pareto diagram, it is obvious that "little or no knowledge of company" has constituted 44% of the most common mistake candidates make during job interviews.

2.36   (a)

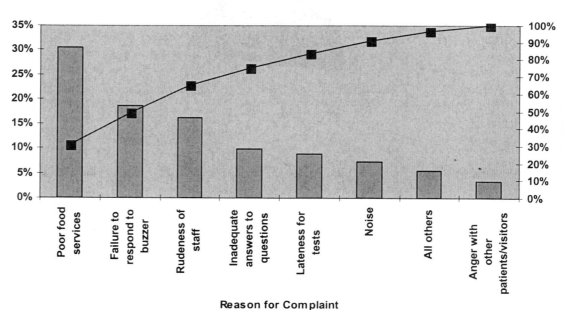

2.36   (b)   To reduce the overall number of complaints, the hospital management should focus
cont.   on improving food service, which accounted for 30.5% of all complaints, followed by
               timely response to patient buzzers and rudeness of staff, each of which accounted for
               18.5% and 16.1% of complaints respectively. Together, the three areas accounted for
               more than 65% of all complaints registered on the patient-satisfaction survey.

2.38

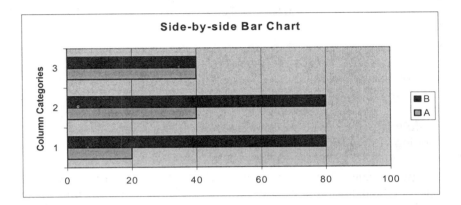

2.40   (a)   Column percentages:

	Total Sales in Millions $	
Apparel Company	**April 2001**	**April 2002**
Gap	31.00%	25.09%
TJX	20.91%	23.45%
Limited	15.95%	16.18%
Kohl's	14.57%	17.71%
Nordstrom	10.77%	10.91%
Talbots	3.74%	3.39%
AnnTaylor	3.05%	3.26%
Total	100.00%	100.00%

(b)

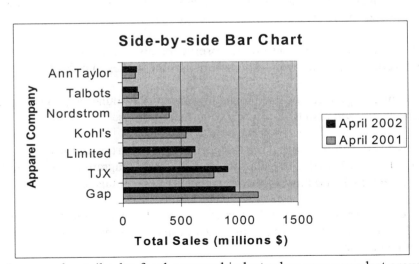

(c)   In general, retail sales for the apparel industry has seen a modest growth between
       April 2001 and April 2002 with the exception of Talbots, whose sales have declined
       slightly and Gap, whose sales have declined by almost 200 million dollars.

2.42

(a) Table of row percentages

Shift

	Day	Evening	
Nonconforming	40%	60%	100%
Conforming	68%	32%	100%
Total	67%	33%	100%

(b) Table of column percentages

Shift

	Day	Evening	
Nonconforming	2%	7%	4%
Conforming	98%	93%	96%
Total	100%	100%	100%

(c)   Table of total percentages

Shift

	Day	Evening	
Nonconforming	2%	2%	4%
Conforming	65%	31%	96%
Total	67%	33%	100%

(d)   The row percentages allow us to block the effect of disproportionate group size and show us that the pattern for day and evening tests among the nonconforming group is very different from the pattern for day and evening tests among the conforming group. Where 40% of the nonconforming group was tested during the day, 68% of the conforming group was tested during the day.

(e)   The director of the lab may be able to cut the number of nonconforming tests by reducing the number of tests run in the evening, when there is a higher percent of tests run improperly.

2.48   (a)   Good features: (1) a bar chart is used correctly for this categorical data; (2) the various percentages are displayed along with the length of the bars.

(b)   Bad features: (1) the background graphic is an example of chartjunk; (2) the shading in the bars reduces the data-ink ratio and do not convey any valuable information.

2.50   (a)   Good features: (1) the bar chart used is an appropriate graphical tool for the categorical data; (2) the various percentages are presented in the bar chart.

(b)   Bad features: (a) the background graphic complicates the presentation of the data and distracts viewers attention from the real data.

2.52   A stem-and-leaf display allows you to observe the distribution of the data within the range of the observations. The ordered array merely lists the values in order from lowest to highest.

2.54   The percentage ogive can be used to approximate the cumulative percentage less than a particular value, and also to compare two or more groups.

2.56   A bar chart is useful for comparing categories. A pie chart is useful when examining the portion of the whole that is in each category. A Pareto diagram is useful in focusing on the categories that make up most of the frequencies or percentages.

2.58   The bar chart is most similar to the Pareto diagram. Both are used for categorical variables, but the Pareto diagram orders the categories from most frequently occurring to least frequently occurring.

2.60   Percentage breakdowns according to the total percentage, the row percentage, and/or the column percentage allow the interpretation of data in a two-way contingency table from several different perspectives.

2.62

(a)

Range	Frequency	Percentage
0 but less than 25	17	34
25 but less than 50	19	38
50 but less than 75	5	10
75 but less than 100	2	4
100 but less than 125	3	6
125 but less than 150	2	4
150 but less than 175	2	4

(b)

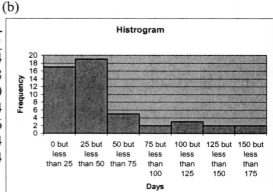

(c)

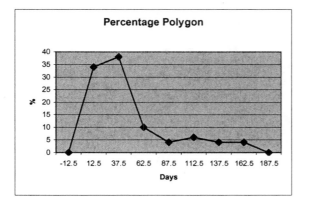

(d)

Range	Cumulative %
0 but less than 25	34
25 but less than 50	72
50 but less than 75	82
75 but less than 100	86
100 but less than 125	92
125 but less than 150	96
150 but less than 175	100

(e)

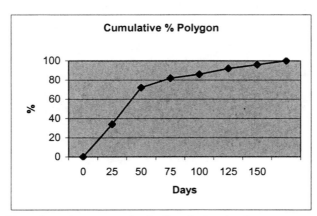

(f)   Yes, there is a great deal of variation in the amount of time it takes to resolve complaints. The number of days ranges from 1 to 165. Although 72% are resolved within 50 days the remaining 28% take up to another 115 days to finally be resolved.

2.62   (g)   You should tell the president of the company that over half of the complaints are
cont.   resolved within a month, but point out that some complaints take as long as three or
             four months to settle.

2.64   (a)

12.6	12.8	13	13.1	13.3	13.3	13.4	13.5	13.6	13.7
13.7	13.7	13.8	13.8	13.9	13.9	14	14	14	14.1
14.1	14.1	14.2	14.2	14.2	14.3	14.3	14.3	14.3	14.3
14.3	14.4	14.4	14.4	14.4	14.4	14.4	14.4	14.4	14.5
14.5	14.5	14.5	14.5	14.5	14.6	14.6	14.6	14.7	14.7
14.8	14.8	14.8	14.8	14.9	14.9	14.9	14.9	14.9	14.9
14.9	15	15	15	15	15.1	15.1	15.1	15.1	15.2
15.2	15.2	15.2	15.2	15.2	15.2	15.2	15.3	15.3	15.3
15.3	15.3	15.4	15.4	15.4	15.4	15.5	15.5	15.6	15.6
15.6	15.6	15.6	15.7	15.7	15.7	15.8	15.8	15.9	15.9
16	16	16	16	16.1	16.1	16.1	16.2	16.3	16.4
16.4	16.5	16.5	16.6	16.8	16.9	16.9	17	17.6	18.6

(b)

Viscosity	Frequency	Percentage	Cumulative %
12 but less than 13	2	1.67%	1.67%
13 but less than 14	14	11.67%	13.33%
14 but less than 15	45	37.50%	50.83%
15 but less than 16	39	32.50%	83.33%
16 but less than 17	17	14.17%	97.50%
17 but less than 18	2	1.67%	99.17%
18 but less than 19	1	0.83%	100.00%

(c)

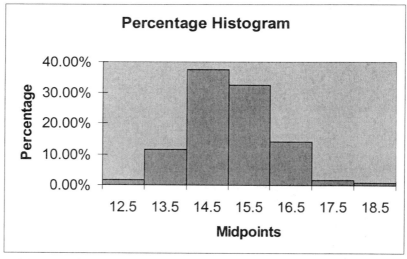

(d)   97.50% of the batches are within company specifications.

2.66   (a)

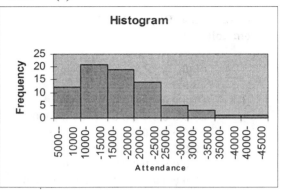

Majority of the games have attendance ranges between 10000 to 25000. The distribution is right-skewed with only 4 games having attendance over 30000. There are 12 games with attendance below 10000.

(b)

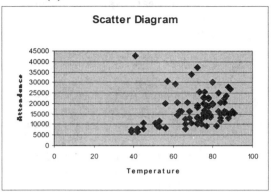

(c) There appear to be a positive relationship between temperature and attendance. Attendance tends to be higher for warmer days. One exception is the opening game of the season in which attendance is the highest while temperature is among the lowest

2.68   (a)

**Stem-and-Leaf Display
for Horsepower
Stem unit: 10**

```
 7|0
 8|
 9|0 0 0
10|0 8
11|0 5
12|5 5 6 7 7 7 9
13|0 0 0 0 1 2 5 5 8
14|0 0 0 0 0 2 3 5 7 8 9 9
15|0 0 0 0 0 5 5 5 7 7
16|0 0 0 5 5 5 8 8
17|0 0 0 0 0 4 5 5
18|0 0 3 4 4 5 5 5 5 5 8
19|4 4 5 7
20|0 0 0 0 3 5 5 5
21|0 0 0 5 5 5 5
22|0 0 0 0 0 0 0 1 5 5 5
23|0 5
24|0 0 0 0 0
25|0 0 5 5
26|
27|0 0 5 5
28|5 5
```

**Stem-and-Leaf Display
for MPG
Stem unit: 10**

```
1|0 3 3 3 4 4 5 5 5 5 5 5 6 6 6 6 6
 |7 7 7 7 7 7 8 8 8 8 8 8 8 8 8
 |9 9 9 9 9 9 9 9 9 9 9 9 9 9 9 9 9 9
2|0 0 0 0 0 0 0 0 0
 |1 1 1 1 1 1 1 1 1 1 1 1 1 1 1 1 1 1 1 1 1
 |2 2 2 2 2 2 2 2 2 2 3 3 3 3 3 3 3
 |4 4 4 4 4 4 5 5 6 6 6 7 7 7 7 8 9 9
3|8
4|1 1
```

2.68   (a)   PHStat output:
cont.

Stem-and-Leaf Display for Length
Stem   10
unit:

```
15|5
16|1 2 3 3 3 5 9
17|0 0 0 2 2 3 3 3 3 4 5 5 5 5 5 5 5
  |6 6 7 7 7 8 8 8 8 8 9 9
18|0 0 1 1 2 3 3 4 4 4 4 4 5 5 5 5 6 6
  |7 7 7 7 8 8 9 9 9 9 9 9
19|0 0 0 0 0 1 1 1 1 2 2 2 2 2 2 3 3
  |4 4 4 4 5 5 6 7 8 8 8 9
20|0 0 0 1 1 1 1 1 1 1 3 4 7 7 9 9
21|2 2 5 9 9
22|7
```

Stem-and-Leaf Display for Width
Stem unit: 1

```
65|0
66|0 0
67|0 0 0 0 0 0 0 0 0
68|0 0 0 0 0 0 0 0 0 0 0 0 0 0 0 0
69|0 0 0 0 0 0 0 0 0
70|0 0 0 0 0 0 0 0 0 0 0 0 0 0 0
71|0 0 0 0 0 0 0 0 0 0 0 0
72|0 0 0 0 0 0 0 0 0 0 0 0 0 0 0 0 0
73|0 0 0 0 0 0 0 0 0
74|0 0 0 0 0 0 0 0 0 0
75|0 0 0 0 0 0 0
76|0 0 0 0
77|
78|0 0 0
79|0 0 0 0
80|0
```

Stem-and-Leaf Display for Turning Circle
Stem unit: 1

```
33|0
34|0
35|0 0 0
36|0 0 0 0 0
37|0 0 0 0 0 0 0 0 0 0 0 0
38|0 0 0 0 0 0 0 0 0
39|0 0 0 0 0 0 0 0 0 0 0 0 0 0 0 0 0 0
40|0 0 0 0 0 0 0 0 0 0 0 0 0 0 0 0 0 0 0 0 0 0 0 0 0
41|0 0 0 0 0 0 0 0 0 0 0 0 0 0 0
42|0 0 0 0 0 0 0 0 0
43|0 0 0 0 0 0 0 0 0
44|0 0 0 0 0
45|0
46|0 0
47|0
48|
49|
50|
51|
52|0
```

2.68   (a)
cont.

Stem-and-Leaf Display
for Weight
Stem unit: 1000

```
2|2 4 4 6 6 6 6 7 7 7 8 8 8 8 8 9 9 9 9 10
3|0 0 1 1 1 1 1 1 1 1 1 1 2 2 2 3 3 3 3 3 3 3 3 3 3 3
 |4 4 4 4 4 4 4 4 5 5 5 5 5 5 5 5 5 5 6 6 6 6 6 6 6 6 6
 |7 7 7 7 8 8 8 8 8 8 9 9 9 9 9 9 10 10 10 10 10 10 10
4|1 1 1 1 1 1 1 2 2 2 2 3 3 3 5 5 7 7 7 7 7 8
5|4 6 6
6|
7|3
```

Stem-and-Leaf Display
for Cargo Volume
Stem unit: 10

```
0|5 5
1|0 0 1 1 1 1 2 2 2 2 2 2 3 3 3 3 3 3 3 3 3 3
 |4 4 4 4 4 4 4 4 4 4 4 4 4 4 5 5 5 5 5 5 5 5 5
 |6 6 6 6 6 6 6 7 7 7 7 7 7 8 8 8 8 8 8 9 9 9 9
2|1 1 1 8 9
3|0 1 2 4 4 4 4 4 5 5 5 6 6 6 6 7 7 7 8 8 9 9 9
4|2 2 4 4 5 6 6 7 8
5|0 7 7 7
6|3 7 7
7|4 4 6 6 6 7 7
8|4
```

(b)

Horsepower	Frequency	Percentage	Cumulative %
Greater than 50 and up to 70	1	0.41%	.83%
Greater than 70 and up to 90	3	1.24%	3.31%
Greater than 90 and up to 110	3	1.24%	5.79%
Greater than 110 and up to 130	12	4.96%	15.70%
Greater than 130 and up to 150	22	9.09%	33.88%
Greater than 150 and up to 170	18	7.44%	48.76%
Greater than 170 and up to 190	14	5.79%	60.33%
Greater than 190 and up to 210	16	6.61%	73.55%
Greater than 210 and up to 230	16	6.61%	86.78%
Greater than 230 and up to 250	8	3.31%	93.39%
Greater than 250 and up to 270	4	1.65%	96.69%
Greater than 270 and up to 290	4	1.65%	100.00%

2.68   (b), (e)
cont.

MPG	Frequency	Percentage	Cumulative %
Greater than 7 and up to 10	1	0.41%	.83%
Greater than 10 and up to 13	3	1.24%	3.31%
Greater than 13 and up to 16	13	5.37%	14.05%
Greater than 16 and up to 19	34	14.05%	42.15%
Greater than 19 and up to 22	41	16.94%	76.03%
Greater than 22 and up to 25	16	6.61%	89.26%
Greater than 25 and up to 28	8	3.31%	95.87%
Greater than 28 and up to 31	2	0.83%	97.52%
Greater than 31 and up to 34	0	0.00%	97.52%
Greater than 34 and up to 37	0	0.00%	97.52%
Greater than 37 and up to 40	1	0.41%	98.35%
Greater than 40 and up to 43	2	0.83%	100.00%

Length	Frequency	Percentage	Cumulative %
Greater than 145 and up to 155	1	0.41%	.83%
Greater than 155 and up to 165	6	2.48%	5.79%
Greater than 165 and up to 175	18	7.44%	20.66%
Greater than 175 and up to 185	29	11.98%	44.63%
Greater than 185 and up to 195	39	16.12%	76.86%
Greater than 195 and up to 205	18	7.44%	91.74%
Greater than 205 and up to 215	7	2.89%	97.52%
Greater than 215 and up to 225	2	0.83%	99.17%
Greater than 225 and up to 235	1	0.41%	100.00%

Width	Frequency	Percentage	Cumulative %
Greater than 63.5 and up to 65	1	0.41%	.83%
Greater than 65 and up to 66.5	2	0.83%	2.48%
Greater than 66.5 and up to 68	25	10.33%	23.14%
Greater than 68 and up to 69.5	9	3.72%	30.58%
Greater than 69.5 and up to 71	29	11.98%	54.55%
Greater than 71 and up to 72.5	17	7.02%	68.60%
Greater than 72.5 and up to 74	19	7.85%	84.30%
Greater than 74 up and to 75.5	7	2.89%	90.08%
Greater than 75.5 and up to 77	4	1.65%	93.39%
Greater than 77 and up to 78.5	3	1.24%	95.87%
Greater than 78.5 and up to 80	5	2.07%	100.00%

2.68   (b),(e)
cont.

Weight	Frequency	Percentage	Cumulative %
Greater than 2000 and up to 2500	3	1.24%	2.48%
Greater than 2500 and up to 3000	16	6.61%	15.70%
Greater than 3000 and up to 3500	39	16.12%	47.93%
Greater than 3500 and up to 4000	37	15.29%	78.51%
Greater than 4000 and up to 4500	15	6.20%	90.91%
Greater than 4500 and up to 5000	7	2.89%	96.69%
Greater than 5000 and up to 5500	1	0.41%	97.52%
Greater than 5500 and up to 6000	2	0.83%	99.17%
Greater than 6000 and up to 6500	0	0.00%	99.17%
Greater than 6500 and up to 7000	0	0.00%	99.17%
Greater than 7000 and up to 7500	1	0.41%	100.00%

Cargo Volume	Frequency	Percentage	Cumulative %
Greater than -5 and up to 5	2	0.83%	1.65%
Greater than 5 and up to 15	45	18.60%	38.84%
Greater than 15 and up to 25	26	10.74%	60.33%
Greater than 25 and up to 35	13	5.37%	71.07%
Greater than 35 and up to 45	16	6.61%	84.30%
Greater than 45 and up to 55	5	2.07%	88.43%
Greater than 55 and up to 65	4	1.65%	91.74%
Greater than 65 and up to 75	4	1.65%	95.04%
Greater than 75 and up to 85	6	2.48%	100.00%

Turning Circle	Frequency	Percentage	Cumulative %
Greater than 32 and up to 34	2	0.83%	1.65%
Greater than 34 and up to 36	9	3.72%	9.09%
Greater than 36 and up to 38	21	8.68%	26.45%
Greater than 38 and up to 40	46	19.01%	64.46%
Greater than 40 and up to 42	24	9.92%	84.30%
Greater than 42 and up to 44	14	5.79%	95.87%
Greater than 44 and up to 46	3	1.24%	98.35%
Greater than 46 and up to 48	1	0.41%	99.17%
Greater than 48 and up to 50	0	0.00%	99.17%
Greater than 50 and up to 52	1	0.41%	100.00%

(c)

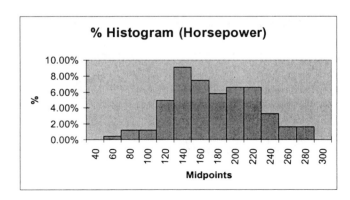

2.68   (c)
cont.

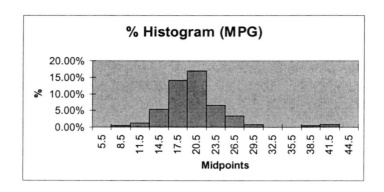

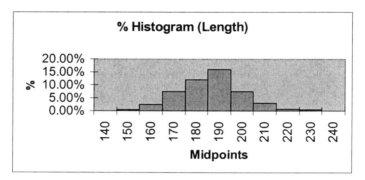

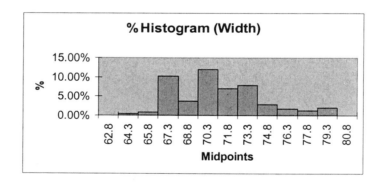

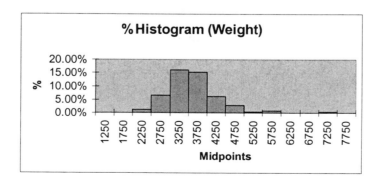

2.68   (c)
cont.

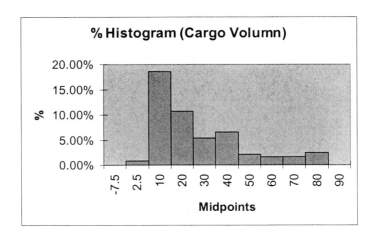

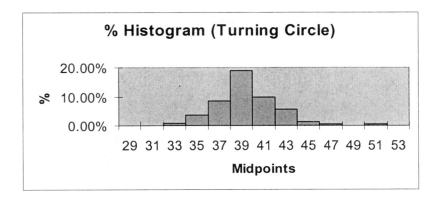

(d)

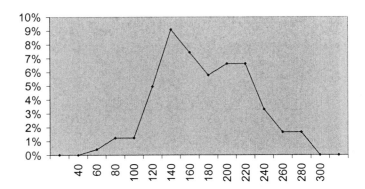

2.68   (d)
cont.

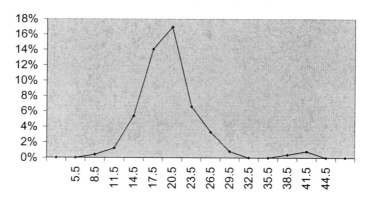

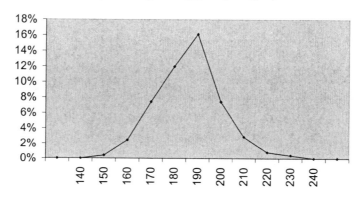

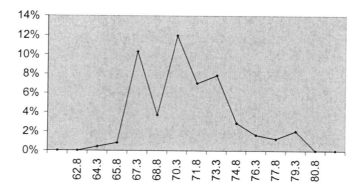

2.68   (d)
cont.

Percentage Polygon (Weight)

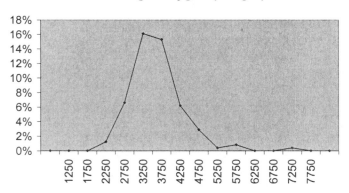

Percentage Polygon (Cargo Volumn)

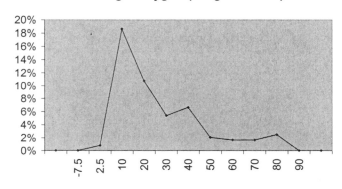

Percentage Polygon (Turning Circle)

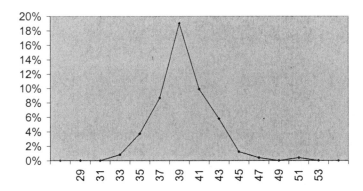

2.68   (f)
cont.

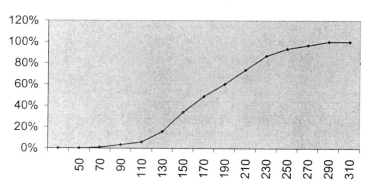

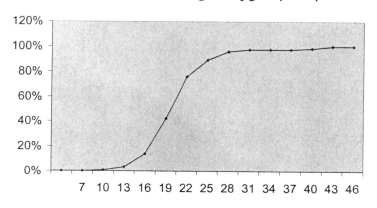

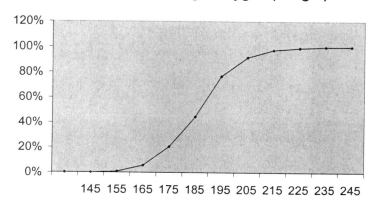

2.68   (f)
cont.

Cumulative Percentage Polygon (Width)

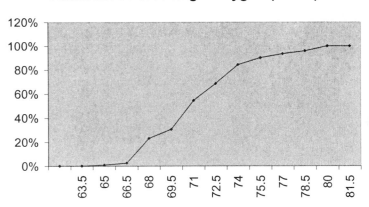

Cumulative Percentage Polygon (Weight)

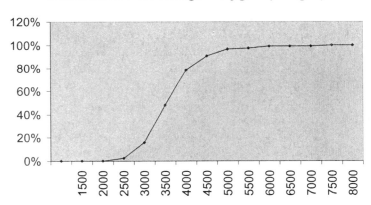

Cumulative Percentage Polygon (Cargo Volumn)

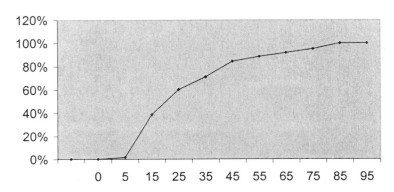

2.68   (f)
cont.

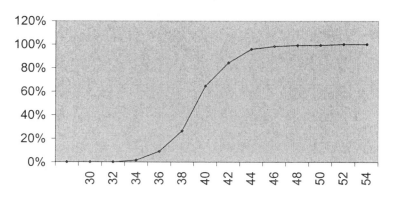

(i)

Count of Drive Type	Fuel Type			
Drive Type	Diesel	Premium	Regular	Grand Total
AWD	0	5	2	7
Front	1	18	63	82
Front, AWD	0	0	1	1
Permanent 4WD	0	3	0	3
Rear	0	11	17	28
Grand Total	1	37	83	121

(j)

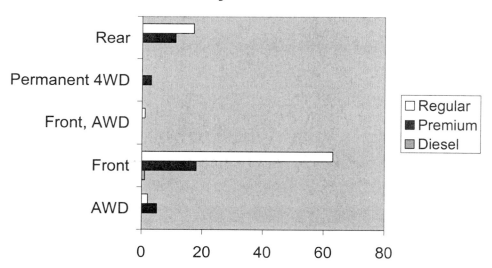

(k)   Based on the results of (i) and (j), the percentage of front-wheels drive cars that use regular gasoline appears to be higher than that for rear-wheel drive cars.

2.70 (a), (d), (e)

Average Ticket$	Frequency	Percentage	Cumulative %
More than 6 and up to 12	3	10.00%	10.00%
More than 12 and up to 18	12	40.00%	50.00%
More than 18 and up to 24	11	36.67%	86.67%
More than 24 and up to 30	3	10.00%	96.67%
More than 30 and up to 36	0	0.00%	96.67%
More than 36 and up to 42	1	3.33%	100.00%

Fan Cost Index	Frequency	Percentage	Cumulative %
More than 80 and up to 105	2	6.67%	6.67%
More than 105 and up to 130	7	23.33%	30.00%
More than 130 and up to 155	10	33.33%	63.33%
More than 155 and up to 180	9	30.00%	93.33%
More than 180 and up to 205	1	3.33%	96.67%
More than 205 and up to 230	1	3.33%	100.00%

Regular season game receipts ($millions)	Frequency	Percentage	Cumulative %
More than 5 and up to 20	5	16.67%	16.67%
More than 20 and up to 35	7	23.33%	40.00%
More than 35 and up to 50	5	16.67%	56.67%
More than 50 and up to 65	6	20.00%	76.67%
More than 65 and up to 80	5	16.67%	93.33%
More than 80 and up to 95	1	3.33%	96.67%
More than 95 and up to 110	1	3.33%	100.00%

Local TV, radio and cable ($millions)	Frequency	Percentage	Cumulative %
More than 0 and up to 10	7	23.33%	23.33%
More than 10 and up to 20	13	43.33%	66.67%
More than 20 and up to 30	5	16.67%	83.33%
More than 30 and up to 40	3	10.00%	93.33%
More than 40 and up to 50	1	3.33%	96.67%
More than 50 and up to 60	1	3.33%	100.00%

Other Local Operating Revenue	Frequency	Percentage	Cumulative %
More than 0 and up to 10	6	20.00%	20.00%
More than 10 and up to 20	3	10.00%	30.00%
More than 20 and up to 30	8	26.67%	56.67%
More than 30 and up to 40	8	26.67%	83.33%
More than 40 and up to 50	3	10.00%	93.33%
More than 50 and up to 60	1	3.33%	96.67%
More than 60 and up to 70	1	3.33%	100.00%

2.70   (a), (d), (e)
cont.

Player compensation and benefits	Frequency	Percentage	Cumulative %
More than 30 and up to 45	5	16.67%	16.67%
More than 45 and up to 60	8	26.67%	43.33%
More than 60 and up to 75	4	13.33%	56.67%
More than 75 and up to 90	5	16.67%	73.33%
More than 90 and up to 105	5	16.67%	90.00%
More than 105 and up to 120	3	10.00%	100.00%

National and other local Expenses	Frequency	Percentage	Cumulative %
More than 30 and up to 40	4	13.33%	13.33%
More than 40 and up to 50	10	33.33%	46.67%
More than 50 and up to 60	9	30.00%	76.67%
More than 60 and up to 70	2	6.67%	83.33%
More than 70 and up to 80	3	10.00%	93.33%
More than 80 and up to 90	2	6.67%	100.00%

Income from Baseball Operations	Frequency	Percentage	Cumulative %
More than -60 and up to -45	2	6.67%	6.67%
More than -45 and up to -30	2	6.67%	13.33%
More than -45 and up to –15	8	26.67%	40.00%
More than -15 and up to 0	8	26.67%	66.67%
More than 0 and up to 15	7	23.33%	90.00%
More than 15 and up to 30	1	3.33%	93.33%
More than 30 and up to 45	2	6.67%	100.00%

(b), (f)

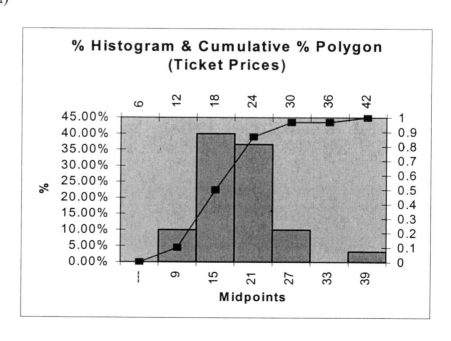

2.70 (b), (f)
cont.

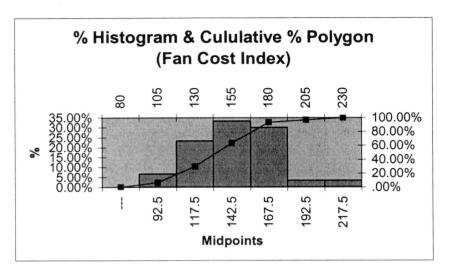

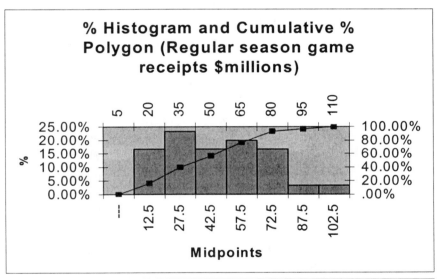

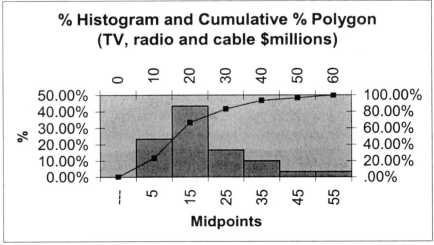

2.70   (b), (f)
cont.

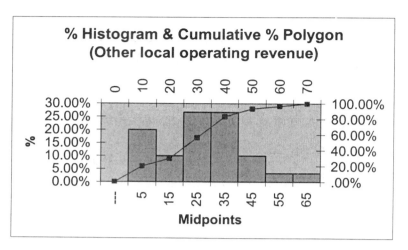

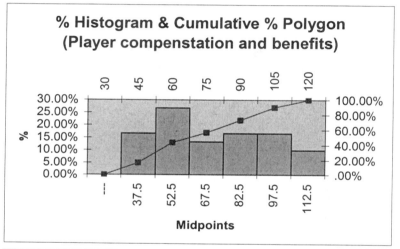

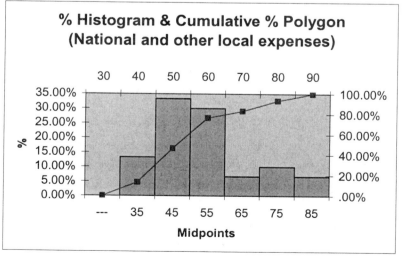

2.70   (b), (f)
cont.

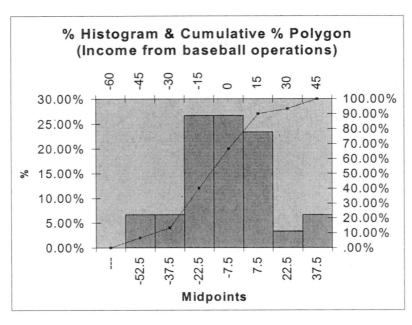

(c)

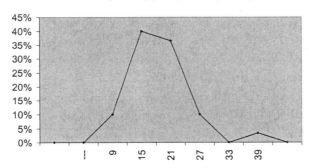

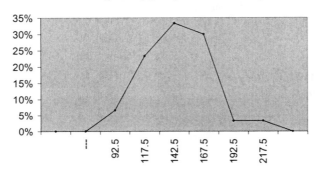

2.70   (c)
cont.

Percentage Polygon (Regular season game receipts)

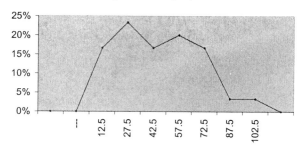

Percentage Polygon (Local TV, radio and cable ($millions))

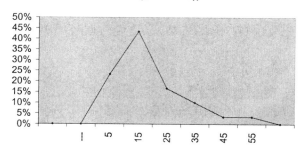

Percentage Polygon (Other Local Operating Revenue)

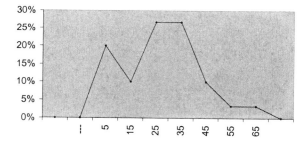

Percentage Polygon (Player compensation and benefits)

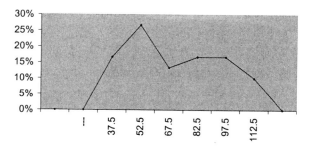

2.70   (c)
cont.

Percentage Polygon (National and other local Expenses)

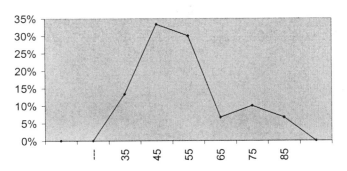

Percentage Polygon (Income from Baseball Operations)

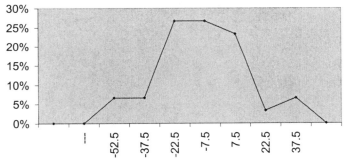

(g)   The percentage histogram and the percentage polygon present essentially the same information. The percentage polygon has the advantage that several polygons can be plotted on the same graph. If cumulative percentage less than a particular value is needed, the cumulative percentage polygon should be used. It is also useful in comparing more than one group.

(h)

Scatter Diagram

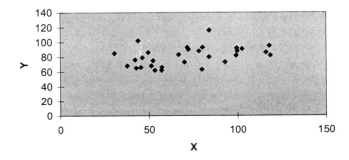

(i)   There appears to be a positive linear relationship between number of wins and player compensation and benefits.

2.72 (a)

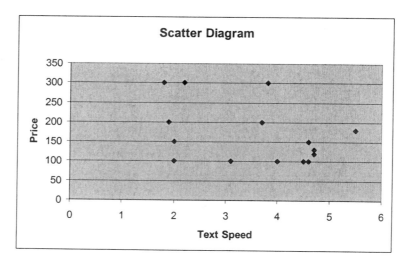

(b)

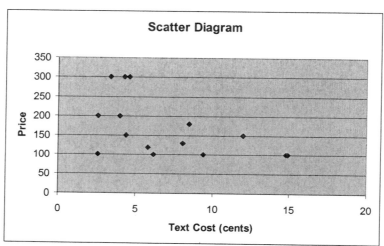

(c)

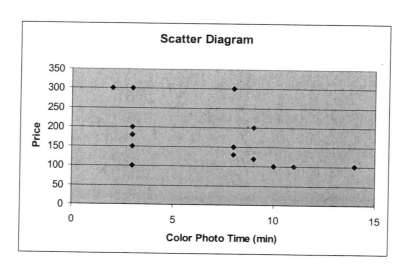

2.72   (d)
cont.

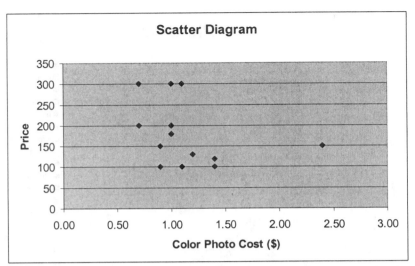

(e)   The only variable that appears to be useful in predicting printer price is text cost. There appears to be a negative relationship between price and text cost. The higher the text cost, the lower is the printer cost.

2.74   (a)

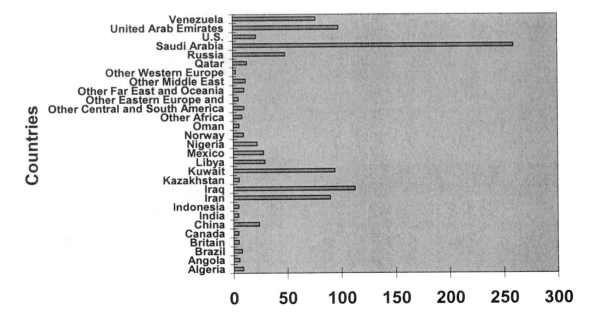

2.74   (b)
cont.

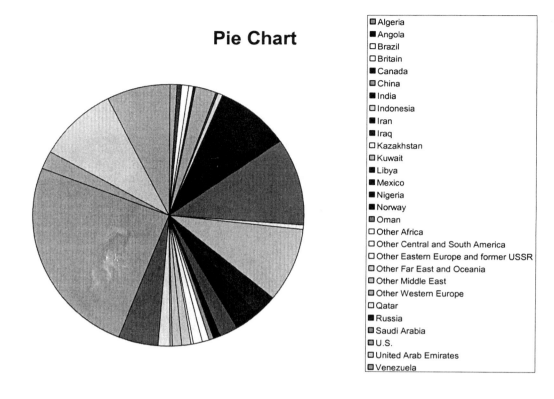

(c)

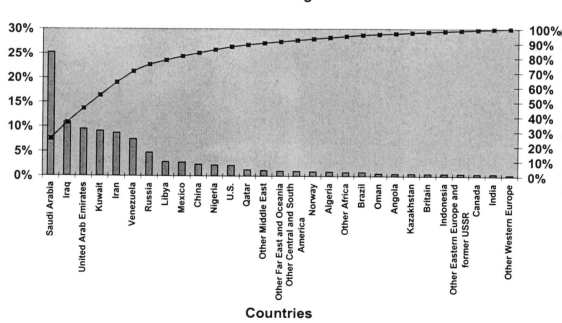

2.74 (d)
cont.

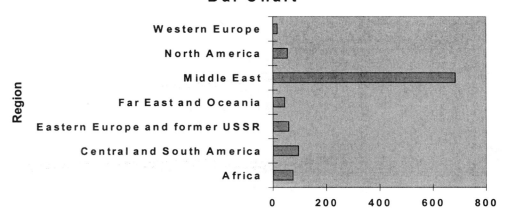

Bar Chart

(e)

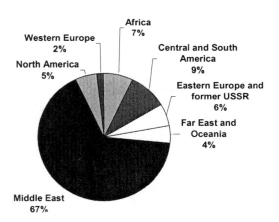

Pie Chart

(f)

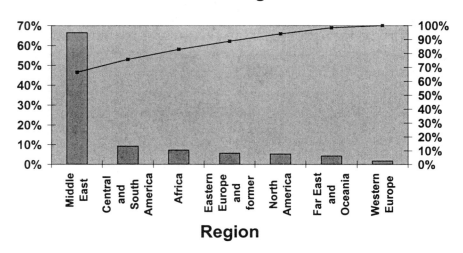

Pareto Diagram

2.74   (g)   The Pareto diagram is most appropriate because it not only sorts the frequencies in
cont.   descending order, it also provides the cumulative polygon on the same scale.

    (h)   The Middle East, with a share of more than 60%, obviously has the largest proven
        conventional reserves. Among the set of countries, Saudi Arabia has the largest share
        of proven conventional reserves followed by Iraq, United Arab Emirates and Kuwait.
        These four countries account for more than half of the reserves among the set of
        countries.

2.76   (a)

Asian/Pacific 3rd Quarter 1999 Pie Chart

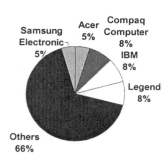

European 3rd Quarter 1999 Pie Chart

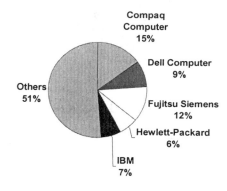

2.76   (a)
cont.

Asian/Pacific 3rd Quarter 2000 Pie Chart

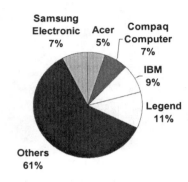

European 3rd Quarter 2000 Pie Chart

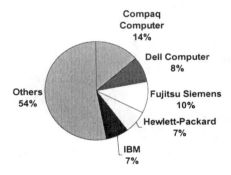

2.76   (b)
cont.

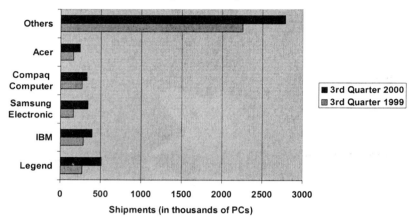

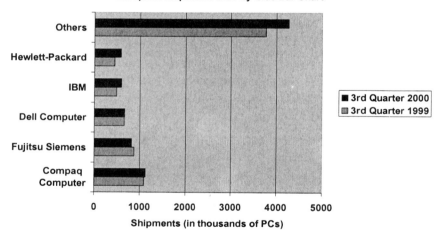

(c)   From the side-by-side bar charts above, it is obvious that the PC shipments experienced a growth from the 3rd quarter of 1999 to the 3rd quarter of 2000 in both markets for all companies except Fujitsu Siemens. The side-by-side bar chart does a better job of illustrating the changes from 1999 to 2000.

(d)   The market share, measured in percentage of the total shipments, for each company can clearly be seen from the pie charts above. The pie chart does a better job illustrating the market share for a particular company.

(e)   In the Europe market, all companies except Fujitsu Siemens experienced growth in PC shipments from the 3rd quarter of 1999 to the 3rd quarter of 2000. The Asia/Pacific market also exhibited similar growth pattern for all the companies.

2.78   (a)

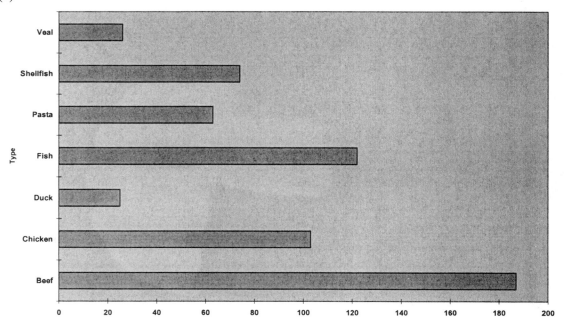

(b)

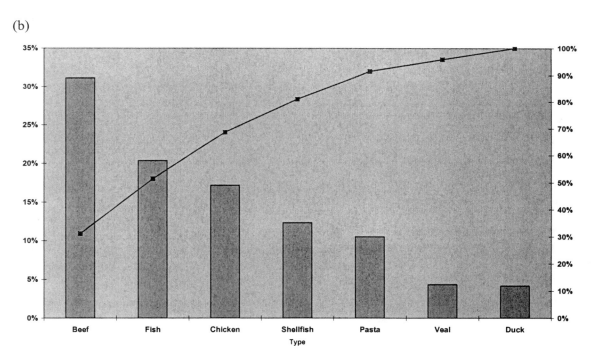

2.78   (c)
cont.

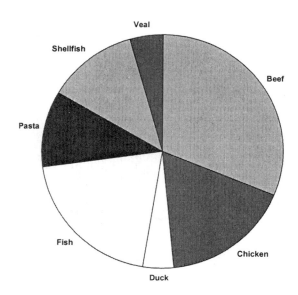

(d)   The Pareto diagram has the advantage of offering the cumulative percentage view of
        the categories and, hence, enable the viewers to separate the "vital few" from the
        "trivial many".

(e)   Beef and fish account for more than 50% of all entrees ordered by weekend patrons
        of a continental restaurant. When chicken is included, better than two-thirds of the
        entrees are accounted for.

(f), (g), (h)

Dessert Ordered	Gender				Beef Entrée			
	Male	Female	Total		Dessert Ordered	Yes	No	Total
Yes	71%	29%	100%		Yes	52%	48%	100%
No	48%	52%	100%		No	25%	75%	100%
Total	53%	47%	100%		Total	31%	69%	100%

(g)

Dessert Ordered	Gender				Beef Entrée			
	Male	Female	Total		Dessert Ordered	Yes	No	Total
Yes	30%	14%	23%		Yes	38%	16%	23%
No	70%	86%	77%		No	62%	84%	77%
Total	100%	100%	100%		Total	100%	100%	100%

(h)

Dessert Ordered	Gender				Beef Entrée			
	Male	Female	Total		Dessert Ordered	Yes	No	Total
Yes	16%	7%	23%		Yes	12%	11%	23%
No	37%	40%	77%		No	19%	58%	77%
Total	53%	47%	100%		Total	31%	69%	100%

2.78   (i)   If the owner is interested in finding out the percentage of joint occurrence of gender
cont.   and ordering of dessert or the percentage of joint occurrence of ordering a beef entrée
                and a dessert among all patrons, the table of total percentages is most informative. If
                the owner is interested in the effect of gender on ordering of dessert or the effect of
                ordering a beef entrée on the ordering of dessert, the table of column percentages will
                be most informative. Since dessert will usually be ordered after the main entree and
                the owner has no direct control over the gender of patrons, the table of row
                percentages is not very useful here.

        (j)   30% of the men sampled ordered desserts compared to 14% of the women. Men are
                more than twice as likely to order desserts as women. Almost 38% of the patrons
                ordering a beef entree ordered dessert compared to less than 16% of patrons ordering
                all other entrees. Patrons ordering beef are better than 2.3 times as likely to order
                dessert as patrons ordering any other entree.

2.80   (a)

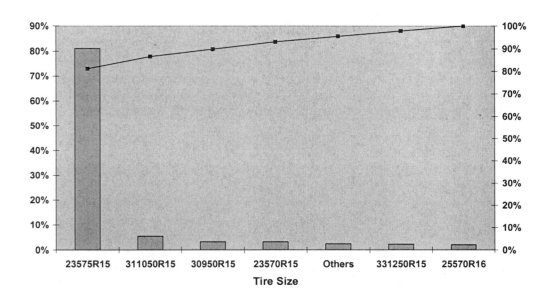

        23575R15 accounts for over 80% of the warranty claims.

2.80   (b)
cont.

Pie Chart

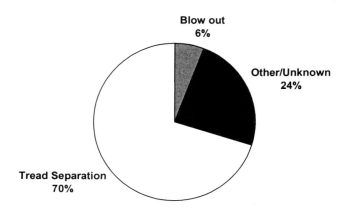

Tread separation accounts for majority (70%) of the warranty claims.

(c)

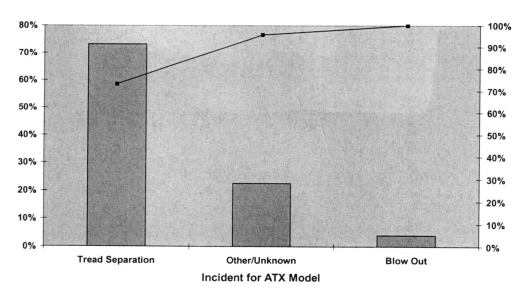

Tread separation accounts for more than 70% of the warranty claims among the ATX model.

2.80   (d)
cont.

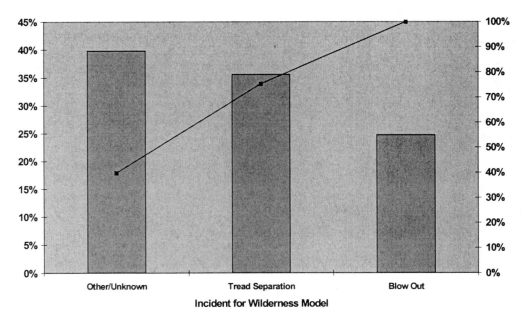

Incident for Wilderness Model

The number of claims is quite evenly distributed among the three incidents with other/unknown incidents account for almost 40% of the claims, tread separation accounts for about 35% of the claim while blow out accounts for about 25% of the claims.

(e)   The tire size 23575R15 accounts for more than 80% of the warranty claims. For this tire size, tread separation is the major incident responsible for claims among the ATX model while there is not any particular incident which accounts for majority of the claims among the Wilderness model. Tread separation among the ATX model accounts for 1365/2504=54.5% of the warranty claims.

CHAPTER 3

OBJECTIVES
- To be able to describe the properties of central tendency, variation, and shape in numerical data
- To be able to develop and interpret a box-and-whisker plot
- To be able to calculate descriptive summary measures from population
- To be able to calculate the coefficient of correlation

OVERVIEW AND KEY CONCEPTS
Measures of Central Tendency

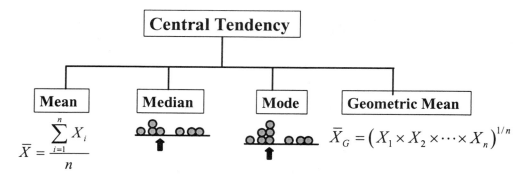

- **Arithmetic mean:** The sum of all the observations in a set of data divided by the total number of observations.
  - $$\overline{X} = \frac{\sum_{i=1}^{n} X_i}{n}$$
  - The arithmetic mean is the most common measure of central tendency.
  - It is very sensitive to extreme values, called outliers.
- **Median:** The value such that 50% of the observations are smaller and 50% of the observations are larger.
  - Median = $\frac{n+1}{2}$ ranked observation.
  - If n is odd, the median is the middle ranked observation.
  - If n is even, the median is the average of the two middle ranked observations.
  - The median is not affected by extreme values.

- **Mode:** The value that occurs most often in a set of data.
  - It is not affected by extreme values.
  - There may be several modes or there may be no mode in a set of data.
  - It can be used for either numerical or categorical data.
- **Geometric mean:** The nth root of the product of n values.
  - $$\overline{X}_G = \left(X_1 \times X_2 \times \cdots \times X_n \right)^{1/n}$$
  - It is useful in the measure of rate of change of a variable over time.
  - The geometric mean rate of return can be used to measure the status of an investment over time. $\overline{R}_G = \left[\left(1 + R_1 \right) \times \left(1 + R_2 \right) \times \cdots \times \left(1 + R_n \right) \right]^{1/n} - 1$
- **Quartiles:** The most widely used measures of noncentral location.
  - The ordered data is split into four equal portions.
  - The first quartile (Q_1) is the value for which 25% of the observations are smaller and 75% are larger.

    $Q_1 = \dfrac{n+1}{4}$ ordered observation.
  - The third quartile (Q_3) is the value for which 75% of the observations are smaller and 25% are larger.

    $Q_3 = \dfrac{3(n+1)}{4}$ ordered observation.
  - The median is the second quartile.

    $Q_2 = \dfrac{(n+1)}{2}$ ordered observation.

Measures of Variation

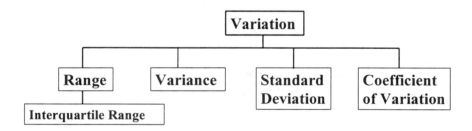

- **Range:** The largest value minus the smallest value.
  - The range ignores how the data are distributed.
  - It is very sensitive to extreme values.
- **Interquartile range (mid-spread):** The 3rd quartile minus the 1st quartile.
  - It is not affected by extreme values.
  - It measures the spread of the middle 50% of the observations.

- **Sample variance:** The sum of the squared differences around the arithmetic mean divided by the sample size minus 1.

  - $$S^2 = \frac{\sum_{i=1}^{n}(X_i - \bar{X})^2}{n-1}$$

  - Sample variance measures the average scatter around the mean.
- **Sample standard deviation:** The square root of the sample variance.

  - $$S = \sqrt{\frac{\sum_{i=1}^{n}(X_i - \bar{X})^2}{n-1}}$$

  - Sample standard deviation has the same units of measurement as the original data.
- **Coefficient of Variation:** The standard deviation divided by the arithmetic mean, multiplied by 100%.

  - $$CV = \left(\frac{S}{\bar{X}}\right)100\%$$

  - It is a relative measure of variation.
  - It is used in comparing two or more sets of data measured in different units.

Shape of a Distribution

- The shape describes how data is distributed.
- Measures of shapes can be symmetric or skewed.

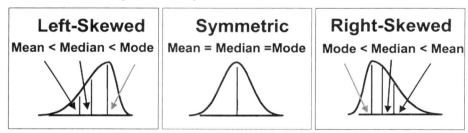

Left-Skewed	**Symmetric**	**Right-Skewed**
Mean < Median < Mode	Mean = Median =Mode	Mode < Median < Mean

Exploratory Data Analysis

- A five-number summary consists of $X_{smallest}$, Q_1, Median, Q_3, $X_{largest}$.
- **Box-and-whisker plot:** Provides a graphical representation of the data based on the five-number summary.

Distribution Shape and Box-and-Whisker Plot

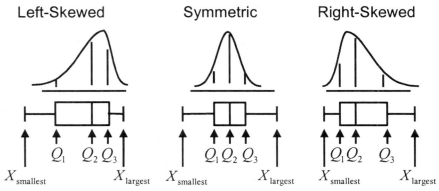

- In right-skewed distributions, the distance from the median to $X_{largest}$ is greater than the distance from $X_{smallest}$ to the median.
- In right-skewed distribution, the distance from Q_3 to $X_{largest}$ is greater than the distance from $X_{smallest}$ to Q_1.
- In left-skewed distributions, the distance from the median to $X_{largest}$ is smaller than the distance from $X_{smallest}$ to the median.
- In left-skewed distribution, the distance from Q_3 to $X_{largest}$ is smaller than the distance from $X_{smallest}$ to Q_1.

Obtaining Descriptive Summary Measures from a Population

- **Population mean:** $\mu = \dfrac{\sum\limits_{i=1}^{N} X_i}{N}$

- **Population variance:** $\sigma^2 = \dfrac{\sum\limits_{i=1}^{N} (X_i - \mu)^2}{N}$

- **Population standard deviation:** $\sigma = \sqrt{\dfrac{\sum\limits_{i=1}^{N} (X_i - \mu)^2}{N}}$

- **The empirical rule:** In bell-shaped distributions, roughly 68% of the observations are contained within a distance of ± 1 standard deviation around the mean, approximately 95% of the observations are contained within a distance of ± 2 standard deviation around the mean and approximately 99.7% are contained within a distance of ± 3 standard deviation around the mean.

- **The Bienaymé-Chebyshev rule:** Regardless of how skewed a set of data is distributed, the percentage of observations that are contained within distances of k standard deviations around the mean must be at least $\left(1 - \dfrac{1}{k^2}\right)100\%$

    - At least 75% of the observations must be contained within distances of ± 2 standard deviation around the mean.
    - At least 88.89% of the observations must be contained within distances of ± 3 standard deviation around the mean.
    - At least 93.75% of the observations must be contained within distances of ± 4 standard deviation around the mean.

Correlation Coefficient as a Measure of Strength between Two Numerical Variables

- **The coefficient of correlation:** $r = \dfrac{\displaystyle\sum_{i=1}^{n}\left(X_i - \bar{X}\right)\left(Y_i - \bar{Y}\right)}{\sqrt{\displaystyle\sum_{i=1}^{n}\left(X_i - \bar{X}\right)^2 \sum_{i=1}^{n}\left(Y_i - \bar{Y}\right)^2}}$

    - Measures the strength of a linear relationship between 2 numerical variables X and Y.
    - Is unit free.
    - The values are between -1 and 1.
    - The closer r is to -1, the stronger the negative linear relationship.
    - The closer r is to $+1$, the stronger the positive linear relationship.
    - If r is close to 0, little or no linear relationship exists.

SOLUTIONS TO END OF SECTION
AND CHAPTER REVIEW EVEN PROBLEMS

3.2   (a)   Mean = 7   Median = 7   Mode = 7
      (b)   Range = 9   Variance = 10.8   Interquartile range = 5
                  Standard deviation = 3.286   Coefficient of variation = (3.286/7)•100% = 46.94%
      (c)   Since the mean equals the median, the distribution is symmetrical.

3.4   (a)   Mean = 2   Median = 7   Mode = 7
      (b)   Range = 17   Variance = 62   Interquartile range = 14.5
                  Standard deviation = 7.874   Coefficient of variation = (7.874/2)•100% = 393.7%
      (c)   Since the mean is less than the median, the distribution is left-skewed.

3.6 $\bar{R}_G = \left[(1+0.1)(1+0.3)\right]^{1/2} - 1 = 19.58\%$

3.8   (a), (b)

	Burger	Chicken
Minimum	19	7
First Quartile	31	15
Median	35	18
Third Quartile	39	27
Maximum	43	39
Mean	34.28571	20.63636
Standard Deviation	7.80415	9.770084
Sample Variance	60.90476	95.45455
Range	24	32
Interquartile Range	8	12
Coefficient of Variation	22.7621%	47.3440%

      (c)

Box-and-whisker Plot

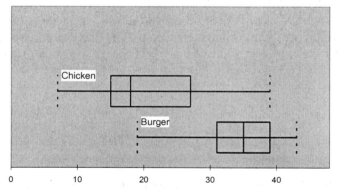

      The data for chicken items are skewed to the right and the data for burgers are skewed to the
      left.
      (d)   In general, burgers have more total fat than chicken items. The least total fat among burgers is
            still higher than 50% of the total fat among chicken items. About 25% of the burgers have
            higher total fat than the highest total fat among the chicken items.

3.10 (a)   Mean = 20.73   median = 18   mode = 18   range = 49   variance = 83.93
        standard deviation = 9.16

(b)   The average P/E ratio for the 30 stocks traded on the New York Stock Exchange is 20.73. T
        P/E ratio that occurs most is 18 while the middle ranked P/E ratio is 18. The average of the
        squared differences between all the P/E ratio in the sample and the sample average P/E ratio
        83.93.

3.12 (a) $\bar{X} = 44.69$. median = 46.25   There is no mode.

(b)   range = 60 $S^2 = 370.4241$ $S = 19.2464$

(c)   The average percentage of the total code written for a software system that is part of the reus
        data base is 44.69%. The middle ranked percentage of reuse is 46.25. There is no particular
        reuse rate that occurs more than once. The average of the squared differences between all the
        reuse rates in the sample and the sample mean is 370.4241. According to the empirical rule,
        roughly 2 out of 3 reuse rates in the population will scatter within 19.25% of 44.69%.

3.14 (a)   Mean = 4.287   Median = 4.5 $Q_1 = 3.20$ $Q_3 = 5.55$

(b)   Variance = 2.683   Standard deviation = 1.638   Range = 6.08
        Interquartile range = 2.35   Coefficient of variation = 38.21%

(c)   Since the mean is less than the median, the distribution is left-skewed.

(d)   The mean and median are both under 5 minutes and the distribution is left-skewed,
        meaning that there are more unusually low observations than there are high observations.
        But six of the 15 bank customers sampled (or 40%) had wait times in excess of 5
        minutes. So, although the customer is more likely to be served in less than 5 minutes, the
        manager may have been overconfident in responding that the customer would "almost
        certainly" not wait longer than 5 minutes for service.

(e)   According to the empirical rule, between 90% to 95% of the observations will fall within
        2 standard deviation around the mean. Hence, using a cutoff of $4.287 + 2(1.638) = 7.563$
        minutes will result in roughly a 5% chance of having to pay this small payment of gift.

3.16 (a) $\bar{X} = \dfrac{(0.88\% + 3.38\%)}{2} = 2.13\%$

(b) $\bar{R}_G = \left[(1+0.88\%)(1+3.38\%)\right]^{1/2} - 1 = 2.1224\%$

(c)   Even though the arithmetic mean rate of return and the geometric mean rate of return for
        Dell Computer Corporation's stock between March 2002 and April 2002 are about the
        same, the geometric mean rate of return is a better measure for stock price changes that
        are expressed as rate of change over time.

3.18 $\bar{R}_G = \left[(1+0.099)(1-0.289)(1+0.089)(1+0.226)(1+0.041)(1+0.161)(1+0.064)(1-0.029)(1+0.022)\right]^{1/9}$
        $-1 = 3.23\%$

3.20 (a)   Population Mean = 6

(b)   Population Variance, $\sigma^2 = 9.4$ Population Standard Deviation, $\sigma = 3.066$

3.22 (a)   Stem-and-leaf of Quarterly Sales Tax Receipts

5	3
6	57
7	3568
8	04679
9	02335689
10	00123345567
11	011125668
12	555789
13	00
14	5
15	1

(b)   Mean = 10.28

(c) $\sigma^2 = 4.1820$ $\sigma = 2.045$

(d)   64%   (e) 94%   (f) 100%

(g)   These percentages are lower than the empirical rule would suggest.

3.24 (a)   Population Mean = 17.15
The average year-to-date return of the DJ-US real estimate investment group is 17.15 percentage points.

(b)   Population variance = 260.60   Population Standard Deviation = 16.14
The average squared distances between all year-to-date returns and the population mean is 260.60. The majority of the year-to-date returns are within 16.14 percentage point around 17.15.

(c)   Since the population standard deviation is roughly equal to the value of the population mean, there is considerable variability in the YTD returns of the REITs in the DJ-US real estate investment group as majority of the YTD returns are within 16.14 percentage points around 17.15.

3.26 (a)   mean = –10.06. On average, the 52-week return of the 10 largest mutual funds experienced a loss of 10.06%.

(b)   variance = 30.4724; std. dev. = 5.5202. The average squared distances between all 52-week returns and the population average return is 30.47. If the distribution is approximately symmetrical, about 68% of the 52-week returns will be within 5.52% around –10.06%.

(c)   The five-number summary are –17.3, –15.9, –9.9, –6.7, and –0.9. Since the distribution does not appear to be symmetrical, the Bienayme-Chebyshev rule is more appropriate for explaining the variation in this data set. According to the Bienayme-Chebyshev rule, at least 75% of the observations will fall within two standard deviations from the mean, i.e., between –21.10 and 0.98. In this data set, 100% of the observations falls in this interval.

(d)   Since all the observations falls within two standard deviations from the mean, there is no outlier in this data set.

(e)   The five largest bond funds given in Table 3.1 experienced the highest average return on investment. The ten largest mutual funds experienced the largest variability in return on investment.

3.28

m_j	f_j	$m_j f_j$	$(m_j - \bar{X})^2 f_j$
5	10	50	4000
15	20	300	2000
25	40	1000	0
35	20	700	2000
45	10	450	4000
$n = 100$		$\Sigma(m_j f_j) = 2500$	$\Sigma(m_j - \bar{X})^2 f_j = 12000$

(a) $\bar{X} = \dfrac{\sum_{j=1}^{c} m_j f_j}{n} = \dfrac{2500}{100} = 25$

(b) $S = \sqrt{\dfrac{\sum_{j=1}^{c} (m_j - \bar{X})^2 f_j}{n-1}} = 11.01$

3.30 Excel output for March:

m_j	f_j	$m_j f_j$	$(m_j - \bar{X})^2 f_j$
1000	6	6000	83030400
3000	13	39000	38459200
5000	17	85000	1332800
7000	10	70000	51984000
9000	4	36000	73273600
11000	0	0	0
$n = 50$		$\Sigma(m_j f_j) = 236000$	$\Sigma(m_j - \bar{X})^2 f_j = 2.48E+08$

Excel output for April:

m_j	f_j	$m_j f_j$	$(m_j - \bar{X})^2 f_j$
1000	10	10000	1.16E+08
3000	14	42000	27440000
5000	13	65000	4680000
7000	10	70000	67600000
9000	0	0	0
11000	3	33000	1.31E+08
$n = 50$		$\Sigma(m_j f_j) = 220000$	$\Sigma(m_j - \bar{X})^2 f_j = 3.46E+08$

(a) March: $\bar{X} = \dfrac{\sum_{j=1}^{c} m_j f_j}{n} = \dfrac{236000}{50} = 4720$ April: $\bar{X} = \dfrac{\sum_{j=1}^{c} m_j f_j}{n} = \dfrac{220000}{50} = 4400$

(b) March: $S = \sqrt{\dfrac{\sum_{j=1}^{c} (m_j - \bar{X})^2 f_j}{n-1}} = 2250.0794$

April: $S = \sqrt{\dfrac{\sum_{j=1}^{c} (m_j - \bar{X})^2 f_j}{n-1}} = 2657.2965$

3.30 (c) The arithmetic mean has declined by $320 while the standard deviation has increased by
cont. $407.2171.

3.32 Excel output:

Division A				Division B			
m_j	f_j	$m_j f_j$	$(m_j - \bar{X})^2 f_j$	m_j	f_j	$m_j f_j$	$(m_j - \bar{X})^2 f_j$
25	8	200	1905.86	25	15	375	2099.583
35	17	595	502.1267	35	32	1120	107.2803
45	11	495	229.2533	45	20	900	1334.656
55	8	440	1697.164	55	4	220	1320.452
65	2	130	1206.9	65	0	0	0

$n = 46$ $\Sigma(m_j f_j) = 1860$ $\Sigma(m_j - \bar{X})^2 f_j =$ 5541.304

$n = 71$ $\Sigma(m_j f_j) = 2615$ $\Sigma(m_j - \bar{X})^2 f_j =$ 4861.972

(a) Division A: $\bar{X} = 40.4348$ Division B: $\bar{X} = 36.8310$
(b) Division A: $S = 11.0969$ Division B: $S = 8.3341$
(c) Division A has a higher average and standard deviation in age than division B.

3.34 (a) Five-number summary: 3 4 7 9 12
(b)

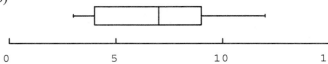

The distribution is almost symmetrical.
(c) The data set is almost symmetrical since the median line almost divides the box in half.

3.36 (a) Five-number summary: -8 -6.5 7 8 9
(b)

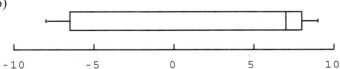

The distribution is left-skewed.
(c) The box-and-whisker plot shows a longer left box from Q_1 to Q_2 than from Q_2 to Q_3,
     visually confirming our conclusion that the data are left-skewed.

3.38 (a) Minimum = 3, 1st quartile = 16, median = 18, 3rd quartile = 24 and maximum = 52
(b) **PHStat output:**

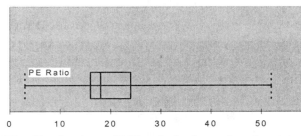

Box-and-whisker Plot

The distribution of P/E ratio is skewed to the right.

3.40

Box-and-whisker Plot

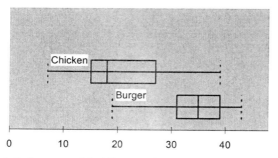

(a)   Minimum = 19, 1st quartile = 31, median = 35, 3rd quartile = 39 and maximum = 43
(b)   The distribution is skewed to the left.
(c)   Minimum = 7, 1st quartile = 15, median = 18, 3rd quartile = 27 and maximum = 39.
(d)   The distribution is skewed to the right.
(e)   While there are a few chicken items that have higher total fat than the rest and a few burgers have lower total fat than the rest, burgers have higher total fat than chicken items in general.

3.42 (a)   minimum = 15, 1st quartile = 25, median =46.25, 3rd quartile = 62.5 and maximum = 75
       (b)

Box-and-whisker Plot

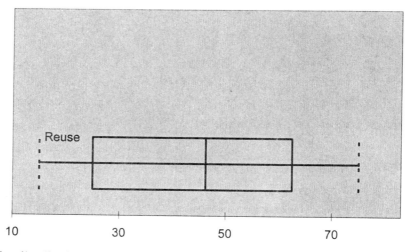

The distribution is skewed to the left.

3.44 (a) $SSX = 217.64$, $SSY = 1958.73$, $SSXY = 652.91$.
$$r = \frac{SSXY}{\sqrt{SSX}\sqrt{SSY}} = \frac{652.91}{\sqrt{217.64}\sqrt{1958.73}} = +1.0$$

       (b)   There is a perfect positive linear relationship between X and Y because all the points lie exactly on a straight line with a positive slope.

3.46 (a)   Quarterly net earnings for Baltimore Gas & Electric Company will be negatively correlated to the average temperature of that period. The lower the average temperature, the higher will be the demand for gas or electric for heating appliances, which translate into higher earnings for the company.

(b)   Investors might use the average temperature in a particular quarter to predict the stock prices of Baltimore Gas & Electric Company since stock prices are positively correlated to earnings as well. When the average temperature of a particular quarter is exceptionally low, one will predict that the stock prices of the company will increase in the following quarter.

(c)   The relationship between stock prices and average temperature should be relevant only for a subset of natural resource stocks that are closely related to the heating industry.

3.48 (a) $r = -0.4014$

(b)   The coefficient of correlation between turnover rate and security violations indicates that there is a rather weak negative linear relationship between the two.

3.50 (a) $r = 0.4838$

(b)   The coefficient of correlation between the cold-cranking amps and the price indicates that there is a moderate positive linear relationship between the two.

(c)   The expectation that batteries with higher ranking amps to have a higher price is only somewhat borne out by the data.

3.52   Central tendency or location refers to the fact that most sets of data show a distinct tendency to group or cluster about a certain central point.

3.54   Measures of central tendency measure a central point in a set of data. Measures of noncentral tendency such as quartiles, measure other points in the distribution.

3.56   The range is a simple measure, but only measures differences between the extremes. The interquartile range measures differences in the center fifty percent of the data. The standard deviation measures variation around the mean while the variance measures the squared variation around the mean, and these are the only measures that take into account each observation. The coefficient of variation measures the variation around the mean relative to the mean.

3.58   Shape is the manner in which the data are distributed.

3.60 (a)   mean = 5.5014   median = 5.515

(b)   first quartile = 5.44   third quartile = 5.57

(c)   range = 0.52   interquartile range = 0.13   variance = 0.0112
standard deviation = 0.10583   coefficient of variation = 1.924%

(d)   The average weight of the tea bags in the sample is 5.5014 grams while the middle ranked weight is 5.515. The company should be concerned about the central tendency because that is where majority of the weight will scatter around.

3.60   (e) The average of the squared differences between the weights in the sample and the sample
cont.   mean is 0.0112 whereas the square-root of it is 0.106 grams. The difference between the
              lightest and the heaviest tea bags in the sample is 0.52. 50% of the tea bags in the
              sample weigh between 5.44 and 5.57 grams. According to the empirical rule, about 68%
              of the tea bags produced will have weight that falls within 0.106 grams around 5.5014
              grams. The company producing the tea bags should be concerned about the variation
              because tea bags will not weigh exactly the same due to various factors in the production
              process, e.g. temperature and humidity inside the factory, differences in the density of
              the tea, etc. Having some idea about the amount of variation will enable the company to
              adjust the production process accordingly.

        (f)

Box-and-whisker Plot

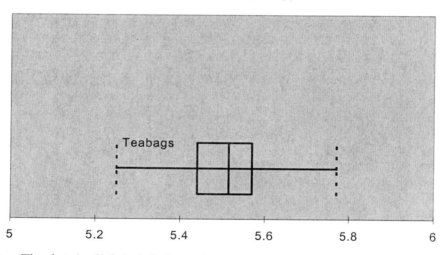

        (g)   The data is slightly left skewed.
        (h)   On average, the weight of the teabags is quite close to the target of 5.5 grams.
        (i)   Even though the average weight is close to the target weight of 5.5 grams, the standard
              deviation of 0.106 indicates that about 75% of the teabags will fall within 0.212 grams
              around the target weight of 5.5 grams. The interquartile range of 0.13 also indicates that
              half of the teabags in the sample fall in an interval 0.13 grams around the median weight
              of 5.515 grams. The process can be adjusted to reduce the variation of the weight around
              the target mean.

3.62   (a)   Mean = 43.04   Median = 28.5
        (b) $Q_1 = 14$ $Q_3 = 54$
        (c)   Range = 164   Interquartile range = 40   Variance = 1,757.79
              Standard deviation = 41.926   Coefficient of variation = 97.41%
        (d)   Box-and-whisker plot for Days to Resolve Complaints

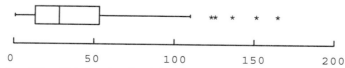

        (e)   The distribution is right-skewed.

3.62   (f) Half of all customer complaints that year were resolved in less than a month (median = 28.5 days), 75% of them within 54 days. There were five complaints that were particularly difficult to settle which brought the overall average up to 43 days. No complaint took longer than 165 days to resolve.

3.64 (a)   mean = 8.42, median = 8.42, range = 0.186 and standard deviation = 0.046. On average, the width is 8.42 inches. The width of the middle ranked observation is 8.42. The difference between the largest and smallest width is 0.186 and majority of the widths fall between 0.046 inches around the mean of 8.42 inches.

      (b)   Minimum = 8.312, 1st quartile = 8.404, median = 8.42, 3rd quartile = 8.459 and maximum = 8.498

      (c)

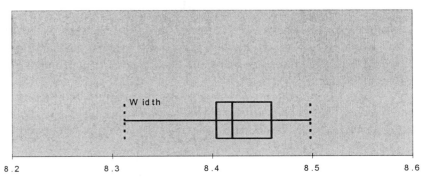

Box-and-whisker Plot

Even though the median equals to the mean, the distribution is not symmetrical but skewed to the left.

      (d)   All the troughs fall within the limit of 8.31 and 8.61 inches.

3.66   (a), (b), (c)

	Time	
	Office I	Office II
Mean	2.214	2.0115
Standard Error	0.384165	0.422998
Median	1.54	1.505
Mode	1.48	3.75
Standard Deviation	1.718039	1.891706
Sample Variance	2.951657	3.57855
Kurtosis	0.285677	2.405845
Skewness	1.126671	1.466424
Range	5.8	7.47
Minimum	0.52	0.08
Maximum	6.32	7.55
Sum	44.28	40.23
Count	20	20
First Quartile	0.93	0.6
Third Quartile	3.93	3.75
Interquartile Range	3	3.15
Coefficient of Variation	77.60%	94.04%

3.66   (d)
cont.

Box-and-whisker Plot

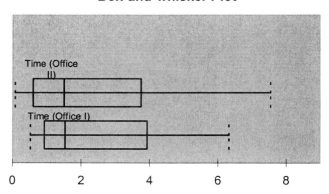

(e)   Times to clear problems at both central offices are right-skewed.
(f)   Times to clear problems for Office I are less dispersed about the mean than times to clear
         problems for Office II, even though the average for Office I times is higher (2.214) than
         that for Office II (2.012).
(g)   If the value 7.55 were incorrectly recorded as 27.55, the mean would be one minute
         higher (from 2.012 to 3.012) and the standard deviation would be over 3 times as large
         (from 1.892 to 5.936).

3.68   (a), (b), (c)

	Cost (per ounce)	Calories	Fiber (grams)	Sugar (grams)
Minimum	0.100000	50.000000	5.000000	0.000000
First Quartile	0.130000	135.000000	5.000000	6.000000
Median	0.170000	190.000000	6.000000	11.000000
Third Quartile	0.200000	200.000000	8.000000	17.500000
Maximum	0.270000	210.000000	13.000000	23.000000
Mean	0.170606	165.757576	6.909091	11.393939
Mode	0.150000	200.000000	5.000000	18.000000
Standard Deviation	0.046900	51.782617	2.402650	6.651783
Sample Variance	0.002200	2681.439394	5.772727	44.246212
Range	0.170000	160.000000	8.000000	23.000000
Interquartile range	0.070000	65.000000	3.000000	11.500000
Coefficient of Variations	27.4903%	31.2400%	34.7752%	58.3800%

3.68 (d)
cont.

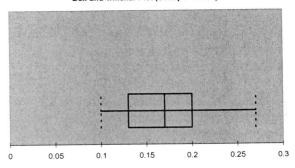

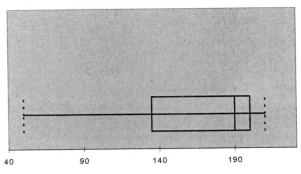

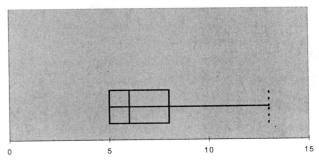

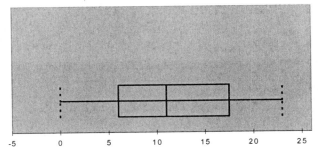

3.68 (e)   The distributions for cost per ounce and fiber content are skewed to the right while the
cont.   distribution for calories is skewed to the left. The distribution for sugar content is quite
                 symmetrical.

      (f)   Cost: The average cost is about 17 cents per ounce, most cereals cluster around this cost
               with a few high priced cereals. The average scatter around the mean is about 5 cents per
               ounce.
               Calories: The average calories is about 166 and a middle value of 190, with an average
               scatter around the mean of about 52. Since the data are left skewed most of the calories
               are clustered at the high end with a few lower calorie cereals.

3.70 (a)-(b)   Excel output:
                   Five-number Summary
                                          Boston   Vermont
                   Minimum   0.04   0.02
                   First Quartile   0.17   0.13
                   Median   0.23   0.2
                   Third Quartile   0.32   0.28
                   Maximum   0.98   0.83

      (c)-(d)

Box-and-whisker Plot

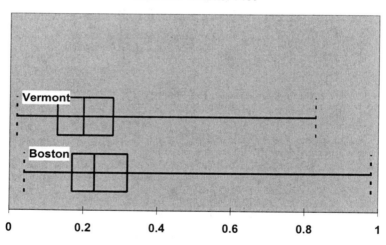

72 (a), (b), (c) Excel output:

	Average Ticket$	Fan Cost Index	Regular season game receipts ($millions)	Local TV, radio and cable ($millions)	Other Local Operating Revenue	Player compensation and benefits	National and other local Expenses	Income from Baseball Operations
Minimum	6.61	84.89	6.4	0.5	2.8	30.5	35	-52.9
First Quartile	15.2	124.25	30.2	10.9	13.9	49.4	46.9	-18.5
Median	17.83	143.475	47.55	16.35	29.05	70.8	50.5	-8.35
Third Quartile	20.84	160.76	62.1	23.6	37	92.8	58.5	1.9
Maximum	39.68	228.73	98	56.8	61.5	118.5	84.2	40.9
Mean	18.1333	144.5737	46.1367	19.0467	27.5933	71.3567	54.6467	-8.3733
Variance	35.9797	843.4552	512.5445	151.0184	234.6186	663.8405	176.4081	428.1531
Standard Dev	5.9983	29.0423	22.6394	12.2890	15.3173	25.7651	13.2819	20.6919
Range	33.07	143.84	91.60	56.30	58.70	88.00	49.20	93.80
Interquartile Range	5.64	36.51	31.90	12.70	23.10	43.40	11.60	20.40
Coefficient of Variation	33.08%	20.09%	49.07%	64.52%	55.51%	36.11%	24.30%	-247.12%

(d)

Box-and-whisker Plot

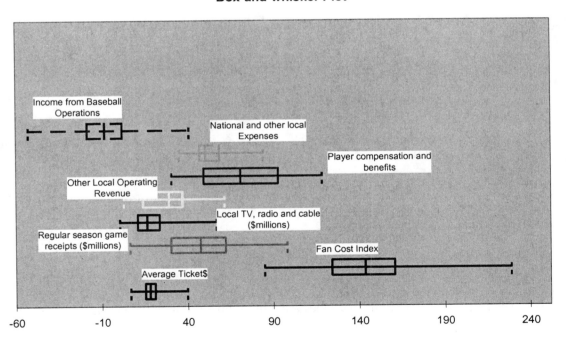

(e)   Average ticket prices, local TV, radio and cable receipts, national and other local expenses are skewed to the right; fan cost index is slightly skewed to the right; all other variables are pretty symmetrical.

(f) $r = 0.3985$. There is a moderate positive linear relationship between the number of wins and player compensation and benefits.

3.74 (a) $r = -0.3842$ (b) $r = -0.5123$ (c) $r = -0.5443$ (d) $r = -0.2614$

(e)   Color photo time has the strongest relationship with price of the four variables, although it is still only a moderate relationship, so it would be the most helpful in predicting price. As the price increases the color photo time tends to decrease. All three variables have a negative (inverse) relationship with price.

3.76 (a), (b), (c)

	Food (NYC)	Décor (NYC)	Service (NYC)	Price (NYC)	Food (LI)	Décor (LI)	Service (LI)	Price (LI)
Minimum	14	10	13	14	15	11	14	23
First Quartile	19	16	17	34	19	16	17	28
Median	20	17	19	39	21	18	19	32
Third Quartile	21	19	20	48	23	20	21	38
Maximum	24	23	23	63	27	27	24	55
Mean	20.1000	17.1200	18.4000	39.7400	20.5400	17.6400	19.0400	33.7400
Variance	4.3367	7.2506	5.3469	93.1759	8.1718	12.1535	5.6310	59.5841
Std. Dev	2.0825	2.6927	2.3123	9.6528	2.8586	3.4862	2.3730	7.7191
Range	10	13	10	49	12	16	10	32
Interquartile Range	2	3	3	14	4	4	4	10
Coefficient Variation	10.36%	15.73%	12.57%	24.29%	13.92%	19.76%	12.46%	22.88%

(d)

Box-and-whisker Plot

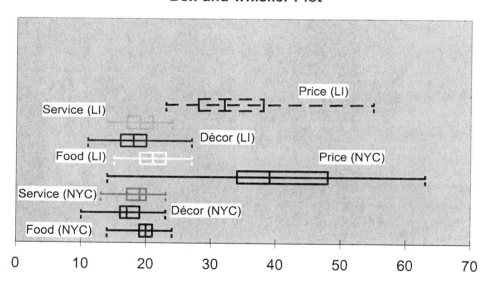

(e)   The distribution for all the variables are quite symmetric with the exception of the price in Long Island, which is skewed to the right.

(f)   There is no noticeable difference in terms of the rating of food, décor, and service between New York City and Long Island restaurants. The price of restaurants in New York City is on average higher and has a higher variation than the price of restaurants in Long Island. The most expensive restaurant in New York City costs $8 more than the most expensive restaurant in Long Island while the least expensive restaurant in New York City costs about $9 less than the least expensive restaurant in Long Island.

CHAPTER 4

OBJECTIVES
- To understand the basic probability concepts
- To understand conditional probability
- To use Bayes theorem to revise probability in the light of new information
- To use rules for counting the number of possible events

OVERVIEW AND KEY CONCEPTS
Some Basic Probability Concepts
- **A priori probability:** The probability is based on prior knowledge of the process involved.
- **Empirical probability:** The probability is based on observed data.
- **Subjective probability:** Chance of occurrence assigned to an event by particular individual.
- **Sample space:** Collection of all possible outcomes, e.g., the set of all six faces of a die.
- **Simple event:** Outcome from a sample space with one characteristic, e.g., a red card from a deck of cards.
- **Joint event:** Involves two or more characteristics simultaneously, e.g., an Ace that is also a Red Card from a deck of cards.
- **Impossible event:** Event that will never happen, e.g., a club and diamond on a single card.
- **Complement event:** The complement of event A, denoted as A', includes all events that are not part of event A, e.g., If event A is the queen of diamonds, then the complement of event A is all the cards in a deck that are not the queen of diamonds.
- **Mutually exclusive events:** Two events are mutually exclusive if they cannot occur together. E.g., If event A is the queen of diamonds and event B is the queen of clubs, then both event A and event B cannot occur together on one card. An event and its complement are always mutually exclusive.
- **Collectively exhaustive events:** A set of events is collectively exhaustive if one of the events must occur. The set of collectively exhaustive events covers the whole sample space. E.g., Event A: all the aces, event B: all the black cards, event C: all the diamonds, event D: all the hearts. Then events A, B, C, and D are collectively exhaustive and so are events B, C, and D. An event and its complement are always collectively exhaustive.
- **Rules of probability:** (1) Its value is between 0 and 1; (2) the sum of probabilities of all collectively exhaustive and mutually exclusive events is 1.
- **The addition rule:** $P(A \text{ or } B) = P(A) + P(B) - P(A \text{ and } B)$
  - For two mutually exclusive events: $P(A \text{ and } B) = 0$
- **The multiplication rule:** $P(A \text{ and } B) = P(A|B)P(B) = P(B|A)P(A)$
- **Conditional probability:** $P(A|B) = \dfrac{P(A \text{ and } B)}{P(B)}$; $P(B|A) = \dfrac{P(A \text{ and } B)}{P(A)}$
- **Statistically independent events:** Two events are statistically independent if $P(A|B) = P(A)$, $P(B|A) = P(B)$ or $P(A \text{ and } B) = P(A)P(B)$. That is, any information about a given event does not affect the probability of the other event.

- **Bayes theorem:** $P(B_i \mid A) = \dfrac{P(A \mid B_i)P(B_i)}{P(A \mid B_1)P(B_1) + \cdots + P(A \mid B_k)P(B_k)} = \dfrac{P(B_i \text{ and } A)}{P(A)}$

  - **E.g.** We know that 50% of borrowers repaid their loans. Out of those who repaid, 40% had a college degree. Ten percent of those who defaulted had a college degree. What is the probability that a randomly selected borrower who has a college degree will repay the loan?

    Solution: Let R represent those who repaid and C represent those who have a college degree. $P(R) = 0.50$, $P(C \mid R) = 0.4$, $P(C \mid R') = 0.10$.

    $$P(R \mid C) = \frac{P(C \mid R)P(R)}{P(C \mid R)P(R) + P(C \mid R')P(R')} = \frac{(.4)(.5)}{(.4)(.5) + (.1)(.5)} = \frac{.2}{.25} = .8$$

  - Bayes theorem is used if $P(A \mid B)$ is needed when $P(B \mid A)$ is given or vice-versa.

Viewing and Computing Marginal (Simple) Probability and Joint Probability Using a Contingency Table

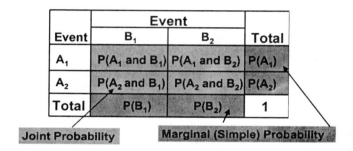

Viewing and Computing Compound Probability Using a Contingency Table

$$P(A_1 \text{ or } B_1) = P(A_1) + P(B_1) - P(A_1 \text{ and } B_1)$$

Event	Event B₁	B₂	Total
A₁	P(A₁ and B₁)	P(A₁ and B₂)	P(A₁)
A₂	P(A₂ and B₁)	P(A₂ and B₂)	P(A₂)
Total	P(B₁)	P(B₂)	1

For Mutually Exclusive Events: P(A or B) = P(A) + P(B)

Viewing and Computing Conditional Probability Using a Contingency Table

First setup the contingency table.

Type	Color		
	Red	Black	Total
Ace	2	2	4
Non-Ace	24	24	48
Total	26	26	52

Revised Sample Space

To find $P(\text{Ace}|\text{Red})$, we only need to focus on the revised sample space of
$P(\text{Red}) = 26/52$.

Out of this, 2/52 belongs to Ace and Red. Hence, $P(\text{Ace}|\text{Red})$ is the ratio of 2/52 to 26/52 or 2/26.
Likewise,

$$P(\text{Red} \mid \text{Ace}) = \frac{P(\text{Ace and Red})}{P(\text{Ace})} = \frac{2/52}{4/52} = \frac{2}{4}$$

Applying Bayes theorem Using a Contingency Table

- **E.g.** We know that 50% of borrowers repaid their loans. Out of those who repaid, 40% had a college degree. Ten percent of those who defaulted had a college degree. What is the probability that a randomly selected borrower who has a college degree will repay the loan?
Solution: Let R represents those who repaid and C represents those who have a college degree. We know that $P(R) = 0.50$, $P(C \mid R) = 0.4$, $P(C \mid R') = 0.10$.

	Repay	$\overline{\text{Repay}}$	Total
College	.2	.05	.25
$\overline{\text{College}}$	.3	.45	.75
Total	.5	.5	1.0

First we fill in the marginal probabilities of $P(R) = 0.5$ and $P(R') = 0.5$ in the contingency table. Then we make use of the conditional probability $P(C \mid R) = 0.4$. It says that if R has already occurred, the probability of C is 0.4. Since R has already occurred, we are restricted to the revised sample space of $P(R) = 0.5$. Forty percent or 0.4 of this $P(R) = 0.5$ belongs to $P(C \text{ and } R)$. Hence, the $0.4(0.5) = 0.2$ for $P(C \text{ and } R)$ in the contingency table. Likewise, given that R' has already occurred, the probability of C is 0.10. Hence, $P(C \text{ and } R')$ is 10% of $P(R') = 0.5$, which is 0.05. Utilizing the fact that the joint probabilities add up vertically and horizontally to their respective marginal probabilities, the contingency table is completed.
We want the probability of R given C. Now we are restricted to the revised sample space of $P(C) = 0.25$ since we know that C has already occurred. Out of this 0.25, 0.2 belongs to $P(C \text{ and } R)$. Hence, $P(R \mid C) = \dfrac{0.2}{0.25} = 0.8$

Counting Rules

- If any one of the k different mutually exclusive and collectively exhaustive events can occur on each of the n trials, the number of possible outcomes is equal to k^n
- If there are k_1 events on the first trial, k_2 events on the second trials, ..., and k_n events on the nth trial, then the number of possible outcomes is $(k_1)(k_2)\cdots(k_n)$
- The number of ways that all n objects can be arranged in order is $n! = n(n-1)\cdots(1)$
  - $n!$ is called n *factorial*
  - $0! = 1$
- **Permutation**: The number of ways of arranging X objects selected from n objects in order is
$$\frac{n!}{(n-X)!}$$
- **Combination**: The number of ways of selecting X objects out of n objects, irrespective or order, is
$$\binom{n}{X} = \frac{n!}{X!(n-X)!}$$

SOLUTIONS TO END OF SECTION
AND CHAPTER REVIEW EVEN PROBLEMS

4.2   (a)   Simple events include selecting a red ball.   (b)   Selecting a white ball

4.4   (a) $40/100 = 2/5 = 0.4$ (g) $\dfrac{40}{100} + \dfrac{35}{100} - \dfrac{10}{100} = \dfrac{65}{100} = \dfrac{13}{20} = 0.65$

       (b) $35/100 = 7/20 = 0.35$

       (c) $60/100 = 3/5 = 0.6$ (h) $\dfrac{40}{100} + \dfrac{65}{100} - \dfrac{30}{100} = \dfrac{75}{100} = \dfrac{3}{4} = 0.75$

       (d) $10/100 = 1/10 = 0.1$

       (e) $30/100 = 3/10 = 0.3$ (i) $\dfrac{60}{100} + \dfrac{65}{100} - \dfrac{35}{100} = \dfrac{90}{100} = \dfrac{9}{10} = 0.9$

       (f) $35/100 = 7/20 = 0.35$

4.6   (a)   Mutually exclusive, not collectively exhaustive
       (b)   Not mutually exclusive, not collectively exhaustive
       (c)   Mutually exclusive, not collectively exhaustive
       (d)   Mutually exclusive, collectively exhaustive
       (e)   Mutually exclusive, collectively exhaustive

4.8   (a)   "A wafer is good."
       (b)   "A wafer is good and no particle was found on the die."
       (c)   "bad wafer."
       (d)   A wafer can be a "good wafer" and was produced by a die "with particles".

       (e) $P(\text{no particles}) = \dfrac{400}{450} = 0.8889$ (f) $P(\text{bad}) = \dfrac{116}{450} = 0.2578$

       (g) $P(\text{bad and no particles}) = \dfrac{80}{450} = 0.1778$

       (h) $P(\text{good and no particles}) = \dfrac{320}{450} = 0.7111$

       (i) $P(\text{good or no particles}) = \dfrac{334}{450} + \dfrac{400}{450} - \dfrac{320}{450} = 0.92$

       (j) $P(\text{bad or particles}) = \dfrac{116}{450} + \dfrac{50}{450} - \dfrac{36}{450} = 0.2889$

       (k)   The probability of "good or no particles" includes the probability of "good and no particles", the probability of "good and particles" and the probability of "bad and no particles".

90   Chapter 4: Basic Probability

4.10   (a)

		Company Size		
		Large	Small-to-midsized	
Stock	Yes	40	43	83
Options	No	149	137	286
		189	180	369

(b)   "A large company"
(c)   "A large company that offers stock options to their board members as part of their non-cash compensation."
(d)   "Did not offer stock options to their board members"
(e)   A company can be "large" and at the same time "offer stock options to their board members".
(f) $P(\text{large}) = 189/369 = 0.5122$
(g) $P(\text{offered stock options}) = 83/369 = 0.2249$
(h) $P(\text{large and offered stock options}) = 40/369 = 0.1084$
(i) $P(\text{small-to-midsized and did not offer stock options}) = 137/369 = 0.3713$
(j) $P(\text{large or offered stock options}) = (189 + 83 - 40)/369 = 0.6287$
(k) $P(\text{small-to-midsized or offered stock options}) = (180 + 83 - 43)/369 = 0.5962$
(l)   The probability of "large or offered stock options" includes the probability of "large and offered stock options", the probability of "large but did not offer stock options" and the probability of "small-to-midsized and offered stock options".

4.12   (a)

Enjoy Clothes Shopping	Male	Female	Total
Yes	136	224	360
No	104	36	140
Total	240	260	500

(b)   Since simple events have only one criterion specified, an example could be any one of the following:
(1) Being a male,
(2) Being a female,
(3) Enjoying clothes shopping,
(4) Not enjoying clothes shopping.
(c)   Since joint events specify two criteria simultaneously, an example could be any one of the following:
(1) Being a male and enjoying clothes shopping,
(2) Being a male and not enjoying clothes shopping,
(3) Being a female and enjoying clothes shopping,
(4) Being a female and not enjoying clothes shopping.
(d)   "Not enjoying clothes shopping" is the complement of "enjoying shopping for clothes," since it involves all events other than enjoying clothes shopping.
(e) $P(\text{male}) = 240/500 = 12/25 = 0.48$
(f) $P(\text{enjoys clothes shopping}) = 360/500 = 18/25 = 0.72$
(g) $P(\text{female and enjoys clothes shopping}) = 224/500 = 56/125 = 0.448$
(h) $P(\text{male and does not enjoy clothes shopping}) = 104/500 = 26/125 = 0.208$
(i) $P(\text{female or enjoys clothes shopping}) = 396/500 = 99/125 = 0.792$
(j) $P(\text{male or does not enjoy clothes shopping}) = 276/500 = 69/125 = 0.552$
(k) $P(\text{male or female}) = 500/500 = 1.00$

4.14   (a) $P(A \mid B) = 10/30 = 1/3 = 0.33$
       (b) $P(A \mid B') = 20/60 = 1/3 = 0.33$
       (c) $P(A' \mid B') = 40/60 = 2/3 = 0.67$
       (d)   Since $P(A \mid B) = P(A) = 1/3$, events A and B are statistically independent.

4.16 $P(A \mid B) = \dfrac{P(A \text{ and } B)}{P(B)} = \dfrac{0.4}{0.8} = \dfrac{1}{2} = 0.5$

4.18   Since $P(A \text{ and } B) = .20$ and $P(A)\, P(B) = 0.12$, events A and B are not statistically independent.

4.20   (a) P(book tickets on the internet | research ticket prices on the internet) = 88/212
             = 0.4151
       (b) P(researches ticket prices on the internet | book tickets on the internet) = 88/108
             = 0.8148
       (c)   The conditional events are reversed.
       (d)   Since P(book tickets on the internet) = 108/400 = 0.27 is not equal to P(book tickets on the internet | research ticket prices on the internet) = 88/212 = 0.4151, researching airline ticket prices on the internet and booking airline tickets on the internet are not statistically independent.

4.22   (a) P(claimed bias | white) = 29/56 = 0.5179
       (b) P(while | claim bias) = 29/155 = 0.1871
       (c)   The conditional events are reversed.
       (d)   Since P(white | claim bias) = 0.1871 is not equal to P(white) = 0.1210, being white and claiming bias are not statistically independent.

4.24   (a) P(needs warranty repair | manufacturer based in U.S.) = 0.025/0.6 = 0.0417
       (b) P(needs warranty repair | manufacturer not based in U.S.) = 0.015/0.4
             = 0.0375
       (c)   Since P(needs warranty repair | manufacturer based in U.S.) = 0.0417 and P(needs warranty repair) = 0.04, the two events are not statistically independent.

4.26   (a) $P(\text{both queens}) = \dfrac{4}{52} \cdot \dfrac{3}{51} = \dfrac{12}{2{,}652} = \dfrac{1}{221} = 0.0045$
       (b) $P(\text{10 followed by 5 or 6}) = \dfrac{4}{52} \cdot \dfrac{8}{51} = \dfrac{32}{2{,}652} = \dfrac{8}{663} = 0.012$
       (c) $P(\text{both queens}) = \dfrac{4}{52} \cdot \dfrac{4}{52} = \dfrac{16}{2{,}704} = \dfrac{1}{169} = 0.0059$
       (d) $P(\text{blackjack}) = \dfrac{16}{52} \cdot \dfrac{4}{51} + \dfrac{4}{52} \cdot \dfrac{16}{51} = \dfrac{128}{2{,}652} = \dfrac{32}{663} = 0.0483$

4.28

$$P(B \mid A) = \frac{P(A \mid B) \cdot P(B)}{P(A \mid B) \cdot P(B) + P(A \mid B') \cdot P(B')}$$

$$= \frac{0.8 \cdot 0.05}{0.8 \cdot 0.05 + 0.4 \cdot 0.95} = \frac{0.04}{0.42} = \mathbf{0.095}$$

4.30   (a) D = has disease T = test positive

$$P(D \mid T) = \frac{P(T \mid D) \cdot P(D)}{P(T \mid D) \cdot P(D) + P(T \mid D') \cdot P(D')}$$

$$= \frac{0.9 \cdot 0.03}{0.9 \cdot 0.03 + 0.01 \cdot 0.97} = \frac{0.027}{0.0367} = 0.736$$

(b)

$$P(D' \mid T') = \frac{P(T' \mid D') \cdot P(D')}{P(T' \mid D') \cdot P(D') + P(T' \mid D) \cdot P(D)}$$

$$= \frac{0.99 \cdot 0.97}{0.99 \cdot 0.97 + 0.10 \cdot 0.03} = \frac{0.9603}{0.9633} = 0.997$$

4.32   (a) B = Base Construction Co. enters a bid
O = Olive Construction Co. wins the contract

$$P(B' \mid O) = \frac{P(O \mid B') \cdot P(B')}{P(O \mid B') \cdot P(B') + P(O \mid B) \cdot P(B)}$$

$$= \frac{0.5 \cdot 0.3}{0.5 \cdot 0.3 + 0.25 \cdot 0.7} = \frac{0.15}{0.325} = 0.4615$$

(b) $P(O) = 0.175 + 0.15 = 0.325$

4.34   (a)   P(huge success | favorable review) = 0.099/0.459 = 0.2157
P(moderate success | favorable review) = 0.14/0.459 = 0.3050
P(break even | favorable review) = 0.16/0.459 = 0.3486
P(loser | favorable review) = 0.06/0.459 = 0.1307

(b)   P(favorable review) = 0.99(0.1) + 0.7(0.2) + 0.4(0.4) + 0.2(0.3) = 0.459

4.36 $3^{10} = 59049$

4.38   (a) $2^7 = 128$ (b) $6^7 = 279936$
(c) There are two mutually exclusive and collective exhaustive outcomes in (a) and six in
(b).

4.40 $n! = 4! = (4)(3)(2)(1) = 24$

4.42 $\dfrac{n!}{(n-X)!} = \dfrac{5!}{1!} = 120$

4.44 $\dfrac{n!}{(n-X)!} = \dfrac{12!}{9!} = (12)(11)(10) = 1320$

4.46 $\dfrac{n!}{X!(n-X)!} = \dfrac{7!}{4!(3!)} = \dfrac{(7)(6)(5)}{(3)(2)(1)} = 35$

4.48 $\dfrac{n!}{X!(n-X)!} = \dfrac{20!}{3!(17!)} = \dfrac{(20)(19)(18)}{(3)(2)(1)} = 1140$

4.52   A simple event can be described by a single characteristic. Joint probability refers to phenomena containing two or more events.

4.54   Events are mutually exclusive if both cannot occur at the same time. Events are collectively exhaustive if one of the events must occur.

4.56   When events A and B are independent, the probability of A and B is the product of the probability of event A and the probability of event B. When events A and B are not independent, the probability of A and B is the product of the conditional probability of event A given event B and the probability of event B.

4.58   In a permutation, the order of the outcomes is important while the order is irrelevant in combination.

4.60   (a)   P(good relationship with boss is important) = (0.63)(0.5)+(0.77)(0.5) = 0.7
       (b)   P(easy commute is important) = (0.48)(0.5)+(0.60)(0.5) = 0.54
       (c)   P(male and good relationship with boss is important) = (0.63)(0.5) = 0.315
       (d)   P(female and flexible hours is important) = (0.53)(0.5) = 0.265
       (e)   P(male | good relationship with boss is important)
             = (0.63)(0.5)/((0.63)(0.5)+(0.77)(0.5)) = 0.45
       (f)   Since P(easy commute is important | male) = 0.48 is not equal to P(easy commute is important) = 0.54, easy commute is important is not statistically independent of male. Similarly, none of the probability of any of the things workers say are extremely important aspects of a job is equal to the corresponding probability conditioned on gender, none of the things workers say are extremely important aspects of a job are statistically independent of gender.

4.62   (a)   P(dessert) = 136/600 = 17/75 = 0.227
       (b)   P(no beef entrée) = 413/600 = 0.688
       (c)   P(dessert *or* beef entrée) = 252/600 = 21/50 = 0.42
       (d)   P(female *and* no dessert) = 240/600 = 2/5 = 0.4
       (e)   P(dessert *and* beef entrée) = 71/600 = 0.118
       (f)   P(female *or* no dessert) = 504/600 = 21/25 = 0.84
       (g)   P(no dessert | female) = 240/280 = 6/7 = 0.8571
       (h)   P((dessert | beef entrée) = 71/187 = 0.3797
       (i)   Not statistically independent
       (j)   Not statistically independent

4.64   (a) P(fewer products) = 272/400 = 0.68
     (b) P(same products) = 96/400 = 0.24
     (c) P(same or more products) = (96 + 32)/400 = 0.32
     (d) P(fewer products and changed brands) = 262/400 = 0.655
     (e) P(same products and same brands) = 14/400 = 0.035
     (f) P(few products | changed brands) = 262/352 = 0.7443
     (g) P(same products | changed brands) = 82/ 352 = 0.233
     (h) P(same or more products | changed brands) = (82 + 8)/352 = 0.2557

4.64   (i)   The results from (a) – (c) involve all consumers while the results from (f) – (g) are
cont.   limited only to those consumers who have changed the brands they have purchased.

4.66 P(HIV is present | ELISA has given a positive result)
     = (0.995)(0.015)/((0.995)(0.015)+(0.01)(0.985)) = 0.6024

CHAPTER 5

OBJECTIVES

- To understand the properties of a probability distribution
- To be able to compute the expected value, variance, and covariance of a probability distribution
- To understand how to compute probabilities from binomial, hypergeometric, and Poisson distributions
- To know when to use the binomial, hypergeometric, and Poisson distributions

OVERVIEW AND KEY CONCEPTS

Some Basic Concepts of Discrete Probability Distribution

- **Random variable:** Outcomes of an experiment expressed numerically, e.g., Toss a die twice and count the number of times the number four appears (0, 1 or 2 times).
- **Discrete random variable:** A random variable that can have only certain distinct values. It is usually obtained by counting. E.g., Toss a coin five times and count the number of tails (0, 1, 2, 3, 4 or 5 tails).
- **Discrete probability distribution:** A mutually exclusive listing of all possible numerical outcomes for a discrete random variable such that a particular probability of occurrence is associated with each outcome.

Concepts of Expectation for a Discrete Random Variable

- **Expected value of a discrete random variable:** A weighted average over all possible outcomes.
    - The weights being the probabilities associated with each of the outcomes.
    - $$\mu = E(X) = \sum_{i=1}^{N} X_i P(X_i)$$
- **Variance of a discrete random variable:** The weighted average of the squared differences between each possible outcome and its mean
    - The weights being the probabilities of each of the respective outcomes.
    - $$\sigma^2 = \sum_{i=1}^{N} \left[X_i - E(X) \right]^2 P(X_i)$$
- **Standard deviation of a discrete random variable:** The square root of the variance.
    - $$\sigma = \sqrt{\sum_{i=1}^{N} \left[X_i - E(X) \right]^2 P(X_i)}$$

Covariance and Its Applications

- **Covariance:** $\sigma_{XY} = \sum_{i=1}^{N} \left[X_i - E(X) \right] \left[Y_i - E(Y) \right] P(X_i Y_i)$

  - A positive covariance indicates a positive relationship between the two discrete random variables.
  - A negative covariance indicates a negative relationship between the two discrete random variables.
  - The unit of the covariance depends on the units of the two discrete random variables, hence, its magnitude cannot be used to measure the strength of the relationship but only the direction of the relationship.

- **The expected value of the sum of two discrete random variables:** The expected value of the sum equals to the sum of the expected values.

  - $E(X+Y) = \mu_{X+Y} = E(X) + E(Y) = \mu_X + \mu_Y$

- **The variance of the sum of two discrete random variables:** The variance of the sum equals the sum of the variances plus twice the covariance.

  - $Var(X+Y) = \sigma_{X+Y}^2 = \sigma_X^2 + \sigma_Y^2 + 2\sigma_{XY}$

- **The standard deviation of the sum of two discrete random variables:**

  $\sigma_{X+Y} = \sqrt{\sigma_{X+Y}^2}$

- **Portfolio expected return:** The portfolio expected returns for a two-asset investment is equal to the weight (w) assigned to asset X multiplied by the expected return of asset X plus the weight ($1-w$) assigned to asset Y multiplied by the expected return of asset Y.

  - $E(P) = \mu_P = wE(X) + (1-w)E(Y)$

- **Portfolio risk:** The standard deviation of the portfolio.

  - $\sigma_P = \sqrt{w^2 \sigma_X^2 + (1-w)^2 \sigma_Y^2 + 2w(1-w)\sigma_{XY}}$

  - The smaller the value of σ_P, the less risky is an investment portfolio.

The Binomial Distribution

- **Properties of the binomial distribution:**
  - The sample has n observations.
  - Each observation is classified into one of the two mutually exclusive and collectively exhaustive categories, usually called *success* and *failure*.
  - The probability of getting a *success* is p while the probability of a *failure* is ($1-p$).
  - The outcome (i.e., *success* or *failure*) of any observation is independent of the outcome of any other observation. This can be achieved by selecting each observation randomly either from an *infinite population without replacement* or from a *finite population with replacement*.

- **The binomial probability distribution function:**

  - $$P(X) = \frac{n!}{X!(n-X)!} p^X (1-p)^{n-X}$$

    where

    $P(X)$: probability of X successes given n and p

    X: number of "successes" in the sample $(X = 0, 1, \cdots, n)$

    p: the probability of "success"

    $(1-p)$: the probability of "failure"

    n: sample size

- **The mean and variance of a binomial distribution:**

  - $\mu = E(X) = np$

  - $\sigma^2 = np(1-p)$

  - $\sigma = \sqrt{np(1-p)}$

- **Applications:** Useful in evaluating the probability of X successes in a sample of size n drawn with replacement from a finite population or without replacement from an infinite population.

The Poisson Distribution

- **Properties of the Poisson distribution:**
  1. The area of opportunity, in which the number of times a particular event occurs is of interest, is defined by time, length, surface area, etc.
  2. The probability that an event occurs in a given area of opportunity is the same for all of the areas of opportunity.
  3. The number of events that occur in one area of opportunity is independent of the number of events that occur in other areas of opportunity.
  4. The probability that two or more events will occur in an area of opportunity approaches zero as the area of opportunity becomes smaller.

- **The Poisson probability distribution function:**

  - $$P(X) = \frac{e^{-\lambda} \lambda^X}{X!}$$

    where

    $P(X)$: probability of X "successes" given λ

    X: number of "successes" per unit

    λ: expected (average) number of "successes"

    e: 2.71828 (base of natural logs)

- **The mean and variance of a Poisson Distribution**

  - $\mu = E(X) = \lambda$

  - $\sigma^2 = \lambda$

  - $\sigma = \sqrt{\lambda}$

- **Applications:** Useful in modeling the number of successes in a given continuous interval of time, length, surface area, etc.

The Hypergeometric Distribution

- **Properties of the hypergeometric distribution:**
    - There are "n" trials in a sample taken randomly from a finite population of size N.
    - The sample is drawn without replacement.
    - The "n" trials are dependent.
- **The hypergeometric probability distribution function:**

    - $$P(X) = \frac{\binom{A}{X}\binom{N-A}{n-X}}{\binom{N}{n}}$$

    where

    $P(X)$: probability that X successes given $n, N,$ and A

    n: sample size

    N: population size

    A: number of "successes" in population

    X: number of "successes" in sample $(X = 0,1,2,\cdots,n)$

- **The mean and variance of a hypergeometric distribution:**

    - $$\mu = E(X) = \frac{nA}{N}$$

    - $$\sigma = \sqrt{\frac{nA(N-A)}{N^2}}\sqrt{\frac{N-n}{N-1}}$$

- **Applications:** Useful in evaluating the probability of A successes in a sample containing n observations drawn without replacement from a finite population of N observations.

SOLUTIONS TO END OF SECTION
AND CHAPTER REVIEW EVEN PROBLEMS

5.2   (a)

Distribution C

X	P(X)	X*P(X)
0	0.20	0.00
1	0.20	0.20
2	0.20	0.40
3	0.20	0.60
4	0.20	0.80
	1.00	2.00 $\mu = 2.00$

Distribution D

X	P(X)	X*P(X)
0	0.10	0.00
1	0.20	0.20
2	0.40	0.80
3	0.20	0.60
4	0.10	0.40
	1.00	2.00 $\mu = 2.00$

(b)   Distribution C

X	$(X-\mu)^2$	P(X)	$(X-\mu)^2*P(X)$
0	$(-2)^2$	0.20	0.80
1	$(-1)^2$	0.20	0.20
2	$(0)^2$	0.20	0.00
3	$(1)^2$	0.20	0.20
4	$(2)^2$	0.20	0.80
		$\sigma^2 =$	2.00

$$\sigma = \sqrt{\Sigma(X-\mu)^2 \cdot P(X)} = \sqrt{2.00} = 1.414$$

Distribution D

X	$(X-\mu)^2$	P(X)	$(X-\mu)^2*P(X)$
0	$(-2)^2$	0.10	0.40
1	$(-1)^2$	0.20	0.20
2	$(0)^2$	0.40	0.00
3	$(1)^2$	0.20	0.20
4	$(2)^2$	0.10	0.40
		$\sigma^2 =$	1.20

$$\sigma = \sqrt{\Sigma(X-\mu)^2 \cdot P(X)} = \sqrt{1.20} = 1.095$$

(c)   Distribution C is uniform and symmetric; D is unimodal and symmetric. Means are the same but variances are different.

5.4   (a)-(b)

X	P(x)	X*P(X)	$(X-\mu_X)^2$	$(X-\mu_X)^2*P(X)$
0	0.10	0.00	4	0.40
1	0.20	0.20	1	0.20
2	0.45	0.90	0	0.00
3	0.15	0.45	1	0.15
4	0.05	0.20	4	0.20
5	0.05	0.25	9	0.45
	(a) Mean =	2.00	variance =	1.40
			(b) Stdev =	1.18321596

5.6   (a)

X	P(X)
$ - 1$	21/36
$ + 1$	15/36

(b)

X	P(X)
$ - 1$	21/36
$ + 1$	15/36

(c)

X	P(X)
$ - 1$	30/36
$ + 4$	6/36

(d) $ - 0.167$ for each method of play

5.8   (a) $E(X) = (0.2)(\$-100) + (0.4)(\$50) + (0.3)(\$\ 200) + (0.1)(\$300) = \$90$
       (b) $E(Y) = (0.2)(\$50) + (0.4)(\$30) + (0.3)(\$\ 20) + (0.1)(\$20) = \$30$
       (c)

$$\sigma_X = \sqrt{(0.2)(-100-90)^2 + (0.4)(50-90)^2 + (0.3)(200-90)^2 + (0.1)(300-90)^2}$$
$$= \sqrt{15900} = 126.10$$

       (d)

$$\sigma_Y = \sqrt{(0.2)(50-30)^2 + (0.4)(30-30)^2 + (0.3)(20-30)^2 + (0.1)(20-30)^2}$$
$$= \sqrt{120} = 10.95$$

       (e) $\sigma_{XY} = (0.2)(-100-90)(50-30) + (0.4)(50-90)(30-30)$
                     $+ (0.3)(200-90)(20-30) + (0.1)(300-90)(20-30) = -1300$
       (f) $E(X+Y) = E(X) + E(Y) = \$90 + \$30 = \$120$
       (g) $\sigma_{X+Y} = \sqrt{15900+120+2(-1300)} = \sqrt{13420} = 115.84$

5.10   (a) $E(P) = 0.3(105) + 0.7(35) = \$56$

$$\sigma_P = \sqrt{(0.3)^2(14,725) + (0.7)^2(11,025) + 2(0.3)(0.7)(-12,675)} = \$37.47$$

$$CV = \frac{\sigma_P}{E(P)} = \frac{37.47}{56}(100\%) = 66.91\%$$

        (b) $E(P) = 0.7(105) + 0.3(35) = \$84$

$$\sigma_P = \sqrt{(0.7)^2(14,725) + (0.3)^2(11,025) + 2(0.7)(0.3)(-12,675)} = \$53.70$$

$$CV = \frac{\sigma_P}{E(P)} = \frac{53.70}{84}(100\%) = 63.93\%$$

        (c)   Investing 50% in the Dow Jones index fund will yield the lowest risk per unit
               average return at $CV = \dfrac{\sigma_P}{E(P)} = \dfrac{10}{70}(100\%) = 14.29\%$.

5.12   (a) $E(X) = \$71$ (b) $E(Y) = \$97$
        (c) $\sigma_X = 61.88$ (d) $\sigma_Y = 84.27$
        (e) $\sigma_{XY} = 5113$
        (f)   Stock Y gives the investor a higher expected return than stock X, but also has a
               higher standard deviation. A risk-averse investor should invest in stock X, but an
               investor willing to sustain a higher risk can expect a higher return from stock Y.
        (g) $E(P) = \$94.40$ $\sigma_P = 81.92$
        (h) $E(P) = \$89.20$ $\sigma_P = 77.28$
        (i) $E(P) = \$84.00$ $\sigma_P = 72.73$
        (j) $E(P) = \$78.80$ $\sigma_P = 68.28$
        (k) $E(P) = \$73.60$ $\sigma_P = 63.98$
        (l)   Based on the results of (g)-(k), you should recommend a portfolio with 10%
               stock X and 90% stock Y if you make the decision solely on the expected return
               but recognize that as your expected return increases, so does the portfolio risk.

5.14   (a)   0.5997 (c)   0.0439   (e)   0.3874
        (b)   0.0016 (d)   0.4018

5.16   Given $p = 0.5$ and $n = 5$, $P(X = 5) = 0.0312$.

5.18   (a)   An operational definition of *aware* can be "remembering having seen the commercials on TV".

(b)   Since the 68% and 24% figures are obtained from the survey results conducted by the networks, they are best classified as empirical classical probability.

(c) $P(X < 5) = 1.4 \cdot 10^{-5} = 0.000014$ (d) $P(X \geq 10) = 0.9721$

(e) $P(X \geq 15) = 0.3426$ (f) $P(X = 20) = 0.000447$

(g) $\mu = n \cdot p = 13.6$

(h)   (c) $P(X < 5) = 0.4561$ (d) $P(X \geq 10) = 0.0103$

(e) $P(X \geq 15) = 2.2 \cdot 10^{-6} = 0.0000022$

(f) $P(X = 20) = 4.02 \cdot 10^{-13} = 0.00000$

(g) $\mu = n \cdot p = 4.8$

5.20   If $p = 0.25$ and $n = 5$,

(a) $P(X = 5) = 0.0010$

(b) $P(X \geq 4) = P(X = 4) + P(X = 5) = 0.0146 + 0.0010 = 0.0156$

(c) $P(X = 0) = 0.2373$

(d) $P(X \leq 2) = P(X = 0) + P(X = 1) + P(X = 2)$
$= 0.2373 + 0.3955 + 0.2637 = 0.8965$

(e)   Two assumptions: (1) Independence of her answers, (2) Only two outcomes - answer correct or answer incorrect.

(f)   Mean: $\mu = 1.25$ Standard deviation: $\sigma = 0.968$

(g)   If $p = 0.25$ and $n = 50$, $P(X \geq 30) = 1 - P(X \leq 29)$ $= 1 - 0.99999984$
$= 0.00000016$ or 1.6423×10^{-7}.

5.22   (a) $P(X = 3) = \dfrac{\binom{5}{3} \cdot \binom{10-5}{4-3}}{\binom{10}{4}} = \dfrac{\frac{5 \cdot 4 \cdot 3!}{3! \cdot 2 \cdot 1} \cdot \frac{5 \cdot 4!}{4! \cdot 1!}}{\frac{10 \cdot 9 \cdot 8 \cdot 7 \cdot 6!}{6! \cdot 4 \cdot 3 \cdot 2 \cdot 1}} = \dfrac{5}{3 \cdot 7} = 0.2381$

(b) $P(X = 1) = \dfrac{\binom{3}{1} \cdot \binom{6-3}{4-1}}{\binom{6}{4}} = \dfrac{\frac{3 \cdot 2!}{2! \cdot 1} \cdot \frac{3!}{3! \cdot 0!}}{\frac{6 \cdot 5 \cdot 4!}{4! \cdot 2 \cdot 1}} = \dfrac{1}{5} = 0.2$

(c) $P(X = 0) = \dfrac{\binom{3}{0} \cdot \binom{12-3}{5-0}}{\binom{12}{5}} = \dfrac{\frac{3!}{3! \cdot 0!} \cdot \frac{9 \cdot 8 \cdot 7 \cdot 6 \cdot 5!}{5! \cdot 4 \cdot 3 \cdot 2 \cdot 1}}{\frac{12 \cdot 11 \cdot 10 \cdot 9 \cdot 8 \cdot 7!}{7! \cdot 5 \cdot 4 \cdot 3 \cdot 2 \cdot 1}} = \dfrac{7}{44} = 0.1591$

(d) $P(X = 3) = \dfrac{\binom{3}{3} \cdot \binom{7-0}{3-3}}{\binom{10}{3}} = \dfrac{\frac{3!}{3! \cdot 0!} \cdot \frac{7!}{7! \cdot 0!}}{\frac{10 \cdot 9 \cdot 8 \cdot 7!}{7! \cdot 3 \cdot 2 \cdot 1}} = \dfrac{1}{120} = 0.0083$

5.24   (a)   If $n = 6$, $A = 25$, and $N = 100$, $P(X \geq 2) = 1 - [P(X = 0) + P(X = 1)]$
$= 1 - [0.1689 + 0.3620] = 0.4691$

(b)   If $n = 6$, $A = 30$, and $N = 100$, $P(X \geq 2) = 1 - [P(X = 0) + P(X = 1)]$
$= 1 - [0.1100 + 0.3046] = 0.5854$

(c)   If $n = 6$, $A = 5$, and $N = 100$, $P(X \geq 2) = 1 - [P(X = 0) + P(X = 1)]$
$= 1 - [0.7291 + 0.2430] = 0.0279$

(d)   If $n = 6$, $A = 10$, and $N = 100$, $P(X \geq 2) = 1 - [P(X = 0) + P(X = 1)]$
$= 1 - [0.5223 + 0.3687] = 0.1090$

(e)   The probability that the entire group will be audited is very sensitive to the true number of improper returns in the population. If the true number is very low ($A = 5$), the probability is very low (0.0279). When the true number is increased by a factor of six ($A = 30$), the probability the group will be audited increases by a factor of almost 21 (0.5854).

5.26   (a)--(c) PHStat output:

Data	
Sample size	8
No. of successes in population	12
Population size	48

Hypergeometric Probabilities Table			
		X	P(X)
		0	(b) 0.080192
		1	0.265463
		2	0.340677
		3	0.219792
		4	0.077271
		5	0.014986
		6	0.001543
		7	7.56E-05
		8	(a) 1.31E-06

$P(X = 8) = 1.31178E-06$
$P(X = 0) = 0.0802$
$P(X \geq 1) = 0.9198$

(d) PHStat output:

Data	
Sample size	8
No. of successes in population	6
Population size	48

Hypergeometric Probabilities Table			
		X	P(X)
		0	0.312788
		1	0.428966
		2	0.208525
		3	0.045087
		4	0.004449
		5	0.000183
		6	2.28E-06

$P(X = 8) = 2.28E-06$
$P(X = 0) = 0.3128$
$P(X \geq 1) = 0.6872$

5.28   (a)--(c)

	A	B	C
1	Defective Disks		
2			
3	Sample size	4	
4	No. of successes in population	5	
5	Population size	15	
6			
7	Hypergeometric Probabilities Table		
8		X	P(x)
9		0	0.153846
10		1	0.43956
11		2	0.32967
12		3	0.07326
13		4	0.003663

(d) $\mu = n \cdot p = 4 \cdot (0.333) = 1.33$

5.30   (a)   If $\lambda = 2.0$, $P(X \geq 2) = 1 - [P(X = 0) + P(X = 1)] = 1 - [0.1353 + 0.2707]$
$= 0.5940$

(b)   If $\lambda = 8.0$, $P(X \geq 3) = 1 - [P(X = 0) + P(X = 1) + P(X = 2)]$
$= 1 - [0.0003 + 0.0027 + 0.0107] = 1 - 0.0137 = 0.9863$

(c)   If $\lambda = 0.5$, $P(X \leq 1) = P(X = 0) + P(X = 1) = 0.6065 + 0.3033 = 0.9098$

(d)   If $\lambda = 4.0$, $P(X \geq 1) = 1 - P(X = 0) = 1 - 0.0183 = 0.9817$

(e)   If $\lambda = 5.0$, $P(X \leq 3) = P(X = 0) + P(X = 1) + P(X = 2) + P(X = 3)$
$= 0.0067 + 0.0337 + 0.0842 + 0.1404 = 0.2650$

5.32   (a)   For the number of phone call received in a 1-hour period to be distributed as a Poisson random variable, we need to assume that (i) the probability that a phone call is received in a given 1-hour period is the same for all the other 1-hour periods, (ii) the number of phone call received in a given 1-hour period is independent of the number of phone call received in any other 1-hour period, (iii) the probability that two or more phone call received in a time period approaches zero as the duration of the time period becomes smaller.

(b) $\lambda = 0.4$, $P(X = 0) = 0.6703$ (c) $\lambda = 0.4$, $P(X = 1) = 0.2681$

(d) $\lambda = 0.4$, $P(X = 2) = 0.0536$ (e) $\lambda = 0.4$, $P(X \geq 3) = 0.0079$

(f) $\lambda = 0.4$, $P(X \leq 4) = 0.99994$. A maximum of 4 phone calls will be received in a 1-hour period 99.99% of the time.

5.34   (a) – (c) Portion of PHStat output

Data						
Average/Expected number of successes:			6			
Poisson Probabilities Table						
	X	P(X)	P(<=X)	P(<X)	P(>X)	P(>=X)
	0	0.002479	0.002479	0.000000	0.997521	1.000000
	1	0.014873	0.017351	0.002479	0.982649	0.997521
	2	0.044618	0.061969	0.017351	0.938031	0.982649
	3	0.089235	0.151204	0.061969	0.848796	0.938031
	4	0.133853	0.285057	0.151204	0.714943	0.848796
	5	**(b)** 0.160623	0.445680	**(a)** 0.285057	0.554320	**(c)** 0.714943
	6	0.160623	0.606303	0.445680	0.393697	0.554320
	7	0.137677	0.743980	0.606303	0.256020	0.393697
	8	0.103258	0.847237	0.743980	0.152763	0.256020
	9	0.068838	0.916076	0.847237	0.083924	0.152763
	10	0.041303	0.957379	0.916076	0.042621	0.083924
	11	0.022529	0.979908	0.957379	0.020092	0.042621
	12	0.011264	0.991173	0.979908	0.008827	0.020092
	13	0.005199	0.996372	0.991173	0.003628	0.008827
	14	0.002228	0.998600	0.996372	0.001400	0.003628
	15	0.000891	0.999491	0.998600	0.000509	0.001400
	16	0.000334	0.999825	0.999491	0.000175	0.000509
	17	0.000118	0.999943	0.999825	0.000057	0.000175

(d) $P(X = 4$ or $X = 5) = P(X = 4) + P(X = 5) = 0.294476$

(e)   (a) – (c) If $\lambda = 5.0$, portion of PHStat output:

Data						
Average/Expected number of successes:			5			
Poisson Probabilities Table						
	X	P(X)	P(<=X)	P(<X)	P(>X)	P(>=X)
	0	0.006738	0.006738	0.000000	0.993262	1.000000
	1	0.033690	0.040428	0.006738	0.959572	0.993262
	2	0.084224	0.124652	0.040428	0.875348	0.959572
	3	0.140374	0.265026	0.124652	0.734974	0.875348
	4	0.175467	0.440493	0.265026	0.559507	0.734974
	5	**(b)** 0.175467	0.615961	**(a)** 0.440493	0.384039	**(c)** 0.559507
	6	0.146223	0.762183	0.615961	0.237817	0.384039
	7	0.104445	0.866628	0.762183	0.133372	0.237817
	8	0.065278	0.931906	0.866628	0.068094	0.133372
	9	0.036266	0.968172	0.931906	0.031828	0.068094
	10	0.018133	0.986305	0.968172	0.013695	0.031828
	11	0.008242	0.994547	0.986305	0.005453	0.013695
	12	0.003434	0.997981	0.994547	0.002019	0.005453
	13	0.001321	0.999302	0.997981	0.000698	0.002019
	14	0.000472	0.999774	0.999302	0.000226	0.000698
	15	0.000157	0.999931	0.999774	0.000069	0.000226
	16	0.000049	0.999980	0.999931	0.000020	0.000069
	17	0.000014	0.999995	0.999980	0.000005	0.000020

(d) $P(X = 4$ or $X = 5) = P(X = 4) + P(X = 5) = 0.350935$

5.36 $\lambda = 9.0$,
    (a) $P(X < 3) = 0.00623$
    (b) $P(X = 3) = 0.01499$
    (c) $P(X \geq 3) = 1 - P(X < 3) = 0.99377$
    (d) $P(X > 3) = 0.97877$

5.38   The expected value is the average of a probability distribution. It is the value that can be expected to occur on the average, in the long run.

5.40   The Poisson distribution is different than the binomial distribution in that we are determining the probability of a specific number of successes in an area of opportunity or time interval. As such, there is no finite sample size as there is in the binomial distribution. The Poisson distribution also assumes that the probability of the occurrence of success in one interval is statistically independent of that in any other interval.

5.42   A positive covariance will increase the portfolio risk. A negative covariance will decrease the portfolio risk.

5.44   (a)-(e)   Portion of the PHStat output:

Binomial Probabilities						
Data						
Sample size	10					
Probability of success	0.4					
Statistics						
Mean	4					
Variance	2.4					
Standard deviation	1.549193					
Binomial Probabilities Table						
	X	P(X)	P(<=X)	P(<X)	P(>X)	P(>=X)
	0	(a) 0.006047	0.006047	0	0.993953	1
	1	(b) 0.040311	0.046357	0.006047	0.953643	0.993953
	2	(c) 0.120932	(d) 0.16729	0.046357	0.83271	0.953643
	10	(e) 0.000105	1	0.999895	0	0.000105

    (f)   The probability is essentially zero that all ten automatically opt to talk to a live operator if the probability of a randomly selected caller will automatically opt to go to a live operator is 40%. Hence, the 40% figure given in the article does not appear to apply to this particular system.

5.46   (a)-(d) Portion of the PHStat output:

Binomial Probabilities						
Data						
Sample size	10					
Probability of success	0.19					
Statistics						
Mean	(d) 1.9					
Variance	1.539					
Standard deviation	(d) 1.240564					
Binomial Probabilities Table						
	X	P(X)	P(<=X)	P(<X)	P(>X)	P(>=
	0	(a) 0.121577	0.121577	0	0.878423	
	1	(b) 0.28518	0.406756	0.121577	0.593244	0.878
	2	0.301023	0.70778	0.406756	0.29222	0.592
	10	6.13E-08	1	1	0	6.13E

(e)   (a)-(d) Portion of the PHStat output:

Binomial Probabilities				
Data				
Sample size	10			
Probability of success	0.33			
Statistics				
Mean	(d) 3.3			
Variance	2.211			
Standard deviation	(d) 1.486943			
Binomial Probabilities Table				
	X	P(X)	P(<=X)	P(>=X)
	0	(a) 0.018228	0.018228	1
	1	(b) 0.089782	0.10801	0.981772
	2	0.198993	0.307003	(c) 0.89199
	10	1.53E-05	1	1.53E-05

.48   (a) – (e) Portion of the PHStat output:

Binomial Probabilities						
Data						
Sample size	10					
Probability of success	0.44					
Statistics						
Mean	(f) 4.4					
Variance	2.464					
Standard deviation	1.569713					
Binomial Probabilities Table						
	X	P(X)	P(<=X)	P(<X)	P(>X)	P(>=X)
	0	0.003033	0.003033	0	0.996967	1
	5	(b) 0.228878	0.759297	(d) 0.530419	0.240703	(c) 0.469581
	6	0.149861	0.909157	0.759297	0.090843	(e) 0.240703
	7	0.067284	0.976442	0.909157	0.023558	0.090843
	8	0.019825	0.996267	0.976442	0.003733	0.023558
	9	0.003461	0.999728	0.996267	0.000272	0.003733
	10	(a) 0.000272	1	0.999728	0	0.000272

(f)   On average 4.4 people will refuse to participate out of every 10 people.

5.50   (a)   The assumptions needed to model the number of shipments made on time by the binomial distribution are (i) the probability of on time delivery of each shipment is the same and (ii) the result of one delivery does not affect the result of the other.
        (b) $P(X = 10) = 0.3487$
        (c) $P(X = 9) = 0.3874$
        (d) $P(X = 8) = 0.1937$
        (e) $P(X = 7) = 0.0574$
        (f) $P(X \le 9) = 0.6513$
        (g) $P(X \le 6) = 0.0128$

5.52   (a)   0.74
        (b)   0.74
        $p = 0.74,\ n = 5$
        (c) $P(X = 4) = 0.3898$ (d) $P(X = 0) = 0.0012$
        (e)   Stock prices tend to rise in the years when the economy is expanding and fall in the years of recession or contraction. Hence, the probability that the price will rise in one year is not likely to be independent from year to year.

5.54   (a) $P(\text{jackpot}) = \dfrac{\dbinom{5}{5}\dbinom{47}{0}}{\dbinom{52}{5}} \dfrac{\dbinom{1}{1}}{\dbinom{52}{1}} = 7.39941 \cdot 10^{-9}$

(b) $P(\$175,000) = \dfrac{\dbinom{5}{5}}{\dbinom{52}{5}} \dfrac{\dbinom{52}{1}}{\dbinom{52}{1}} = 3.84769 \cdot 10^{-7}$

(c) $P(\$5,000) = \dfrac{\dbinom{5}{4}\dbinom{47}{1}}{\dbinom{52}{5}} \dfrac{\dbinom{1}{1}}{\dbinom{52}{1}} = 1.73886 \cdot 10^{-6}$

(d) $P(\$150) = \dfrac{\dbinom{5}{4}\dbinom{47}{1}}{\dbinom{52}{5}} \dfrac{\dbinom{52}{1}}{\dbinom{52}{1}} + \dfrac{\dbinom{5}{3}\dbinom{47}{2}}{\dbinom{52}{5}} \dfrac{\dbinom{1}{1}}{\dbinom{52}{1}}$

$= 9.04208 \cdot 10^{-5} + 7.99876 \cdot 10^{-5} = 0.0001704084$

(e) $P(\$10) = \dfrac{\dbinom{5}{2}\dbinom{47}{3}}{\dbinom{52}{5}} \dfrac{\dbinom{1}{1}}{\dbinom{52}{1}} = 0.001199814$

(f) $P(\$7) = \dfrac{\dbinom{5}{3}\dbinom{47}{2}}{\dbinom{52}{5}} \dfrac{\dbinom{52}{1}}{\dbinom{52}{1}} = 0.004159356$

(g) $P(\$3) = \dfrac{\dbinom{5}{1}\dbinom{47}{4}}{\dbinom{52}{5}} \dfrac{\dbinom{1}{1}}{\dbinom{52}{1}} = 0.006598978$

(h) $P(\$2) = \dfrac{\dbinom{1}{1}}{\dbinom{52}{1}} = 0.019230769$

(i) $P(\$0) = 1 - P(\$2) - P(\$3) - P(\$7) - P(\$10) - P(\$150) - P(\$5,000) - P(\$175,000)$
$- P(\text{jackpot}) = 0.968638543$

5.56   (a) $\lambda = 0.4$, $P(X = 0) = 0.67032$
        (b) $\lambda = 0.4$, $P(X = 1) = 0.26813$
        (c) $\lambda = 0.4$, $P(X \geq 2) = 0.06155$
        (d) $\lambda = 0.4$, $P(X \geq 5) = 0.00006$
        (e) $\lambda = 0.16$, $P(X = 0) = 0.85214$
        (f) $\lambda = 0.16$, $P(X = 1) = 0.13634$
        (g) $\lambda = 0.16$, $P(X \geq 2) = 0.01151$
        (h) $\lambda = 0.16$, $P(X \geq 10) = 0.00000$

CHAPTER 6

OBJECTIVES

- To know how to compute probabilities from the normal distribution
- To be able to use the normal probability plot to assess whether a distribution is normally distributed
- To know how to compute probabilities from the uniform distribution
- To know how to compute probabilities from the exponential distribution

OVERVIEW AND KEY CONCEPTS

Some Basic Concepts of Continuous Probability Density Function

- **Continuous random variable:** A variable that can take an infinite number of values within a specific range, e.g. Weight, height, daily changes in closing prices of stocks, and time between arrivals of planes landing on a runway.

- **Continuous probability density function:** A mathematical expression that represents the continuous phenomenon of a continuous random variable, and can be used to calculate the probability that the random variable occurs within certain ranges or intervals.

- The probability that a continuous random variable is equal to a *particular value* is 0. This distinguishes continuous phenomena, which are measured, from discrete phenomena, which are counted. For example, the probability that a task can be completed in between 20 and 30 seconds can be measured. With a more precise measuring instrument, we can compute the probability that the task can be completed between a very small interval such as 19.99 to 20.01. However, the probability that the task can be completed in *exactly* 21 seconds is 0.

- Obtaining probabilities or computing expected values and standard deviations for continuous random variables involves mathematical expressions that require knowledge of integral calculus. In this book, these are achieved via special probability tables or computer statistical software like Minitab or PHStat.

The Normal Distribution

- **Properties of the normal distribution:**
    - Bell-shaped (and thus symmetrical) in its appearance.
    - Its measures of central tendency (mean, median, and mode) are all identical.
    - Its "middle spread" (interquartile range) is equal to 1.33 standard deviations.
    - Its associated random variable has an infinite range $(-\infty < X < +\infty)$.

- **The normal probability density function:**

  - $f(X) = \dfrac{1}{\sqrt{2\pi\sigma^2}} e^{-\frac{1}{2\sigma^2}(X-\mu)^2}$ where

    $f(X)$: density of random variable X

    $\pi = 3.14159;$ $e = 2.71828$

    μ: population mean

    σ: population standard deviation

    X: value of random variable $(-\infty < X < \infty)$

  - A particular combination of μ and σ will yield a particular normal probability distribution.

- **Standardization or normalization of a normal continuous random variable:** By standardizing (normalizing) a normal random variable, we need only one table to tabulate the probabilities of the whole family of normal distributions.

- **The transformation (standardization) formula:** $Z = \dfrac{X - \mu}{\sigma}$

  - The standardized normal distribution is one whose random variable Z always has a mean 0 and a standard deviation 1.

- **Finding range probability of a normal random variable:**
  1.   Standardize the value of X into Z.
  2.   Lookup the cumulative probabilities from the cumulative standardized normal distribution table.

  E.g., For $\mu = 5$ and $\sigma = 10$, $P(2.9 < X < 7.1) = ?$

$$Z = \frac{X - \mu}{\sigma} = \frac{2.9 - 5}{10} = -.21 \qquad Z = \frac{X - \mu}{\sigma} = \frac{7.1 - 5}{10} = .21$$

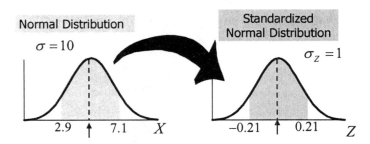

Cumulative Standardized Normal
Distribution Table (Portion) $\mu_z = 0$ $\sigma_z = 1$

Z	.00	.01	.02
0.0	.5000	.5040	.5080
0.1	.5398	.5438	.5478
0.2	.5793	**.5832**	.5871
0.3	.6179	.6217	.6255

Cumulative Standardized Normal
Distribution Table (Portion) $\mu_z = 0$ $\sigma_z = 1$

Z	.00	.01	.02
-03	.3821	.3783	.3745
-02	.4207	**.4168**	.4129
-0.1	.4602	.4562	.4522
0.0	.5000	.4960	.4920

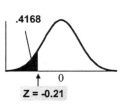

$$P(2.9 < X < 7.1) = P(-0.21 < Z < 0.21) = 0.5832 - 0.4168 = 0.1664$$

E.g., For $\mu = 5$ and $\sigma = 10$, $P(X \geq 8) = ?$

$$Z = \frac{X - \mu}{\sigma} = \frac{8-5}{10} = .30$$

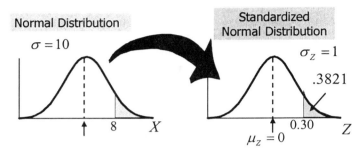

Cumulative Standardized Normal
Distribution Table (Portion)

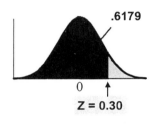

Z	.00	.01	.02
0.0	.5000	.5040	.5080
0.1	.5398	.5438	.5478
0.2	.5793	.5832	.5871
0.3	**.6179**	.6217	.6255

$$P(X \geq 8) = P(Z \geq 0.30) = 1 - 0.6179 = 0.3821$$

- **Recovering X values for known probabilities:**
    1. Lookup the Z value from the cumulative standardized normal distribution table.
    2. Recover the value of X using the formula $X = \mu + Z\sigma$

    E.g., For $\mu = 5$ and $\sigma = 10$, $P(X \leq A) = 0.6179$, what is the value of A?

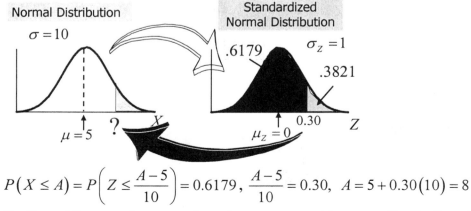

$$P(X \leq A) = P\left(Z \leq \frac{A-5}{10}\right) = 0.6179, \quad \frac{A-5}{10} = 0.30, \quad A = 5 + 0.30(10) = 8$$

- **Applications:** Many continuous random phenomena are either normally distributed or can be approximated by a normal distribution. Hence, it is important to know how to assess whether a distribution is normally distributed.

Evaluating the Normality Assumption

- For small and moderate-sized data sets, construct a stem-and-leaf display and box-and-whisker plot. For large data sets, construct the frequency distribution and plot the histogram or polygon.
- Obtain the mean, median, and mode, and note the similarities or differences among these measures of central tendency.
- Obtain the interquartile range and standard deviation. Note how well the interquartile range can be approximated by 1.33 times the standard deviation.
- Obtain the range and note how well it can be approximated by 6 times the standard deviation.
- Determine whether approximately 2/3 of the observations lie between the mean ± 1 standard deviation. Determine whether approximately 4/5 of the observations lie between the mean ± 1.28 standard deviations. Determine whether approximately 19/20 of the observations lie between the mean ± 2 standard deviations.
- Construct a normal probability plot and evaluate the likelihood that the variable of interest is at least approximately normally distributed by inspecting the plot for evidence of linearity (i.e., a straight line).

The Normal Probability Plot

- **The normal probability plot:** A two-dimensional plot of the observed data values on the vertical axis with their corresponding quantile values from a standardized normal distribution on the horizontal axis.

Left-Skewed

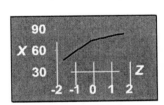

Right-Skewed

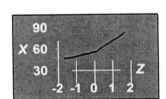

Rectangular

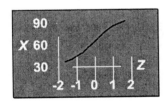

U-Shaped

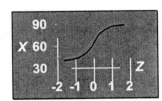

The Uniform Distribution

- **Properties of the uniform distribution:**
  - The probability of occurrence of a value is equally likely to occur anywhere in the range between the smallest value a and the largest value b.
  - Also called the **rectangular distribution.**
  - $\mu = \dfrac{a+b}{2}$
  - $\sigma^2 = \dfrac{(b-a)^2}{12}$
  - $\sigma = \sqrt{\dfrac{(b-a)^2}{12}}$
- **The uniform probability density function:**
  - $f(X) = \dfrac{1}{b-a}$ if $a \leq X \leq b$ and 0 elsewhere, where

    a is the minimum value of X and b is the maximum value of X
- **Applications:** Selection of random numbers.

The Exponential Distribution

- **The exponential distribution:**

  $$P(\text{arrival time} < X) = 1 - e^{-\lambda X}$$

  where

  X : any value of continuous random variable

  λ : the population average number of arrivals per unit of time

  $1/\lambda$: average time between arrivals

  $e = 2.71828$
- **Applications:** The exponential distribution is useful in waiting line (or queuing) theory to model the length of time between arrivals in processes such as customers at fast-food restaurants, and patients entering a hospital emergency room.

SOLUTIONS TO END OF SECTION
AND CHAPTER REVIEW EVEN PROBLEMS

6.2   (a) $P(Z > 1.34) = 1.0 - 0.9099 = 0.0901$
      (b) $P(Z < 1.17) = 0.8790$
      (c) $P(0 < Z < 1.17) = 0.8790 - 0.5 = 0.3790$
      (d) $P(Z < -1.17) = 0.1210$
      (e) $P(-1.17 < Z < 1.34) = 0.9099 - 0.1210 = 0.7889$
      (f) $P(-1.17 < Z < -0.50) = 0.3085 - 0.1210 = 0.1875$

6.4   (a) $P(Z > 1.08) = 1 - 0.8599 = 0.1401$
      (b) $P(Z < -0.21) = 0.4168$
      (c) $P(-1.96 < Z < -0.21) = 0.4168 - 0.0250 = 0.3918$
      (d) $P(-1.96 < Z < 1.08) = 0.8599 - 0.0250 = 0.8349$
      (e) $P(1.08 < Z < 1.96) = 0.9750 - 0.8599 = 0.1151$
      (f)   Since the Z-distribution is symmetric about its mean, half of the area will be below $Z = 0$.
      (g)   If $P(Z < A) = 0.1587$, $A = -1.00$.
      (h)   If $P(Z > A) = 0.1587$, $P(Z < A) = 0.8413$. So $A = +1.00$.

6.6   (a) $P(X > 43) = P(Z > -1.75) = 1 - 0.0401 = 0.9599$
      (b) $P(X < 42) = P(Z < -2.00) = 0.0228$
      (c) $P(X > 57.5) = P(Z > 1.88) = 1.0 - 0.9699 = 0.0301$
      (d) $P(42 < X < 48) = P(-2.00 < Z < -0.50) = 0.3085 - 0.0228 = 0.2857$
      (e) $P(X < 40) = P(Z < -2.50) = 0.0062$
            $P(X > 55) = P(Z > 1.25) = 1.0 - 0.8944 = 0.1056$
            $P(X < 40) + P(X > 55) = 0.0062 + 0.1056 = 0.1118$
      (f) $P(X < A) = 0.05$,
            $$Z = -1.645 = \frac{A - 50}{4} \qquad A = 50 - 1.645(4) = 43.42$$
      (g) $P(X_{\text{lower}} < X < X_{\text{upper}}) = 0.60$
            $P(Z < -0.84) = 0.20$ and $P(Z < 0.84) = 0.80$
            $$Z = -0.84 = \frac{X_{\text{lower}} - 50}{4} \qquad Z = +0.84 = \frac{X_{\text{upper}} - 50}{4}$$
            $X_{\text{lower}} = 50 - 0.84(4) = 46.64$ and $X_{\text{upper}} = 50 + 0.84(4) = 53.36$
      (h) $P(X > A) = 0.85$, so $P(X < A) = 0.15$
            $$Z = -1.04 = \frac{A - 50}{4}$$
            $A = 50 - 1.04(4) = 45.84$

6.8   (a) $P(34 < X < 50) = P(-1.33 < Z < 0) = 0.4082$
       (b) $P(34 < X < 38) = P(-1.33 < Z < -1.00) = 0.1587 - 0.0918 = 0.0669$
       (c) $P(X < 30) + P(X > 60) = P(Z < -1.67) + P(Z > 0.83)$
              $= 0.0475 + (1.0 - 0.7967) = 0.2508$
       (d) $1000(1 - 0.2508) = 749.2 \cong 749$ trucks

       (e) $P(X > A) = 0.80 \qquad P(Z < -0.84) \cong 0.20 \qquad Z = -0.84 = \dfrac{A - 50}{12}$

              $A = 50 - 0.84(12) = 39.92$ thousand miles or 39,920 miles
       (f)   The smaller standard deviation makes the Z-values larger.
              (a) $P(34 < X < 50) = P(-1.60 < Z < 0) = 0.4452$
              (b) $P(34 < X < 38) = P(-1.60 < Z < -1.20) = 0.1151 - 0.0548$
                     $= 0.0603$
              (c) $P(X < 30) + P(X > 60) = P(Z < -2.00) + P(Z > 1.00)$
                     $= 0.0228 + (1.0 - 0.8413) = 0.1815$
              (d) $1000(1 - 0.1815) = 818.5 \cong 819$ trucks
              (e) $A = 50 - 0.84(10) = 41.6$ thousand miles or 41,600 miles

6.10   (a) $P(X < 91) = P(Z < 2.25) = 0.9878$
       (b) $P(65 < X < 89) = P(-1.00 < Z < 2.00) = 0.9772 - 0.1587 = 0.8185$
       (c) $P(81 < X < 89) = P(1.00 < Z < 2.00) = 0.9772 - 0.8413 = 0.1359$
       (d) $P(X > A) = 0.05 \qquad\qquad P(Z < 1.645) = 0.9500$

              $Z = 1.645 = \dfrac{A - 73}{8} \qquad A = 73 + 1.645(8) = 86.16\%$

       (e)   Option 1: $P(X > A) = 0.10 \qquad\qquad P(Z < 1.28) \cong 0.9000$
              $Z = \dfrac{81 - 73}{8} = 1.00$

              Since your score of 81% on this exam represents a Z-score of 1.00, which is below
              the minimum Z-score of 1.28, you will not earn an "A" grade on the exam under this
              grading option.
              Option 2: $Z = \dfrac{68 - 62}{3} = 2.00$

              Since your score of 68% on this exam represents a Z-score of 2.00, which is well
              above the minimum Z-score of 1.28, you will earn an "A" grade on the exam under
              this grading option. You should prefer Option 2.

6.12   (a) $P(X > 90) = P(Z > 1.62) = 1 - 0.9747 = 0.0526$
       (b) $P(60 < X < 90) = P(-0.38 < Z < 1.62) = 0.5954$
       (c) $P(X > A) = 0.80 \qquad\qquad A = 53.08$
       (d) $P(A < X < B) = 0.90 \qquad A = 41.03 \qquad\qquad B = 90.37$
       (e)   It is reasonable to assume that the length of a visit follows a normal distribution.

6.14   With 19 observations, the 18th largest observation covers an area under the normal curve of
       .90. The corresponding Z-value is +1.28. The largest observation covers an area under the
       normal curve of .95. The corresponding Z-value is either + 1.645, + 1.64, or + 1.65
       depending on the "rule" used for this selection.

6.16   Area under normal curve covered: 0.1429 0.2857 0.4286 0.5714 0.7143 0.8571
       Standardized normal quantile value: -1.07 -0.57 -0.18 $+0.18$ $+0.57$ $+1.07$

6.18   (a)   Interquartile range = 0.6 $S_X = 0.5606$ Range = 2.65

1.33 (S_X) = 0.7456   6 (S_X) = 3.3634

Since the interquartile range is quite different than 1.33 (S_X) and the range is also quite different than 6 (S_X), the data does not appear to be approximately normally distributed.

   (b)

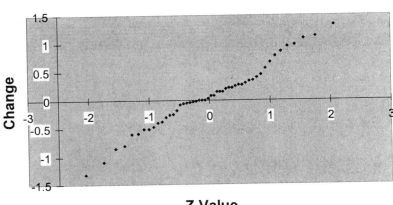

Normal Probability Plot

The normal probability plot suggests that the data appears to be slightly skewed to the left.

6.20   (a)   Five-number summary: 8.5   8.59   8.63   8.66   8.75   mode = 8.65
mean = 8.62   standard deviation = 0.0522   range = 0.25
interquartile   range = 0.07
The mean and median are quite close together. The five-number summary suggests that the distribution of the data is quite symmetrical around the median. Interquartile range is very close to 1.33 times the standard deviation. The range is slightly smaller than 6 times the standard deviation. Also, 67.5% of the data falls within one standard deviation of the mean as compared to the 2/3 in a normal distribution. 82.5% of the observations fall within 1.28 standard deviation of the mean as compared to the 4/5 in a normal distribution. 95% of the observations fall within 2 standard deviation of the mean as compared to the 19/20 in a normal distribution. In general, the actual properties of the data appear to be quite close to the theoretical properties of a normal distribution.

6.20   (b)
cont.

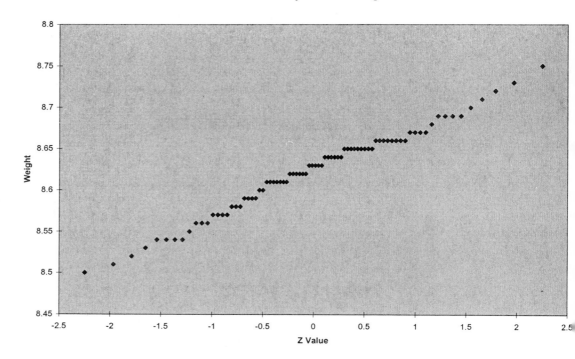

Normal Probability of Rubber Weight

The normal probability plot confirms that the data appear to be approximately normally distributed.

6.22 (a)   Office I: $\overline{X} = 2.214$ $S = 1.718$
Five-number summary   0.52   0.93   1.54   3.93   6.32
The distribution is right-skewed.
Note: The quartiles are obtained using PHStat without any interpolation.

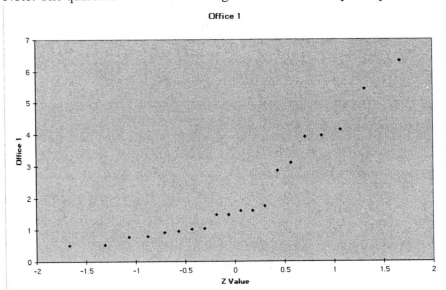

Office II: $\overline{X} = 2.011$ $S = 1.892$
Five-number summary   0.08   0.60   1.505   3.75   7.55
The distribution is right-skewed.
Note: The quartiles are obtained using PHStat without any interpolation.

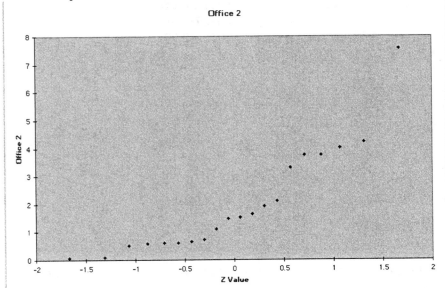

6.24 (a) $P(5 < X < 7) = (7 - 5)/10 = 0.2$
(b) $P(2 < X < 3) = (3 - 2)/10 = 0.1$

(c) $\mu = \dfrac{0+10}{2} = 5$ (d) $\sigma = \sqrt{\dfrac{(10-0)^2}{12}} = 2.8868$

6.26   (a) $P(10 < X < 20) = (20-10)/(25-10) = 0.6667$
        (b) $P(20 < X < 22) = (22-20)/(25-10) = 0.1333$
        (c) $P(18 < X < 25) = (25-18)/(25-10) = 0.4667$

        (d) $\mu = \dfrac{10+25}{2} = 17.5$ (e) $\sigma = \sqrt{\dfrac{(25-10)^2}{12}} = 4.3301$

6.28   (a) $P(0 < X < 0.6) = (0.6)/2 = 0.3$
        (b) $P(0.4 < X < 1.6) = (1.6-0.4)/2 = 0.6$
        (c) $P(1.8 < X < 2) = (2-1.8)/2 = 0.1$
        (d) $P(X > 2) = 0$

        (e) $\mu = \dfrac{0+2}{2} = 1$ (f) $\sigma = \sqrt{\dfrac{(2-0)^2}{12}} = 0.5774$

6.30   (a) $P(\text{arrival time} \le 0.1) = 1 n e^{-\lambda x} = 1 n e^{-(30)(0.1)} = 0.9502$
        (b) $P(\text{arrival time} > 0.1) = 1 - P(\text{arrival time} \le 0.1) = 1 - 0.9502 = 0.0498$
        (c) $P(0.1 < \text{arrival time} < 0.2) = P(\text{arrival time} < 0.2) - P(\text{arrival time} < 0.1)$
               $= 0.9975 - 0.9502 = 0.0473$
        (d) $P(\text{arrival time} < 0.1) + P(\text{arrival time} > 0.2) = 0.9502 + 0.0025 = 0.9527$

6.32   (a) $P(\text{arrival time} \le 0.05) = 1 - e^{-(50)(0.05)} = 0.9179$
        (b) $P(\text{arrival time} \le 0.0167) = 1 - 0.4339 = 0.5661$
        (c)   If $\lambda = 60$, $P(\text{arrival time} \le 0.05) = 0.9502$,
                      $P(\text{arrival time} \le 0.0167) = 0.6329$
        (d)   If $\lambda = 30$, $P(\text{arrival time} \le 0.05) = 0.7769$
                      $P(\text{arrival time} \le 0.0167) = 0.3941$

6.34   (a) $P(\text{arrival time} \le 0.05) = 1 - e^{-(15)(0.05)} = 0.5276$
        (b) $P(\text{arrival time} \le 0.25) = 0.9765$
        (c)   If $\lambda = 25$, $P(\text{arrival time} \le 0.05) = 0.7135$,
                      $P(\text{arrival time} \le 0.25) = 0.9981$

6.36   (a) $P(X \le 14) = = 1 - e^{-(1/20)(14)} = 0.5034$
        (b) $P(X > 21) = = 1 - \left(1 - e^{-(1/20)(21)}\right) = 0.3499$

        (c) $P(X \le 7) = = 1 - e^{-(1/20)(7)} = 0.2953$

6.38   Using the tables of the normal distribution with knowledge of μ_X and σ_X^2 along with the transformation formula, we can find any probability under the normal curve.

6.40   Find the Z value corresponding to the given percentile and then use the equation
        $X = \mu + z\sigma$.

6.42   The normal distribution is bell-shaped; its measures of central tendency are all equal; its middle 50% is within 1.33 standard deviations of its mean; and 99.7% of its values are contained within three standard deviations of its mean.

6.44   The exponential distribution is used to determine the probability that the next arrival will occur within a given length of time.

6.46   (a) $P(1.90 < X < 2.00) = P(-2.00 < Z < 0) = 0.4772$
          (b) $P(1.90 < X < 2.10) = P(-2.00 < Z < 2.00) = 0.9772 - 0.0228 = 0.9544$
          (c) $P(X < 1.90) = P(Z < -2.00) = 0.0228$
          (d) $P(X < 1.90) + P(X > 2.10) = 1 - P(1.90 < X < 2.10) = 0.0456$
          (e) $P(X > 2.10) = P(Z > 2.00) = 1.0 - 0.9772 = 0.0228$
          (f) $P(2.05 < X < 2.10) = P(1.00 < Z < 2.00) = 0.9772 - 0.8413 = 0.1359$
          (g) $P(X > A) = P(Z > -2.33) = 0.99$ $A = 2.00 - 2.33(0.05) = 1.8835$
          (h) $P(A < X < B) = P(-2.58 < Z < 2.58) = 0.99$
                   $A = 2.00 - 2.58(0.05) = 1.8710$ $B = 2.00 + 2.58(0.05) = 2.1290$
          (i)   Item (g) is one-tailed; that is, it requires 99% of the bottles to be above a value, 1% below the value. Item (h) is two-tailed; that is, it requires 99% of the bottles to be between two values, with 1/2% below the lower limit and 1/2% above the upper limit.
          (j)   (a) $P(1.90 < X < 2.00) = P(-2.40 < Z < -0.40) = 0.3446 - 0.0082 = 0.3364$
                   (b) $P(1.90 < X < 2.10) = P(-2.40 < Z < 1.60) = 0.9452 - 0.0082 = 0.9370$
                   (c) $P(X < 1.90) = P(Z < -2.40) = 0.0082$
                   (d) $P(X < 1.90) + P(X > 2.10) = 1 - P(1.90 < X < 2.10) = 0.0630$
                   (e) $P(X > 2.10) = P(Z > 1.60) = 1.0 - 0.9452 = 0.0548$
                   (f) $P(2.05 < X < 2.10) = P(0.60 < Z < 1.60) = 0.9452 - 0.7257 = 0.2195$
                   (g) $P(X > A) = P(Z > -2.33) = 0.99$ $A = 2.02 - 2.33(0.05) = 1.9035$
                   (h) $P(A < X < B) = P(-2.58 < Z < 2.58) = 0.99$
                            $A = 2.02 - 2.58(0.05) = 1.8910$ $B = 2.02 + 2.58(0.05) = 2.1490$

6.48   (a) $P(X > 0) = P(Z > -0.6019) = 0.7264$
          (b) $P(X < 0) = P(Z < -0.6019) = 0.2736$
          (c) $P(X > 10) = P(Z > -0.1165) = 0.5464$
          (d) $P(X > 20) = P(Z > 0.3689) = 0.3561$
          (e) $P(X > 30) = P(Z > 0.8543) = 0.1965$
          (f) $P(X < -10) = P(Z < -1.0874) = 0.1384$
          (g)   (a) $P(X > 0) = P(Z > -0.6047) = 0.7273$
                   (b) $P(X < 0) = P(Z < -0.6047) = 0.2727$
                   (c) $P(X > 10) = P(Z > 0.5581) = 0.2884$
                   (d) $P(X > 20) = P(Z > 1.7209) = 0.0426$
                   (e) $P(X > 30) = P(Z > 2.8837) = 0.0020$
                   (f) $P(X < -10) = P(Z < -1.7674) = 0.0386$
          (h)   The common stocks have higher average annual returns than the long-term government bonds. But they also have higher volatility as reflected by their larger standard deviation. This is the usual trade-off between high return and high volatility in an investment instrument.
          Note: The above answers are obtained using PHStat. They may be slightly different when Table E.2 is used.

6.50   (a) $P(X < 1) = P(Z < 1) = 0.8413$

(b) $P(0.5 < X < 1.5) = P(-1.5 < Z < 3.5) = 0.9330$

(c) $P(0.5 < X) = P(-1.5 < Z) = 0.9332$

(d) $P(A < X) = 0.99$ $\dfrac{A - 0.8}{0.2} = -2.3263$ $A = 0.3347$

(e) $P(A < X < B) = 0.95$ $\dfrac{A - 0.8}{0.2} = -1.960$ $A = 0.4080$

$\dfrac{B - 0.8}{0.2} = 1.96$ $B = 1.1920$

(f) $P(X < 1) = P(Z < -3) = 0.0013$

(g) $P(0.5 < X < 1.5) = P(-4 < Z < -2) = 0.0227$

(h) $P(0.5 < X) = P(-4 < Z) = $ essentially 1.000

(i) $P(A < X) = 0.99$ $\dfrac{A - 2.5}{0.5} = -2.3263$ $A = 1.3368$

(j) $P(A < X < B) = 0.95$ $\dfrac{A - 2.5}{0.5} = -1.960$ $A = 1.5200$

$\dfrac{B - 2.5}{0.5} = 1.96$ $B = 3.480$

(k)   The IRS web site has a lower average and a smaller standard deviation in download time compared to the H&R Block web site.

CHAPTER 7

OBJECTIVES
- To understand the concept of the sampling distribution
- To be able to compute probabilities related to the sample mean and sample proportion
- To understand and be able to apply the central limit theorem

OVERVIEW AND KEY CONCEPTS

Some Basic Concepts on Sampling Distribution
- **Why do we study sampling distribution?**
    - Sample statistics are used to estimate population parameters, but different samples yield different estimates. The solution is to develop a theoretical basis based on sampling distribution.
- **What is a sampling distribution?**
    - A sampling distribution is a theoretical probability distribution of a sample statistic. A sample statistic (e.g., sample mean, sample proportion) is a random variable because a different sample will yield a different value for the statistic, and, hence, a different estimate for the parameter of interest. The sampling distribution is the probability distribution of the sample statistic as a result of taking all possible samples of the same size from the population.

Sampling Distribution of the Sample Mean
- **Population mean of the sample mean**
    - $\mu_{\bar{x}} = \mu$
    - This is the unbiased property of the sample mean.
- **Standard error (population standard deviation) of the sample mean**
    - $\sigma_{\bar{x}} = \dfrac{\sigma}{\sqrt{n}}$
    - Standard error of the sample mean is smaller than the standard deviation of the population.
    - The larger the sample size, the smaller the standard error.
- **The central limit theorem:** As the sample size (i.e., the number of the observations in a sample) gets *large enough*, the sampling distribution of the mean can be approximated by the normal distribution regardless of the distribution of the individual values in the population.
- **The distribution of the sample mean**
    - If the population is normally distributed, the sampling distribution of the mean is normally distributed regardless of the sample size.
    - If the population distribution is fairly symmetrical, the sampling distribution of the mean is approximately normal if sample size is at least 15.
    - For most population distributions, regardless of the shape, the sampling distribution of the mean is approximately normally distributed if the sample size is at least 30.

- **Finite population correction (Note: the finite population correction factor is covered in section 7.3 on the CD-ROM)**
    - Use the finite population correction factor to modify the standard error if sample size n is large relative to the population size N, i.e. $n/N > 0.05$.

    - Standard error with finite population correction factor: $\sigma_{\bar{X}} = \dfrac{\sigma}{\sqrt{n}} \sqrt{\dfrac{N-n}{N-1}}$

Finding Range Probability of the Sample Mean

1. Standardize the value of the sample mean using $Z = \dfrac{\bar{X} - \mu_{\bar{X}}}{\sigma_{\bar{X}}} = \dfrac{\bar{X} - \mu}{\dfrac{\sigma}{\sqrt{n}}}$.

2. Look up the cumulative probabilities from the cumulative standardized normal distribution table.

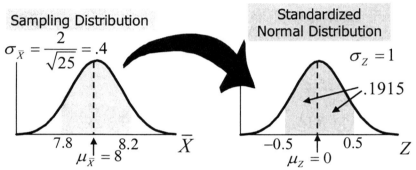

E.g., For $\mu = 8$, $\sigma = 2$, $n = 25$ and X normally distributed. $P(7.8 < \bar{X} < 8.2) = ?$

$$P(7.8 < \bar{X} < 8.2) = P\left(\frac{7.8-8}{2/\sqrt{25}} < \frac{\bar{X} - \mu_{\bar{X}}}{\sigma_{\bar{X}}} < \frac{8.2-8}{2/\sqrt{25}} \right) = P(-.5 < Z < .5) = .3830$$

Sampling Distribution of the Sample Proportion

- **Sample proportion:** $p_S = \dfrac{X}{n} = \dfrac{\text{number of successes}}{\text{sample size}}$
- **Population mean of the sample proportion**
    - $\mu_{p_S} = p$ where p is the probability of success.
- **Standard error of the sample proportion**
    - $\sigma_{p_S} = \sqrt{\dfrac{p(1-p)}{n}}$
- **The distribution of the sample proportion**
    - When np and $n(1-p)$ are each at least 5, the sampling distribution of the sample proportion can be approximated by the normal distribution with mean μ_{p_S} and standard deviation σ_{p_S}.

- **Finite population correction (Note: the finite population correction factor is covered in section 7.3 on the CD-ROM)**
  - Use the finite population correction factor to modify the standard error if sample size n is large relative to the population size N, i.e. $n/N > 0.05$.

  - Standard error with finite population correction factor: $\sigma_{P_s} = \sqrt{\dfrac{p(1-p)}{n}}\sqrt{\dfrac{N-n}{N-1}}$

Finding Range Probability of the Sample Proportion

1. Standardize the value of the sample proportion using $Z = \dfrac{p_S - \mu_{p_S}}{\sigma_{p_S}} = \dfrac{p_S - p}{\sqrt{\dfrac{p(1-p)}{n}}}$.

2. Lookup the cumulative probabilities from the cumulative standardized normal distribution table.

E.g., For $n = 200$, $p = 0.4$. $P(p_S < 0.43) = ?$

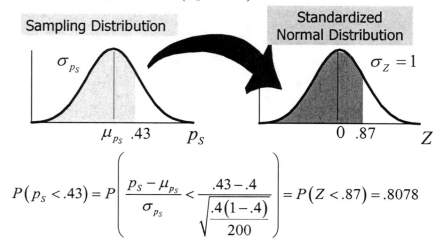

$$P(p_S < .43) = P\left(\frac{p_S - \mu_{p_S}}{\sigma_{p_S}} < \frac{.43 - .4}{\sqrt{\dfrac{.4(1-.4)}{200}}}\right) = P(Z < .87) = .8078$$

SOLUTIONS TO END OF SECTION
AND CHAPTER REVIEW EVEN PROBLEMS

7.2   (a) $P(\bar{X} < 47) = P(Z < -6.00) =$ virtually zero

       (b) $P(47 < \bar{X} < 49.5) = P(-6.00 < Z < -1.00) = 0.1587 - 0.00 = 0.1587$

       (c) $P(\bar{X} > 51.1) = P(Z > 2.20) = 1.0 - 0.9861 = 0.0139$

       (d) $P(49 < \bar{X} < 51) = P(-2.00 < Z < +2.00) = 0.9772 - 0.0228 = 0.9544$

       (e) $P(\bar{X} > A) = P(Z > 0.39) = 0.35$ $\bar{X} = 50 + 0.39(0.5) = 50.195$

       (f)   (a) $P(\bar{X} < 47) = P(Z < -3.00) = 0.00135$

             (b) $P(47 < \bar{X} < 49.5) = P(-3.00 < Z < -0.50)$
                      $= 0.3085 - 0.00135 = 0.30715$

             (c) $P(\bar{X} > 51.1) = P(Z > 1.10) = 1.0 - 0.8643 = 0.1357$

             (d) $P(49 < \bar{X} < 51) = P(-1.00 < Z < +1.00)$
                      $= 0.8413 - 0.1587 = 0.6826$

             (e) $P(\bar{X} > A) = P(Z > 0.39) = 0.35$ $\bar{X} = 50 + 0.39(1) = 50.39$

7.4   (a)   Sampling Distribution of the Mean for $n = 2$ (without replacement)

Sample Number	Outcomes	Sample Means $\bar{X}_i$
1	1, 3	$\bar{X}_1 = 2$
2	1, 6	$\bar{X}_2 = 3.5$
3	1, 7	$\bar{X}_3 = 4$
4	1, 7	$\bar{X}_4 = 4$
5	1, 12	$\bar{X}_5 = 6.5$
6	3, 6	$\bar{X}_6 = 4.5$
7	3, 7	$\bar{X}_7 = 5$
8	3, 7	$\bar{X}_8 = 5$
9	3, 12	$\bar{X}_9 = 7.5$
10	6, 7	$\bar{X}_{10} = 6.5$
11	6, 7	$\bar{X}_{11} = 6.5$
12	6, 12	$\bar{X}_{12} = 9$
13	7, 7	$\bar{X}_{13} = 7$
14	7, 12	$\bar{X}_{14} = 9.5$
15	7, 12	$\bar{X}_{15} = 9.5$

Mean of All Possible Sample Means:

$$\mu_{\bar{x}} = \frac{90}{15} = 6$$

Mean of All Population Elements:

$$\mu = \frac{1 + 3 + 6 + 7 + 7 + 12}{6} = 6$$

Both means are equal to 6. This property is called unbiasedness.

7.4   (b)   Sampling Distribution of the Mean for $n = 3$ (without replacement)
cont.

Sample Number	Outcomes	Sample Means $\overline{X}_i$
1	1, 3, 6	$\overline{X}_1 = 3\ 1/3$
2	1, 3, 7	$\overline{X}_2 = 3\ 2/3$
3	1, 3, 7	$\overline{X}_3 = 3\ 2/3$
4	1, 3, 12	$\overline{X}_4 = 5\ 1/3$
5	1, 6, 7	$\overline{X}_5 = 4\ 2/3$
6	1, 6, 7	$\overline{X}_6 = 4\ 2/3$
7	1, 6, 12	$\overline{X}_7 = 6\ 1/3$
8	3, 6, 7	$\overline{X}_8 = 5\ 1/3$
9	3, 6, 7	$\overline{X}_9 = 5\ 1/3$
10	3, 6, 12	$\overline{X}_{10} = 7$
11	6, 7, 7	$\overline{X}_{11} = 6\ 2/3$
12	6, 7, 12	$\overline{X}_{12} = 8\ 1/3$
13	6, 7, 12	$\overline{X}_{13} = 8\ 1/3$
14	7, 7, 12	$\overline{X}_{14} = 8\ 2/3$
15	1, 7, 7	$\overline{X}_{15} = 5$
16	1, 7, 12	$\overline{X}_{16} = 6\ 2/3$
17	1, 7, 12	$\overline{X}_{17} = 6\ 2/3$
18	3, 7, 7	$\overline{X}_{18} = 5\ 2/3$
19	3, 7, 12	$\overline{X}_{19} = 7\ 1/3$
20	3, 7, 12	$\overline{X}_{20} = 7\ 1/3$

$$\mu_{\overline{x}} = \frac{120}{20} = 6 \qquad \text{This is equal to } \mu, \text{ the population mean.}$$

(c)   The distribution for $n = 3$ has less variability. The larger sample size has resulted in more sample means being close to μ.

7.4   (d)   (a)   Sampling Distribution of the Mean for $n = 2$ (with replacement)
cont.

Sample Number	Outcomes	Sample Means $\overline{X}_i$
1	1, 1	$\overline{X}_1 = 1$
2	1, 3	$\overline{X}_2 = 2$
3	1, 6	$\overline{X}_3 = 3.5$
4	1, 7	$\overline{X}_4 = 4$
5	1, 7	$\overline{X}_5 = 4$
6	1, 12	$\overline{X}_6 = 6.5$
7	3, 1	$\overline{X}_7 = 2$
8	3, 3	$\overline{X}_8 = 3$
9	3, 6	$\overline{X}_9 = 4.5$
10	3, 7	$\overline{X}_{10} = 5$
11	3, 7	$\overline{X}_{11} = 5$
12	3, 12	$\overline{X}_{12} = 7.5$
13	6, 1	$\overline{X}_{13} = 3.5$
14	6, 3	$\overline{X}_{14} = 4.5$
15	6, 6	$\overline{X}_{15} = 6$
16	6, 7	$\overline{X}_{16} = 6.5$
17	6, 7	$\overline{X}_{17} = 6.5$
18	6, 12	$\overline{X}_{18} = 9$
19	7, 1	$\overline{X}_{19} = 4$
20	7, 3	$\overline{X}_{20} = 5$
21	7, 6	$\overline{X}_{21} = 6.5$
22	7, 7	$\overline{X}_{22} = 7$
23	7, 7	$\overline{X}_{23} = 7$
24	7, 12	$\overline{X}_{24} = 9.5$
25	7, 1	$\overline{X}_{25} = 4$
26	7, 3	$\overline{X}_{26} = 5$
27	7, 6	$\overline{X}_{27} = 6.5$
28	7, 7	$\overline{X}_{28} = 7$
29	7, 7	$\overline{X}_{29} = 7$
30	7, 12	$\overline{X}_{30} = 9.5$
31	12, 1	$\overline{X}_{31} = 6.5$
32	12, 3	$\overline{X}_{32} = 7.5$
33	12, 6	$\overline{X}_{33} = 9$
34	12, 7	$\overline{X}_{34} = 9.5$
35	12, 7	$\overline{X}_{35} = 9.5$
36	12, 12	$\overline{X}_{36} = 12$

7.4   (d)   (a)   Mean of All Possible   Mean of All
cont.   Sample Means: Population Elements:

$$\mu_{\bar{x}} = \frac{216}{36} = 6 \qquad\qquad \mu = \frac{1+3+6+7+7+12}{6} = 6$$

~~replacement~~

Both means are equal to 6. This property is called unbiasedness.

(b)   Repeat the same process for the sampling distribution of the mean for $n = 3$ (with replacement). There will be $6^3 = 216$ different samples.

$\mu_{\bar{x}} = 6$ This is equal to μ, the population mean.

(c)   The distribution for $n = 3$ has less variability. The larger sample size has resulted in more sample means being close to μ.

7.6   (a) $P(-32 < X < -22) = P(-0.3333 < Z < 0.3333) = 0.2611$
      (b) $P(-37 < X < -17) = P(-0.6667 < Z < 0.6667) = 0.4950$
      (c) $P(-47 < X < -7) = P(-1.3333 < Z < 1.3333) = 0.8176$
      (d) $P(X > 0) = P(Z > 1.8) = 0.0359$
      (e) $P(-32 < \bar{X} < -22) = P(-1.0541 < Z < 1.0541) = 0.7082$
      (f) $P(-37 < \bar{X} < -17) = P(-2.1082 < Z < 2.1082) = 0.9650$
      (g) $P(-47 < \bar{X} < -7) = P(-4.2164 < Z < 4.2164) = 1.0000$
      (h) $P(\bar{X} > 0) = P(Z > 5.6921) = 0.0000$
      (i)   When samples of size 10 are taken rather than individual values (samples of $n = 1$), more values lie closer to the mean and fewer values lie farther away from the mean with the increased sample size. This occurs because the standard deviation of the sampling distribution, the standard error, is given by:

$$\sigma_{\bar{X}} = \frac{\sigma}{\sqrt{n}}$$

As n increases, the value of the denominator increases, resulting in a smaller value of the overall fraction. The standard error for the distribution of sample means of size 10 is $\sqrt{1/10}$ of the population standard deviation of individual values and means that the sampling distribution is more concentrated around the population mean.

Note: The above answers are obtained using PHStat. They may be slightly different when Table E.2 is used.

7.8   (a) $P(\bar{X} > 3) = P(Z > -1.00) = 1.0 - 0.1587 = 0.8413$
      (b) $P(\bar{X} < A) = P(Z < 1.04) = 0.85$ $\bar{X} = 3.10 + 1.04(0.1) = 3.204$
      (c)   To be able to use the standard normal distribution as an approximation for the area under the curve, we must assume that the population is symmetrically distributed such that the central limit theorem will likely hold for samples of $n = 16$.
      (d) $P(\bar{X} < A) = P(Z < 1.04) = 0.85$ $\bar{X} = 3.10 + 1.04(0.05) = 3.152$
      (e)   To be able to use the standard normal distribution as an approximation for the area under the curve, we must assume that the central limit theorem will hold for samples of $n = 64$.
      (f)   For $n = 1$, $P(X < 2) = P(Z < -2.75) = 0.0030$
            For $n = 16$, $P(\bar{X} > 3.4) = P(Z > 3.00) = 1.0 - 0.99865 = 0.00135$
            For $n = 100$, $P(\bar{X} < 2.9) = P(Z < -4.00) = $ virtually zero
            It is more likely to have an individual service time below 2 minutes.

7.10   (a) $P(\overline{X} < 55000) = P(Z < -1.227) = 0.1099$
       (b) $P(\overline{X} > 60000) = P(Z > 1.773) = 0.0381$
       (c) $P(\overline{X} > 111600) = P(Z > 32.733) = 0.0000$
       (d)   This indicates that the household income distribution is not normally distributed and is skewed to the right.
       (e)   Since the distribution is not symmetrical about the mean, a sample size of 20 will not be large enough for the central limit to take effect so that the sampling distribution of the sample mean can be approximated by a normal distribution and, hence, the methods used in (a)-(c) will not be appropriate.
       Note: The above answers are obtained using PHStat. They may be slightly different when Table E.2 is used.

7.12   (a) $p_s = 48/64 = 0.75$ (b) $\sigma_{p_s} = \sqrt{\dfrac{0.70(0.30)}{64}} = 0.0573$

7.14   (a) $p_s = 14/40 = 0.35$ (b) $\sigma_{p_s} = \sqrt{\dfrac{0.30(0.70)}{40}} = 0.0725$

7.16   (a) $P(0.50 < p_s < 0.60) = P(0 < Z < 2.83) = 0.4977$
       (b) $P(-1.645 < Z < 1.645) = 0.90$
             $p_s = .50 - 1.645(0.0354) = 0.4418$ $p_s = .50 + 1.645(0.0354) = 0.5582$
       (c) $P(p_s > 0.65) = P(Z > 4.24) =$ virtually zero
       (d)   If $n = 200$, $P(p_s > 0.60) = P(Z > 2.83) = 1.0 - 0.9977 = 0.0023$
             If $n = 1000$, $P(p_s > 0.55) = P(Z > 3.16) = 1.0 - 0.99921 = 0.00079$
             More than 60% correct in a sample of 200 is more likely than more than 55% correct in a sample of 1000.

7.18   (a) $P(0.55 < p_s < 0.60) = P(-0.95 < Z < 0.49) = 0.5168$
       (b) $P(0.50 < p_s < 0.65) = P(-2.38 < Z < 1.92) = 0.9639$
       (c) $P(p_s < 0.45) = P(Z < -3.81) = 0.00007$
       (d)   (a) $P(0.55 < p_s < 0.60) = P(-0.67 < Z < 0.35) = 0.3854$
             (b) $P(0.50 < p_s < 0.65) = P(-1.68 < Z < 1.36) = 0.8666$
             (c) $P(p_s < 0.45) = P(Z < -2.70) = 0.0035$

7.20   (a) $P(0.35 < p_s < 0.40) = P(-0.7303 < Z < 0.7303) = 0.5348$
       (b) $P(A < p_s < B) = P(-1.6449 < Z < 1.6449) = 0.90$
             $A = 0.375 - 1.6449(0.0342) = 0.3187$
             $B = 0.375 + 1.6449(0.0342) = 0.4313$
       (c) $P(A < p_s < B) = P(-1.960 < Z < 1.960) = 0.95$
             $A = 0.375 - 1.960(0.0342) = 0.3079$
             $B = 0.375 + 1.96(0.0342) = 0.4421$
       Note: The above answers are obtained using PHStat. They may be slightly different when Table E.2 is used.

7.22   (a) $P(0.10 < p_s < 0.15) = P(-1.7841 < Z < 1.1894) = 0.8457$
      (b) $P(p_s > 0.18) = P(Z > 2.9735) = 0.0015$
If the proportion of U.S. college students in the population who purchased items from an online bookseller is indeed 13%, the proportion of samples of 400 U.S. college students that will have more than 18% of students who purchased items from an online bookseller will be 0.0015, which is a very low proportion. Hence, the current sample of 400 U.S. college students revealing more than 18% who purchased items from an online bookseller is a rather strong evidence that the population estimate of 13% is very likely to be an under estimation.

      (c) $P(p_s > 0.18) = P(Z > 1.4868) = 0.0685$
If the proportion of U.S. college students in the population who purchased items from an online bookseller is indeed 13%, the proportion of samples of 100 U.S. college students that will have more than 18% of students who purchased items from an online bookseller will be 0.0685, which is a rather low proportion but not at all unlikely. Hence, the current sample of 100 U.S. college students revealing more than 18% who purchased items from an online bookseller suggests that the population estimate of 13% is probably an under estimation.

Note: The above answers are obtained using PHStat. They may be slightly different when Table E.2 is used.

7.24   Because the average of all the possible sample means is equal to the population mean.

7.26   As larger sample sizes are taken, the effect of extreme values on the sample mean become smaller and smaller. With large enough samples, even though the population is not normally distributed, the sampling distribution of the mean will be approximately normally distributed.

7.28   The probability distribution is the distribution of a particular variable of interest, while the sampling distribution represents the distribution of a statistic.

7.30 $\mu_{\bar{X}} = 0.753$ $\sigma_{\bar{X}} = \dfrac{\sigma_X}{\sqrt{n}} = \dfrac{0.004}{5} = 0.0008$

      (a) $P(0.75 < \bar{X} < 0.753) = P(-3.75 < Z < 0) = 0.5 - 0.00009 = 0.4999$
      (b) $P(0.74 < \bar{X} < 0.75) = P(-16.25 < Z < -3.75) = 0.00009$
      (c) $P(\bar{X} > 0.76) = P(Z > 8.75) =$ virtually zero
      (d) $P(\bar{X} < 0.74) = P(Z < -16.25) =$ virtually zero
      (e) $P(\bar{X} < A) = P(Z < -1.48) = 0.07$ $X = 0.753 - 1.48(0.0008) = 0.7518$

7.32 $\mu_{\bar{X}} = 4.7$ $\sigma_{\bar{X}} = \dfrac{\sigma_X}{\sqrt{n}} = \dfrac{0.40}{5} = 0.08$

      (a) $P(4.60 < \bar{X}) = P(-1.25 < Z) = 1 - 0.1056 = 0.8944$
      (b) $P(A < \bar{X} < B) = P(-1.04 < Z < 1.04) = 0.70$
$A = 4.70 - 1.04(0.08) = 4.6168$ ounces
$X = 4.70 + 1.04(0.08) = 4.7832$ ounces
      (c) $P(\bar{X} > A) = P(Z > -0.74) = 0.77$ $A = 4.70 - 0.74(0.08) = 4.6408$

7.34   (a) $P(0.18 < p_s < 0.22) = P(-1 < Z < 1) = 0.6827$
       (b) $P(0.16 < p_s < 0.24) = P(-2 < Z < 2) = 0.9545$
       (c) $P(0.14 < p_s < 0.26) = P(-3 < Z < 3) = 0.9973$
       (d) $P(0.12 < p_s < 0.28) = P(-4 < Z < 4) = 0.9999$

CHAPTER 8

OBJECTIVES
- To understand confidence interval estimates for the mean and the proportion
- To know how to determine the sample size necessary to obtain a desired confidence interval
- To be able to apply confidence intervals in auditing

OVERVIEW AND KEY CONCEPTS
Why We Need Confidence Interval Estimates in Addition to Point Estimates
- Confidence interval estimates take into consideration variation in sample statistics from sample to sample.
- They provide information about closeness to unknown population parameters.
- The interval estimates are always stated in level of confidence, which is lower than 100%.

Confidence Interval Estimate for the Mean when the Population Variance is Known
- **Assumptions:**
    - Population variance σ^2 is known.
    - Population is normally distributed or the sample size is large.
- **Point estimate for the population mean μ : $\bar{X}$**
- **Confidence interval estimate:**
    - $\bar{X} \pm Z_{\alpha/2} \dfrac{\sigma}{\sqrt{n}}$ where $Z_{\alpha/2}$ is the value corresponding to a cumulative area of $\left(1 - \dfrac{\alpha}{2}\right)$ from a standardized normal distribution, i.e., the right-tail probability of $\alpha/2$.
- **Elements of confidence interval estimate**
    - **Level of confidence:** Measures the level of confidence in which the interval will contain the unknown population parameter.
    - **Precision (range):** Represents the closeness to the unknown parameter.
    - **Cost:** The cost required to obtain a sample of size n.
- **Factors affecting interval width (precision)**
    - **Data variation measured by σ^2 :** The larger is the σ^2, the wider is the interval estimate.
    - **Sample size n:** The larger is the sample size, the narrower is the interval estimate.
    - **The level of confidence $100(1-\alpha)\%$:** The higher is the level of confidence, the wider is the interval estimate.

- **Interpretation of a $100(1-\alpha)\%$ confidence interval estimate:** If all possible samples of size n are taken and their sample means are computed, $100(1-\alpha)\%$ of the intervals contain the true population mean somewhere within the interval around their sample means and only $100(\alpha)\%$ of them do not.

Confidence Interval Estimate for the Mean when the Population Variance is Unknown

- **Assumptions:**
  - Population variance σ^2 is unknown.
  - Population is normally distributed or the sample size is large.
- **Confidence interval estimate:**
  - $\bar{X} \pm t_{\alpha/2,n-1} \dfrac{S}{\sqrt{n}}$ where $t_{\alpha/2,n-1}$ is the value corresponding to a cumulative area of $\left(1-\dfrac{\alpha}{2}\right)$ from a Student's distribution with n-1 degrees of freedom, i.e., the right-tail probability of $\alpha/2$.

Confidence Interval Estimate for the Proportion

- **Assumptions:**
  - Two categorical outcomes
  - Population follows Binomial distribution
  - Normal approximation can be used if $np \geq 5$ and $n(1-p) \geq 5$.
- **Point estimate for the population proportion of success p : p_S**
- **Confidence interval estimate:**
  - $p_S \pm Z_{\alpha/2}\sqrt{\dfrac{p_S(1-p_S)}{n}}$

Confidence Interval Estimate for the Total Amount (Application of Confidence Interval Estimate in Auditing)

- **Point estimate for population total:** $N\bar{X}$
- **Confidence interval estimate:**
  - $N\bar{X} \pm N\left(t_{\alpha/2,n-1}\right)\dfrac{S}{\sqrt{n}}\sqrt{\dfrac{(N-n)}{(N-1)}}$

Confidence Interval Estimate for the Total Difference (Application of Confidence Interval Estimate in Auditing)

- **Point estimate for total difference:** $N\bar{D}$ where $\bar{D} = \dfrac{\sum\limits_{i=1}^{n} D_i}{n}$ is the sample average difference.

- **Confidence interval estimate:**

  - $$N\bar{D} \pm N\left(t_{\alpha/2,n-1}\right)\frac{S_D}{\sqrt{n}}\sqrt{\frac{(N-n)}{(N-1)}} \quad \text{where } S_D = \sqrt{\frac{\sum\limits_{i=1}^{n}\left(D_i - \bar{D}\right)^2}{n-1}}.$$

One-sided Confidence Interval Estimate for the Proportion (Application of Confidence Interval Estimate in Auditing)

- **Confidence interval estimate:**

  - $$p \le p_S + Z_\alpha\sqrt{\frac{p_S(1-p_S)}{n}}\sqrt{\frac{N-n}{N-1}} \quad \text{where } Z_\alpha \text{ is the value corresponding to a}$$
    cumulative area of $(1-\alpha)$ from a standardized normal distribution, i.e., the right-tail probability of α.

Determining Sample Size

- **The sample size needed when estimating the population mean:**

  - $n = \dfrac{Z^2\sigma^2}{e^2}$ where e is the acceptable sampling error and σ^2 is estimated from past data, by an educated guess or by the data obtained from a pilot study.

- **The sample size needed when estimating the population proportion:**

  - $n = \dfrac{Z^2 p(1-p)}{e^2}$ where p is estimated from past information, by an educated guess or use 0.5.

SOLUTIONS TO END OF SECTION AND CHAPTER REVIEW EVEN PROBLEMS

8.2 $\bar{X} \pm Z \cdot \dfrac{\sigma}{\sqrt{n}} = 125 \pm 2.58 \cdot \dfrac{24}{\sqrt{36}}$ $\qquad\qquad$ $114.68 \leq \mu \leq 135.32$

8.4   Since the results of only one sample are used to indicate whether something has gone wrong in the production process, the manufacturer can never know with 100% certainty that the specific interval obtained from the sample includes the true population mean. In order to have every possible interval estimate of the true mean, the entire population (sample size N) would have to be selected.

8.6   Approximately 5% of the intervals will not include the true population mean somewhere in the interval. Since the true population mean is not known, we do not know for certain whether it is in the one interval we have developed, between 10.99408 and 11.00192 inches.

8.8   (a)

	A	B
1	Light Bulbs	
2		
3	Population Standard Deviation	100
4	Sample Mean	350
5	Sample Size	64
6	Confidence Level	95%
7	Standard Error of the Mean	12.5
8	Z Value	-1.95996108
9	Interval Half Width	24.49951353
10	Interval Lower Limit	325.5004865
11	Interval Upper Limit	374.4995135

(b)   No. The manufacturer cannot support a claim that the bulbs last an average 400 hours. Based on the data from the sample, a mean of 400 hours would represent a distance of 4 standard deviations above the sample mean of 350 hours.

(c)   No. Since σ is known and $n = 64$, from the central limit theorem, we may assume that the sampling distribution of $\bar{X}$ is approximately normal.

(d)   An individual value of 320 is only 0.30 standard deviations below the sample mean of 350. The confidence interval represents bounds on the estimate of the mean of a sample of 64, not an individual value.

(e)   The confidence interval is narrower based on a process standard deviation of 80 hours rather than the original assumption of 100 hours.

   (a) $\bar{X} \pm Z \cdot \dfrac{\sigma}{\sqrt{n}} = 350 \pm 1.96 \cdot \dfrac{80}{\sqrt{64}}$ $\qquad$ $330.4 \leq \mu \leq 369.6$

   (b)   Based on the smaller standard deviation, a mean of 400 hours would represent a distance of 5 standard deviations above the sample mean of 350 hours. No, the manufacturer cannot support a claim that the bulbs last an average of 400 hours.

8.10   (a) $t_9 = 2.2622$
         (b) $t_9 = 3.2498$
         (c) $t_{31} = 2.0395$
         (d) $t_{64} = 1.9977$
         (e) $t_{15} = 1.7531$

8.12 $\bar{X} \pm t \cdot \dfrac{s}{\sqrt{n}} = 50 \pm 2.9467 \cdot \dfrac{15}{\sqrt{16}}$ $38.9499 \le \mu \le 61.0501$

8.14   Original data: $5.8571 \pm 2.4469 \cdot \dfrac{6.4660}{\sqrt{7}}$ $-0.1229 \le \mu \le 11.8371$

         Altered data: $4.00 \pm 2.4469 \cdot \dfrac{2.1602}{\sqrt{7}}$ $2.0022 \le \mu \le 5.9978$

         The presence of an outlier in the original data increases the value of the sample mean and greatly inflates the sample standard deviation.

8.16   (a) $\bar{X} \pm t \cdot \dfrac{s}{\sqrt{n}} = 1.67 \pm 2.0930 \cdot \dfrac{0.32}{\sqrt{20}}$ $\$1.52 \le \mu \le \$1.82$

         (b)   The store owner can be 95% confidence that the population mean retail value of greeting cards that it has in its inventory is somewhere in between $1.52 and $1.82. The store owner could multiply the ends of the confidence interval by the number of cards to estimate the total value of her inventory.

8.18   (a) $\bar{X} \pm t \cdot \dfrac{s}{\sqrt{n}} = 43.04 \pm 2.0096 \cdot \dfrac{41.9261}{\sqrt{50}}$ $31.12 \le \mu \le 54.96$

         (b)   The population distribution needs to be normally distribution.
         (c)

Normal Probability Plot

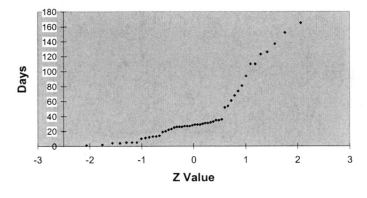

8.18   (c)
cont.

Box-and-whisker Plot

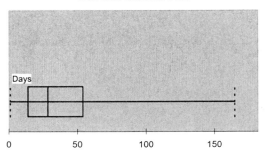

Both the normal probability plot and the box-and-whisker plot suggest that the distribution is skewed to the right.

(d)   Even though the population distribution is not normally distributed, with a sample of 50, the t distribution can still be used due to the central limit theorem.

8.20   (a) $\bar{X} \pm t \cdot \dfrac{s}{\sqrt{n}} = 43.8889 \pm 2.0555 \cdot \dfrac{25.2835}{\sqrt{27}}$ $33.89 \le \mu \le 53.89$

(b)   The population distribution needs to be normally distributed.

(c)

Normal Probability Plot

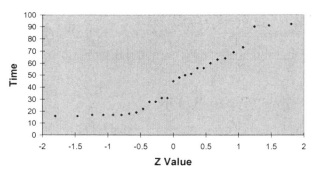

Box-and-whisker Plot

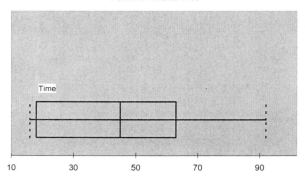

Both the normal probability plot and the box-and-whisker show that the population distribution is not normally distributed and is skewed to the right.

8.20   (d)   With a sample size of 27 and the population distribution that appears to be skewed,
cont.   the method used in (a) is not reliable and, hence, any comparison with Problem 2.64
              is likely to be invalid.

8.22 $p_s = \dfrac{X}{n} = \dfrac{50}{200} = 0.25$ $p_s \pm Z \cdot \sqrt{\dfrac{p_s(1-p_s)}{n}} = 0.25 \pm 1.96\sqrt{\dfrac{0.25(0.75)}{200}}$

$$0.19 \le p \le 0.31$$

8.24   (a)

	A	B
1	Purchase Additional Telephone Line	
2		
3	Sample Size	500
4	Number of Successes	135
5	Confidence Level	99%
6	Sample Proportion	0.27
7	Z Value	-2.57583451
8	Standard Error of the Proportion	0.019854471
9	Interval Half Width	0.05114183
10	Interval Lower Limit	0.21885817
11	Interval Upper Limit	0.32114183

       (b)   The manager in charge of promotional programs concerning residential customers
             can infer that the proportion of households that would purchase an additional
             telephone line if it were made available at a substantially reduced installation cost is
             somewhere between 0.22 and 0.32 with a 99% level of confidence.

8.26   (a) $p_s = \dfrac{X}{n} = 0.41$

$$p_s \pm Z \cdot \sqrt{\dfrac{p_s(1-p_s)}{n}} = 0.41 \pm 1.96\sqrt{\dfrac{0.41(1-0.41)}{1110}}$$

$$0.3810 < p < 0.4388$$

       (b) $p_s \pm Z \cdot \sqrt{\dfrac{p_s(1-p_s)}{n}} = 0.41 \pm 1.6449\sqrt{\dfrac{0.41(1-0.41)}{1110}}$

$$0.3856 < p < 0.4342$$

       (c)   The 95% confidence interval is wider because the critical value used in constructing
             the interval is larger due to the higher level of confidence.

8.28   (a) $p_s = \dfrac{X}{n} = 0.46$

$$p_s \pm Z \cdot \sqrt{\dfrac{p_s(1-p_s)}{n}} = 0.46 \pm 1.96\sqrt{\dfrac{0.46(1-0.46)}{500}}$$

$0.4163 < p < 0.5037$

(b) $p_s = \dfrac{X}{n} = 0.10$

$$p_s \pm Z \cdot \sqrt{\dfrac{p_s(1-p_s)}{n}} = 0.10 \pm 1.96\sqrt{\dfrac{0.10(1-0.10)}{500}}$$

$0.0737 < p < 0.1263$

8.30   (a) $p_s = \dfrac{X}{n} = \dfrac{450}{1000} = 0.45$

$$p_s \pm Z \cdot \sqrt{\dfrac{p_s(1-p_s)}{n}} = 0.45 \pm 1.96\sqrt{\dfrac{0.45(1-0.45)}{1000}}$$

$0.4192 < p < 0.4808$

(b)   We are 95% confidence that the proportion of all working women in North America who believe that companies should hold positions for those on maternity leave for more than six months is somewhere between 0.4192 and 0.4808.

8.32 $n = \dfrac{Z^2\sigma^2}{e^2} = \dfrac{1.96^2 \cdot 15^2}{5^2} = 34.57$ Use $n = 35$

8.34 $n = \dfrac{Z^2 p(1-p)}{e^2} = \dfrac{2.58^2(0.5)(0.5)}{(0.04)^2} = 1{,}040.06$ Use $n = 1{,}041$

8.36   (a) $n = \dfrac{Z^2\sigma^2}{e^2} = \dfrac{1.96^2 \cdot 400^2}{50^2} = 245.86$ Use $n = 246$

(b) $n = \dfrac{Z^2\sigma^2}{e^2} = \dfrac{1.96^2 \cdot 400^2}{25^2} = 983.41$ Use $n = 984$

8.38 $n = \dfrac{Z^2\sigma^2}{e^2} = \dfrac{1.96^2 \cdot (100)^2}{(20)^2} = 96.04$ Use $n = 97$

8.40   (a) $n = \dfrac{Z^2\sigma^2}{e^2} = \dfrac{2.58^2 \cdot 25^2}{5^2} = 166.41$ Use $n = 167$

(b) $n = \dfrac{Z^2\sigma^2}{e^2} = \dfrac{1.96^2 \cdot 25^2}{5^2} = 96.04$ Use $n = 97$

8.42 $n = \dfrac{Z^2\sigma^2}{e^2} = \dfrac{1.96^2 \cdot 20^2}{5^2} = 61.47$ Use $n = 62$

8.44   (a) $n = \dfrac{Z^2 p(1-p)}{e^2} = \dfrac{1.645^2 (0.5)(0.5)}{(0.04)^2} = 422.82$ Use $n = 423$

(b) $n = \dfrac{Z^2 p(1-p)}{e^2} = \dfrac{1.96^2 (0.5)(0.5)}{(0.04)^2} = 600.25$ Use $n = 601$

(c) $n = \dfrac{Z^2 p(1-p)}{e^2} = \dfrac{1.96^2 (0.5)(0.5)}{(0.03)^2} = 1067.07$ Use $n = 1068$

(d)   In general, larger sample size is needed if a higher level of confidence is required holding everything else fixed. This increase in sample size reflects the higher price for the increase in level of confidence. If a higher precision is required, which is reflected in lower acceptable sampling error, the sample size will need to be raised to reflect the higher associated cost holding everything else fixed.

8.46   (a) $p_s = \dfrac{X}{n} = \dfrac{94}{586} = 0.1604$

$p_s \pm Z \cdot \sqrt{\dfrac{p_s(1-p_s)}{n}} = 0.1604 \pm 1.96 \cdot \sqrt{\dfrac{0.1604(1-0.1604)}{586}}$ $0.1307 < p < 0.1901$

(b) $n = \dfrac{Z^2 p(1-p)}{e^2} = \dfrac{1.96^2 (0.1604)(1-0.1604)}{(0.02)^2} = 1293.34$ Use $n = 1294$

(c) $n = \dfrac{Z^2 p(1-p)}{e^2} = \dfrac{2.5758^2 (0.1604)(1-0.1604)}{(0.02)^2} = 2233.84$ Use $n = 2234$

8.48 $n = \dfrac{Z^2 p(1-p)}{e^2} = \dfrac{1.96^2 (0.50)(0.50)}{(0.02)^2} = 2400.91$ Use $n = 2401$

8.50 $N \cdot \bar{X} \pm N \cdot t \cdot \dfrac{s}{\sqrt{n}} \sqrt{\dfrac{N-n}{N-1}} = 500 \cdot 25.7 \pm 500 \cdot 2.7969 \cdot \dfrac{7.8}{\sqrt{25}} \cdot \sqrt{\dfrac{500-25}{500-1}}$

$\$10,721.53 \le$ Population Total $\le \$14,978.47$

8.52   (a) $p_s + Z \cdot \sqrt{\dfrac{p_s(1-p_s)}{n}} = 0.04 + 1.2816 \cdot \sqrt{\dfrac{0.04(1-0.04)}{300}}$ $p < 0.0545$

(b) $p_s + Z \cdot \sqrt{\dfrac{p_s(1-p_s)}{n}} = 0.04 + 1.645 \cdot \sqrt{\dfrac{0.04(1-0.04)}{300}}$ $p < 0.0586$

(c) $p_s + Z \cdot \sqrt{\dfrac{p_s(1-p_s)}{n}} = 0.04 + 2.3263 \cdot \sqrt{\dfrac{0.04(1-0.04)}{300}}$ $p < 0.0663$

8.54 $N \cdot \bar{X} \pm N \cdot t \cdot \dfrac{s}{\sqrt{n}} \sqrt{\dfrac{N-n}{N-1}} = 3000 \cdot \$261.40 \pm 3000 \cdot 1.8331 \cdot \dfrac{\$138.8046}{\sqrt{10}} \cdot \sqrt{\dfrac{3000-10}{3000-1}}$

$\$543,176.96 \le$ Population Total $\le \$1,025,223.04$

8.56 $N \cdot \bar{D} \pm N \cdot t \cdot \dfrac{S_D}{\sqrt{n}} \sqrt{\dfrac{N-n}{N-1}} = 4000 \cdot \$7.45907 \pm 4000 \cdot 2.6092 \cdot \dfrac{\$29.5523}{\sqrt{150}} \sqrt{\dfrac{4000-150}{4000-1}}$

$\$5,125.99 \le$ Total Difference in the Population $\le \$54,546.57$

Note: The t-value of 2.6092 for 95% confidence and $df = 149$ was derived on Excel.

8.58 (a) $p_s + Z \cdot \sqrt{\dfrac{p_s(1-p_s)}{n}} \sqrt{\dfrac{N-n}{N-1}} = 0.0367 + 1.645 \cdot \sqrt{\dfrac{0.0367(1-0.0367)}{300}} \sqrt{\dfrac{10000-300}{10000-1}}$

$p < 0.0542$

(b) Since the upper bound is higher than the tolerable exception rate of 0.04, the auditor should request a larger sample.

8.60 The only way to have 100% confidence is to obtain the parameter of interest, rather than a sample statistic. From another perspective, the range of the normal and t distribution is infinite, so a Z or t value that contains 100% of the area cannot be obtained.

8.62 If the confidence level is increased, a greater area under the normal or t distribution needs to be included. This leads to an increased value of Z or t, and thus a wider interval.

8.64 In some applications such as auditing, interest is primarily on the total amount of a variable rather than the average amount.

8.66 (a) The population from which this sample was drawn was the collection of all subscribers to the *Redbook* magazine who visited the magazine's web site.

(b) The sample is not a random sample from this population. The sample consisted of only those subscribers to the magazine who visited the magazine's web site and chose to fill out the survey.

(c) This is not a statistically valid study. There was selection bias since only those who visited the magazine's web site and chose to answer the survey were represented. There was possibly nonresponse bias as well. Visitors to the web site who chose to fill out the survey might not answer all questions and there was no way for the magazine to get back to them to follow-up on the nonresponses if this was an anonymous survey.

(d) To avoid the above potential pitfalls, the magazine could have drawn a random sample from the list of all subscribers to the magazine and offer them the option of filling out the survey over the Internet or on the survey form that is mailed to the subscribers. The magazine should also keep track of the subscribers who are invited to fill out the survey and follow up on the nonresponses after a specified period of time with mail or telephone to encourage them to participate in the survey.

The sample size needed is $n = \dfrac{Z^2 \cdot p \cdot (1-p)}{e^2} = \dfrac{1.96^2 \cdot (0.6195) \cdot (1-0.6195)}{(0.02)^2} = 2264$

8.68   (a) $p_s \pm Z \cdot \sqrt{\dfrac{p_s(1-p_s)}{n}} = 0.58 \pm 1.96 \cdot \sqrt{\dfrac{0.58(1-0.58)}{200}}$ $\qquad 0.5116 < p < 0.6484$

(b) $p_s \pm Z \cdot \sqrt{\dfrac{p_s(1-p_s)}{n}} = 0.50 \pm 1.96 \cdot \sqrt{\dfrac{0.50(1-0.50)}{200}}$ $\qquad 0.4307 < p < 0.5693$

(c) $p_s \pm Z \cdot \sqrt{\dfrac{p_s(1-p_s)}{n}} = 0.22 \pm 1.96 \cdot \sqrt{\dfrac{0.22(1-0.22)}{200}}$ $\qquad 0.1626 < p < 0.2774$

(d) $p_s \pm Z \cdot \sqrt{\dfrac{p_s(1-p_s)}{n}} = 0.19 \pm 1.96 \cdot \sqrt{\dfrac{0.19(1-0.19)}{200}}$ $\qquad 0.1356 < p < 0.2444$

(e) $n = \dfrac{Z^2 \cdot p \cdot (1-p)}{e^2} = \dfrac{1.96^2 \cdot (0.5) \cdot (0.5)}{(0.02)^2} = 2400.9 \cong 2401$

(f)   The survey has found out that 58% of the 200 managers in the sample have caught sales people cheating on an expense report. This is different from stating that 58% of all sales people cheat on an expense report. The former refers to the proportion in the sample of 200 managers while the latter refers to the proportion in the population.

8.70   (a) $\bar{X} \pm t \cdot \dfrac{s}{\sqrt{n}} = 5.5014 \pm 2.6800 \cdot \dfrac{0.1058}{\sqrt{50}}$ $\qquad 5.46 < \mu < 5.54$

(b)   Since 5.5 gram is within the 99% confidence interval, the company can claim that the average weight of tea in a bag is 5.5 gram with a 99% level of confidence.

8.72   (a) $\bar{X} \pm t \cdot \dfrac{s}{\sqrt{n}} = 3124.2147 \pm 1.9665 \cdot \dfrac{34.713}{\sqrt{368}}$ $\qquad 3120.66 < \mu < 3127.77$

(b) $\bar{X} \pm t \cdot \dfrac{s}{\sqrt{n}} = 3704.0424 \pm 1.9672 \cdot \dfrac{46.7443}{\sqrt{330}}$ $\qquad 3698.98 < \mu < 3709.10$

(c)

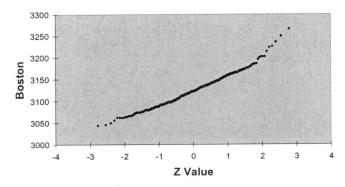

Normal Probability Plot

8.72   (c)
cont.

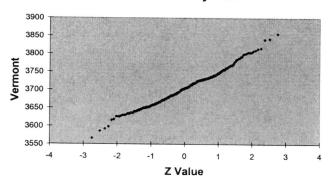

Normal Probability Plot

The weight for Boston shingles is slightly skewed to the right while the weight for Vermont shingles appears to be slightly skewed to the left.

(d)   Since the two confidence intervals do not overlap, the average weight of Vermont shingles is higher than the average weight of Boston shingles.

8.74   (a)   NY, Food: $\bar{X} \pm t \cdot \dfrac{s}{\sqrt{n}} = 20.1 \pm 2.0096 \cdot \dfrac{2.0825}{\sqrt{50}}$ $19.51 < \mu < 20.69$

LI, Food: $\bar{X} \pm t \cdot \dfrac{s}{\sqrt{n}} = 20.54 \pm 2.0096 \cdot \dfrac{2.8586}{\sqrt{50}}$ $19.73 < \mu < 21.35$

NY, Décor: $\bar{X} \pm t \cdot \dfrac{s}{\sqrt{n}} = 17.12 \pm 2.0096 \cdot \dfrac{2.6927}{\sqrt{50}}$ $16.35 < \mu < 17.89$

LI, Décor: $\bar{X} \pm t \cdot \dfrac{s}{\sqrt{n}} = 17.64 \pm 2.0096 \cdot \dfrac{3.4862}{\sqrt{50}}$ $16.65 < \mu < 18.63$

NY, Services: $\bar{X} \pm t \cdot \dfrac{s}{\sqrt{n}} = 18.4 \pm 2.0096 \cdot \dfrac{2.3123}{\sqrt{50}}$ $17.74 < \mu < 19.06$

LI, Services: $\bar{X} \pm t \cdot \dfrac{s}{\sqrt{n}} = 19.04 \pm 2.0096 \cdot \dfrac{2.3730}{\sqrt{50}}$ $18.37 < \mu < 19.71$

NY, Price: $\bar{X} \pm t \cdot \dfrac{s}{\sqrt{n}} = 39.74 \pm 2.0096 \cdot \dfrac{9.6528}{\sqrt{50}}$ $37.00 < \mu < 42.48$

LI, Price: $\bar{X} \pm t \cdot \dfrac{s}{\sqrt{n}} = 33.7400 \pm 2.0096 \cdot \dfrac{7.7191}{\sqrt{50}}$ $31.55 < \mu < 35.93$

(b)   The price per person in New York City is higher on average than that in Long Island with 95% level of confidence. We can conclude that there are no differences in the ratings for food, décor and service between the two cities at 95% level of confidence.

8.76 (a) $\bar{X} \pm t \cdot \dfrac{s}{\sqrt{n}} = 1759 \pm 2.6490 \cdot \dfrac{380}{\sqrt{70}}$ $1{,}638.69 \leq \mu \leq 1{,}879.31$

(b) $p_s \pm Z \cdot \sqrt{\dfrac{p_s(1-p_s)}{n}} = 0.60 \pm 1.96 \cdot \sqrt{\dfrac{0.60(0.40)}{70}}$ $0.485 \leq p \leq 0.715$

8.78 (a) $n = \dfrac{Z^2 \cdot \sigma^2}{e^2} = \dfrac{2.58^2 \cdot 18^2}{5^2} = 86.27$ Use $n = 87$

Note: If the Z-value used is carried out to 2.5758, the value of n is 85.986 and only 86 women would be sampled.

(b) $n = \dfrac{Z^2 \cdot p \cdot (1-p)}{e^2} = \dfrac{1.645^2 \cdot (0.5) \cdot (0.5)}{(0.045)^2} = 334.07$ Use $n = 335$

(c) If a single sample were to be selected for both purposes, the larger of the two sample sizes ($n = 335$) should be used.

8.80 (a) $\bar{X} \pm t \cdot \dfrac{s}{\sqrt{n}} = \$21.34 \pm 1.9949 \cdot \dfrac{\$9.22}{\sqrt{70}}$ $\$19.14 \leq \mu \leq \$23.54$

(b) $p_s \pm Z \cdot \sqrt{\dfrac{p_s(1-p_s)}{n}} = 0.3714 \pm 1.645 \cdot \sqrt{\dfrac{0.3714(0.6286)}{70}}$

$0.2764 \leq p \leq 0.4664$

(c) $n = \dfrac{Z^2 \cdot \sigma^2}{e^2} = \dfrac{1.96^2 \cdot 10^2}{1.5^2} = 170.74$ Use $n = 171$

(d) $n = \dfrac{Z^2 \cdot p \cdot (1-p)}{e^2} = \dfrac{1.645^2 \cdot (0.5) \cdot (0.5)}{(0.045)^2} = 334.08$ Use $n = 335$

(e) If a single sample were to be selected for both purposes, the larger of the two sample sizes ($n = 335$) should be used.

8.82 (a) $n = \dfrac{Z^2 \cdot p \cdot (1-p)}{e^2} = \dfrac{1.96^2 \cdot (0.5) \cdot (0.5)}{(0.05)^2} = 384.16$ Use $n = 385$

If we assume that the population proportion is only 0.50, then a sample of 385 would be required. If the population proportion is 0.90, the sample size required is cut to 103.

(b) $p_s \pm Z \cdot \sqrt{\dfrac{p_s(1-p_s)}{n}} = 0.84 \pm 1.96 \cdot \sqrt{\dfrac{0.84(0.16)}{50}}$

$0.7384 \leq p \leq 0.9416$

(c) The representative can be 95% confidence that the actual proportion of bags that will do the job is between 74.5% and 93.5%. He/she can accordingly perform a cost-benefit analysis to decide if he/she want to sell the Ice Melt product.

8.84 (a) $n_0 = \dfrac{Z^2 \cdot \sigma^2}{e^2} = \dfrac{1.96^2 \cdot 30^2}{5^2} = 138.292$

$n = \dfrac{n_0 N}{n_0 + (N-1)} = \dfrac{138.292 \cdot 25056}{138.292 + (25056 - 1)} = 137.53$ Use $n = 138$

(b) $p_s = \dfrac{12}{138} = 0.087$

$p_s \pm Z \cdot \sqrt{\dfrac{p_s(1-p_s)}{n}} \cdot \sqrt{\dfrac{N-n}{N-1}}$

$= 0.087 \pm 1.645 \cdot \sqrt{\dfrac{0.087(0.913)}{138}} \cdot \sqrt{\dfrac{25,056-138}{25,056-1}}$

$0.0476 \le p \le 0.1263$

(c) Using Excel, we find the t-value for 95% confidence and 137 degrees of freedom is $t = 1.9774$.

$\bar{X} \pm t \cdot \dfrac{s}{\sqrt{n}} \cdot \sqrt{\dfrac{N-n}{N-1}} = \$93.70 \pm 1.9774 \cdot \dfrac{\$34.55}{\sqrt{138}} \cdot \sqrt{\dfrac{25,056-138}{25,056-1}}$

$\$87.90 \le \mu_X \le \$99.50$

(d) $N \cdot \bar{X} \pm N \cdot t \cdot \dfrac{s}{\sqrt{n}} \cdot \sqrt{\dfrac{N-n}{N-1}}$

$= 25,056 \cdot \$93.70 \pm 25,056 \cdot 1.9774 \cdot \dfrac{\$34.55}{\sqrt{138}} \cdot \sqrt{\dfrac{25,056-138}{25,056-1}}$

$\$2,202,427.61 \le \text{Population Total} \le \$2,493,066.79$

(e) $\bar{D} = \dfrac{\sum D}{n} = \dfrac{241}{138} = 1.7463768$ $s_D = \sqrt{\dfrac{\sum (D - \bar{D})^2}{n-1}} = \sqrt{\dfrac{6432.12}{137}} = 6.85199$

$N \cdot \bar{D} \pm N \cdot t \cdot \dfrac{s_D}{\sqrt{n}} \cdot \sqrt{\dfrac{N-n}{N-1}}$

$= 25,056 \cdot \$1.7463768 \pm 25,056 \cdot 1.9774 \cdot \dfrac{\$6.85199}{\sqrt{138}} \cdot \sqrt{\dfrac{25,056-138}{25,056-1}}$

$\$14,937.30 \le \text{Total Difference in the Population} \le \$72,577.14$

CHAPTER 9

OBJECTIVES

- To understand the basic hypothesis testing procedure
- To use hypothesis testing to test a mean, proportion, or variance
- To be aware of the assumptions of each hypothesis testing procedure, how to evaluate the assumptions, and what will be the consequences if the assumptions are seriously violated
- To be familiar with pitfalls involved in hypothesis testing and ethical issues that may be involved

OVERVIEW AND KEY CONCEPTS

Some Basic Concepts in Hypothesis Testing

- **Null hypothesis** (H_0): The hypothesis that is always tested.
  - The null hypothesis always refers to a specified value of the population parameter, not a sample statistic.
  - The statement of the null hypothesis always contains an equal sign regarding the specified value of the population parameter.
- **Alternative hypothesis:** The opposite of the null hypothesis and represents the conclusion supported if the null hypothesis is rejected.
  - The statement of the alternative hypothesis never contains an equal sign regarding the specified value of the population parameter.
- **Critical value:** A value or values that separate the rejection region or regions from the remaining values.
- **Type I error:** A Type I error occurs if the null hypothesis is rejected when in fact it is true and should not be rejected.
- **Type II error:** A Type II error occurs if the null hypothesis is not rejected when in fact it is false and should be rejected.
- **Level of significance** (α): The probability of committing a Type I error.
- **The β risk (the consumer's risk level):** The probability of committing a Type II error.
- **Factors that affect the β risk:** Holding everything else constant,
  - β increases when the difference between the hypothesized parameter and its true value decreases.
  - β increases when α decreases.
  - β increases when σ increases.
  - β increases when the sample size n decreases.
- **The confidence coefficient** $(1-\alpha)$: The probability that the null hypothesis is not rejected when in fact it is true and should not be rejected.
- **The confidence level:** $100(1-\alpha)\%$
- **The power of a test** $(1-\beta)$: The probability of rejecting the null hypothesis when in fact it is false and should be rejected.

- **Risk in decision making:** There is a delicate balance between the probability of committing a Type I error and the probability of a Type II error.

H_0: Innocent

E.g. Jury Trial				Hypothesis Test		
	The Truth				**The Truth**	
Verdict	Innocent	Guilty	Decision	H_0 True	H_0 False
Innocent	Correct	Error	Do Not Reject H_0	$1 - \alpha$	Type II Error (β)
Guilty	Error	Correct	Reject H_0	Type I Error (α)	Power $(1 - \beta)$

  - Reducing the probability of Type I error will inevitably increase the probability of committing a Type II error holding everything else constant.
  - One should choose a smaller Type I error when the cost of rejecting the maintained hypothesis is high.
  - One should choose a larger Type I error when there is an interest in changing the status quo.
- **p-value (the observed level of significance):** The probability of obtaining a test statistic equal to or more extreme than the result obtained from the sample data, given the null hypothesis is true.
  - It is also the smallest level of significance at which the null hypothesis can be rejected.
  - Roughly speaking, it measures the amount of evidence against the null hypothesis. The smaller the p-value, the stronger is the evidence against the null hypothesis.
  - The statistical decision rule is to reject the null hypothesis if the p-value is less than the level of significance (α), and do not reject otherwise.

General Steps in the Traditional Critical Value Approach to Hypothesis Testing
1. State the null hypothesis.
2. State the alternative hypothesis.
3. Choose the level of significance (α).
4. Choose the sample size, n.
5. Choose an appropriate test.
6. Collect data and compute the sample value of the appropriate test statistic.
7. Obtain the critical value(s) based on the level of significance.
8. Compare the computed test statistic to the critical value(s).
9. Make a statistical decision: Reject H_0 when the computed test statistic falls in a rejection region; do not reject H_0 otherwise.
10. Draw the conclusion.

General Steps in the *p* Value Approach to Hypothesis Testing
1. State the null hypothesis.
2. State the alternative hypothesis.
3. Choose the level of significance (α).
4. Choose the sample size, *n*.
5. Choose an appropriate test.
6. Collect data and compute the sample value of the appropriate test statistic.
7. Obtain the *p*-value based on the computed test statistic.
8. Compare the *p*-value to α
9. Make a statistical decision: Reject H_0 when the *p*-value $< \alpha$; do not reject H_0 otherwise.
10. Draw the conclusion.

Z Test for the Population Mean (μ) when σ is Known
*   **Assumptions:**
    *   Population is normally distributed or large sample size.
    * σ is known.
*   **Test statistic:**
    * $Z = \dfrac{\overline{X} - \mu_{\overline{X}}}{\sigma_{\overline{X}}} = \dfrac{\overline{X} - \mu}{\sigma / \sqrt{n}}$
    *   The alternative hypothesis can be one-tail with a right-tail rejection region, one-tail with a left-tail rejection region or two-tail with both right-tail and left-tail rejection regions.

t Test for the Population Mean (μ) when σ Is Unknown
*   **Assumptions:**
    *   Population is normally distributed or large sample size.
    * σ is unknown.
*   **Test statistic:**
    * $t = \dfrac{\overline{X} - \mu}{S / \sqrt{n}}$ with $(n - 1)$ degrees of freedom.
    *   The alternative hypothesis can be one-tail with a right-tail rejection region, one-tail with a left-tail rejection region or two-tail with both right-tail and left-tail rejection regions.

Z Test for the Population Proportion (p)
- **Assumptions:**
  - Population involves 2 categorical values.
  - Both np and $n(1\text{-}p)$ are at least 5.
- **Test statistic:**
  - $$Z = \frac{p_S - \mu_{p_S}}{\sigma_{p_S}} = \frac{p_S - p}{\sqrt{\dfrac{p(1-p)}{n}}}$$
  - The alternative hypothesis can be one-tail with a right-tail rejection region, one-tail with a left-tail rejection region or two-tail with both right-tail and left-tail rejection regions.

χ^2 Test for the Population Variance $\left(\sigma^2\right)$ or Standard Deviation (σ)
- **Assumption:**
  - Population is normally distributed.
- **Test statistic:**
  - $$\chi^2 = \frac{(n-1)S^2}{\sigma^2}$$ with $(n-1)$ degrees of freedom.
  - The alternative hypothesis can be one-tail with a right-tail rejection region, one-tail with a left-tail rejection region or two-tail with both right-tail and left-tail rejection regions.

SOLUTIONS TO END OF SECTION
AND CHAPTER REVIEW EVEN PROBLEMS

9.2 H_1 is used to denote the alternative hypothesis.

9.4 β is used to denote the consumer's risk, or the chance of committing a Type II error.

9.6 α is the probability of making a Type I error – that is, the probability of incorrectly rejecting the null hypothesis when in reality the null hypothesis is true and should not be rejected.

9.8   The power of a test is the complement of the probability β of making a Type II error.

9.10   It is possible to incorrectly fail to reject a false null hypothesis because it is possible for the mean of a single sample to fall in the nonrejection region even though the hypothesized population mean is false.

9.12   Other things being equal, the closer the *hypothesized* mean is to the *actual* mean, the larger is the risk of committing a Type II error.

9.14   Under the French judicial system, unlike ours in the United States, the null hypothesis is that the defendant is assumed to be guilty, the alternative hypothesis is that the defendant is innocent. The meaning of α and β risks would also be switched.

9.16 H_0: $\mu = 20$ minutes. 20 minutes is adequate travel time between classes.
       H_1: $\mu \neq 20$ minutes. 20 minutes is not adequate travel time between classes.

9.18   Decision rule: Reject H_0 if $Z < -1.96$ or $Z > +1.96$.
       Decision: Since $Z_{calc} = +2.21$ is greater than $Z_{crit} = +1.96$, reject H_0.

9.20   Decision rule: Reject H_0 if $Z < -2.58$ or $Z > +2.58$.

9.22 p-value $= 2(1 - .9772) = 0.0456$

9.24 p-value $= 0.1676$

9.26   (a) H_0: $\mu = 70$ pounds. The cloth has an average breaking strength of 70 pounds.
              H_1: $\mu \neq 70$ pounds. The cloth has an average breaking strength that differs from 70 pounds.
       (b)   Decision rule: Reject H_0 if $Z < -1.96$ or $Z > +1.96$.
              Test statistic: $Z = \dfrac{\bar{X} - \mu}{\sigma / \sqrt{n}} = \dfrac{69.1 - 70}{3.5 / \sqrt{49}} = -1.80$

              Decision: Since $Z_{calc} = -1.80$ is between the critical bounds of ± 1.96, do not reject H_0. There is not enough evidence to conclude that the cloth has an average breaking strength that differs from 70 pounds.

9.26   (c) p value $= 2(0.0359) = 0.0718$
cont.   Interpretation: The probability of getting a sample of 49 pieces that yield a mean strength that is farther away from the hypothesized population mean than this sample is 0.0718 or 7.18%.

    (d)   Decision rule: Reject H_0 if $Z < -1.96$ or $Z > +1.96$.

Test statistic: $Z = \dfrac{\overline{X} - \mu}{\sigma/\sqrt{n}} = \dfrac{69.1 - 70}{1.75/\sqrt{49}} = -3.60$

Decision: Since $Z_{calc} = -3.60$ is less than the lower critical bound of -1.96, reject H_0. There is enough evidence to conclude that the cloth has an average breaking strength that differs from 70 pounds.

    (e)   Decision rule: Reject H_0 if $Z < -1.96$ or $Z > +1.96$.

Test statistic: $Z = \dfrac{\overline{X} - \mu}{\sigma/\sqrt{n}} = \dfrac{69 - 70}{3.5/\sqrt{49}} = -2.00$

Decision: Since $Z_{calc} = -2.00$ is less than the lower critical bound of -1.96, reject H_0. There is enough evidence to conclude that the cloth has an average breaking strength that differs from 70 pounds.

9.28   (a) H_0: $\mu = 375$ hours. The average life of the manufacturer's light bulbs is equal to 375 hours.
            H_1: $\mu \neq 375$ hours. The average life of the manufacturer's light bulbs differs from 375 hours.

    (b)   Decision rule: Reject H_0 if $Z < -1.96$ or $Z > +1.96$.

Test statistic: $Z = \dfrac{\overline{X} - \mu}{\sigma/\sqrt{n}} = \dfrac{350 - 375}{100/\sqrt{64}} = -2.00$

Decision: Since $Z_{calc} = -2.00$ is below the critical bound of -1.96, reject H_0. There is enough evidence to conclude that the average life of the manufacturer's light bulbs differs from 375 hours.

    (c) p-value $= 2(0.0228) = 0.0456$

    (d) $\overline{X} \pm Z \cdot \dfrac{\sigma}{\sqrt{n}} = 350 \pm 1.96 \cdot \dfrac{100}{\sqrt{64}}$ $325.50 \leq \mu \leq 374.50$

    (e)   The results are the same. The confidence interval formed does not include the hypothesized value of 375 hours.

9.30   (a), (b), (c)

	A	B
1	Salad Dressings	
2		
3	Null Hypothesis μ=	8
4	Level of Significance	0.05
5	Population Standard Deviation	0.15
6	Sample Size	50
7	Sample Mean	7.983
8	Standard Error of the Mean	0.021213203
9	Z Test Statistic	-0.80138769
10		
11	Two-Tailed Test	
12	Lower Critical Value	-1.95996108
13	Upper Critical Value	1.959961082
14	p-Value	0.422907113
15	Do not reject the null hypothesis	

(a) $H_0: \mu = 8$ $H_1: \mu \neq 8$

(b)   Decision rule: Reject H_0 if $Z < -1.96$ or $Z > 1.96$

Test statistic: $Z = \dfrac{7.983 - 8}{.15/\sqrt{50}} = -.8$

Decision: Do not reject H_0. There is insufficient evidence to conclude that the amount of salad dressing placed in 8 oz bottle is significantly different from 8 oz.

(c) p-value = 0.4229. The probability of observing a Z test statistic more extreme than $-.8$ is 0.4229 if the population average is indeed 8 oz.

(d)   Decision rule: Reject H_0 if $Z < -1.96$ or $Z > +1.96$.

Test statistic: $Z = \dfrac{\bar{X} - \mu}{\sigma/\sqrt{n}} = \dfrac{7.983 - 8}{0.05/\sqrt{50}} = -2.40$

Decision: Since $Z_{calc} = -2.40$ is less than the lower critical bound of -1.96, reject H_0. There is enough evidence to conclude that the machine is filling bottles improperly.

(e)   Decision rule: Reject H_0 if $Z < -1.96$ or $Z > +1.96$.

Test statistic: $Z = \dfrac{\bar{X} - \mu}{\sigma/\sqrt{n}} = \dfrac{7.952 - 8}{0.15/\sqrt{50}} = -2.26$

Decision: Since $Z_{calc} = -2.26$ is less than the lower critical bound of -1.96, reject H_0. There is enough evidence to conclude that the machine is filling bottles improperly.

9.32 $Z = 2.33$

9.34 $Z = -2.33$

9.36 p value $= 1 - .9772 = 0.0228$

9.38 p value $= 0.0838$

9.40 p-value $= P(Z < 1.38) = 0.9162$

9.42   (a) H_0: $\mu \geq 2.8$ feet.

The average length of steel bars produced is at least 2.8 feet and the production equipment does not need immediate adjustment.

H_1: $\mu < 2.8$ feet.

The average length of steel bars produced is less than 2.8 feet and the production equipment does need immediate adjustment.

(b)   Decision rule: If $Z < -1.645$, reject H_0.

Test statistic: $Z = \dfrac{\overline{X} - \mu}{\sigma / \sqrt{n}} = \dfrac{2.73 - 2.8}{0.2 / \sqrt{25}} = -1.75$

Decision: Since $Z_{\text{calc}} = -1.75$ is less than $Z_{\text{crit}} = -1.645$, reject H_0. There is enough evidence to conclude the production equipment needs adjustment.

(c)   Decision rule: If p value < 0.05, reject H_0.

Test statistic: $Z = \dfrac{\overline{X} - \mu}{\sigma / \sqrt{n}} = \dfrac{2.73 - 2.8}{0.2 / \sqrt{25}} = -1.75$

p value $= 0.0401$

Decision: Since p value $= 0.0401$ is less than $\alpha = 0.05$, reject H_0. There is enough evidence to conclude the production equipment needs adjustment.

(d)   The probability of obtaining a sample whose mean is 2.73 feet or less when the null hypothesis is true is 0.0401.

(e)   The conclusions are the same.

9.44   (a) H_0: $\mu \geq 8$ ounces.

The mean amount of salad dressing dispensed is at least 8 ounces. The machine is working properly. No work stoppage should occur.

H_1: $\mu < 8$ ounces.

The mean amount of salad dressing dispensed is less than 8 ounces. The machine is not working properly. The filling line should be stopped.

(b)   Decision rule: If $Z < -1.645$, reject H_0.

Test statistic: $Z = \dfrac{\overline{X} - \mu}{\sigma / \sqrt{n}} = \dfrac{7.983 - 8}{0.15 / \sqrt{50}} = -0.80$

Decision: Since $Z_{\text{calc}} = -0.80$ is greater than $Z_{\text{crit}} = -1.645$, do not reject H_0. There is not enough evidence to conclude that the mean amount of salad dressing dispensed is less than 8 ounces. There is insufficient evidence to conclude the machine is not working properly. The filling line should not be stopped.

(c)   Decision rule: If p value < 0.05, reject H_0.

Test statistic: $Z = \dfrac{\overline{X} - \mu}{\sigma / \sqrt{n}} = \dfrac{7.983 - 8}{0.15 / \sqrt{50}} = -0.80$

p value $= 0.2119$

Decision: Since p value $= 0.2119$ is greater than $\alpha = 0.05$, do not reject H_0. There is not enough evidence to conclude that the mean amount of salad dressing dispensed is less than 8 ounces. There is insufficient evidence to conclude the machine is not working properly. The filling line should not be stopped.

9.44   (d)   The probability of obtaining a sample whose mean is 7.983 ounces or less when the
cont.   null hypothesis is true is 0.2119.
       (e)   The conclusions are the same.

9.46 $t = \dfrac{\overline{X} - \mu}{S/\sqrt{n}} = \dfrac{56 - 50}{12/\sqrt{16}} = 2.00$

9.48   (a) For a two-tailed test with a 0.05 level of confidence, $t_{crit} = \pm 2.1315$.
       (b) For an upper-tailed test with a 0.05 level of confidence, $t_{crit} = + 1.7531$.

9.50   No, you should not use the t test to test the null hypothesis that $\mu = 60$ on a population that is
       left-skewed because the sample size $(n = 16)$ is less than 30. The t test assumes that, if the
       underlying population is not normally distributed, the sample size is sufficiently large to
       enable the test statistic t to be influenced by the central limit theorem. If sample sizes are
       small $(n < 30)$, the t test should not be used because the sampling distribution does not meet
       the requirements of the central limit theorem.

9.52   (a) H_0: $\mu \le \$300$. The average cost of textbooks per semester at a large university is no
              more than $300.
              H_1: $\mu > \$300$. The average cost of textbooks per semester at a large university is more
              than $300.
              Decision rule: $df = 99$. If $t > 1.2902$, reject H_0.
              Test statistic: $t = \dfrac{\overline{X} - \mu}{S/\sqrt{n}} = \dfrac{\$315.40 - \$300.00}{\$43.20/\sqrt{100}} = 3.5648$
              Decision: Since $t_{calc} = 3.5648$ is above the critical bound of $t = 1.2902$, reject H_0.
              There is enough evidence to conclude that the average cost of textbooks per semester
              at a large university is more than $300.
       (b) H_0: $\mu \le \$300$. The average cost of textbooks per semester at a large university is no
              more than $300.
              H_1: $\mu > \$300$. The average cost of textbooks per semester at a large university is more
              than $300.
              Decision rule: $df = 99$. If $t > 1.6604$, reject H_0.
              Test statistic: $t = \dfrac{\overline{X} - \mu}{S/\sqrt{n}} = \dfrac{\$315.40 - \$300.00}{\$75.00/\sqrt{100}} = 2.0533$
              Decision: Since $t_{calc} = 2.0533$ is above the critical bound of $t = 1.6604$, reject H_0.
              There is enough evidence to conclude that the average cost of textbooks per semester
              at a large university is more than $300.

9.52
cont.   (c) H_0: $\mu \leq \$300$. The average cost of textbooks per semester at a large university is no
more than \$300.
H_1: $\mu > \$300$. The average cost of textbooks per semester at a large university is more
than \$300.
Decision rule: $df = 99$. If $t > 1.2902$, reject H_0.
$$\text{Test statistic: } t = \frac{\overline{X} - \mu}{S/\sqrt{n}} = \frac{\$305.11 - \$300.00}{\$43.20/\sqrt{100}} = 1.1829$$
Decision: Since $t_{calc} = 1.1829$ is below the critical bound of $t = 1.2902$, do not reject
H_0. There is not enough evidence to conclude that the average cost of textbooks per
semester at a large university is more than \$300.

9.54   (a) $H_0 : \mu = 2$ \qquad $H_1 : \mu \neq 2$ \qquad $d.f. = 49$
Decision rule: Reject H_0 if $|t| > 2.0096$
$$\text{Test statistic: } t = \frac{\overline{X} - \mu}{S/\sqrt{n}} = \frac{2.0007 - 2}{0.0446/\sqrt{50}} = 0.1143$$
Decision: Since $|t| < 2.0096$, do not reject H_0. There is not enough evidence to
conclude that the mean amount of soft drink filled is different from 2.0 liters.

(b) p-value = 0.9095. The probability of observing a sample of 50 soft drinks that will
result in a sample average amount of fill more different from 2.0 liters is 0.9095 if
the population average amount of soft drink filled is indeed 2.0 liters.

(c)   In order for the t test to be valid, the data are assumed to be independently drawn
from a population that is normally distributed. Since the sample size is 50, which is
considered fairly large, the t distribution will provide a good approximation to the
sampling distribution of the mean as long as the population distribution is not very
skewed.

(d)

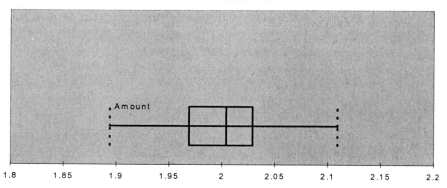

The box-and-whisker plot suggests that the data are rather symmetrically distributed.
Hence, the results in (a) are valid in terms of the normality assumption.

9.54 (e)
cont.

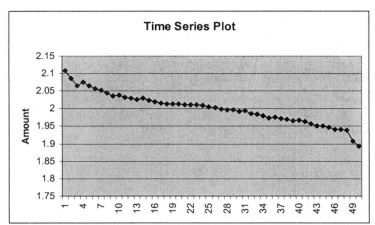

The time series plot of the data reveals that there is a downward trend in the amount of soft drink filled. This violates the assumption that data are drawn independently from a normal population distribution because the amount of fill in consecutive bottles appears to be closely related. As a result, the t test in (a) becomes invalid.

9.56   (a) $H_0 : \mu \le 20$ $H_1 : \mu > 20$

Decision rule: Reject H_0 if $t > 1.6766$ $d.f. = 49$

Test statistic: $t = \dfrac{\overline{X} - \mu}{S / \sqrt{n}} = \dfrac{43.04 - 20}{41.9261 / \sqrt{50}} = 3.8858$

Decision: Since $t > 1.6766$, reject H_0. There is enough evidence to conclude that the average number of days is greater than 20.

(b)   The population distribution needs to be normal.

(c)

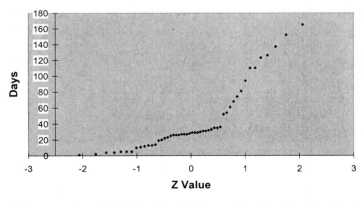

The normal probability plot indicates that the distribution is skewed to the right.

(d)   Even though the population distribution is probably not normally distributed, the result obtained in (a) should still be valid due to the central limit theorem as a result of the relatively large sample size of 50.

9.58   (a) $H_0 : \mu = 45$ $H_1 : \mu \neq 45$

Decision rule: Reject H_0 if $|t| > 2.0555$ $d.f. = 26$

Test statistic: $t = \dfrac{\overline{X} - \mu}{S/\sqrt{n}} = \dfrac{43.8889 - 45}{25.2835/\sqrt{27}} = -0.2284$

Decision: Since $|t| < 2.0555$, do not reject H_0. There is not enough evidence to conclude that the mean processing time has changed from 45 days.

(b)   The population distribution needs to be normal.

(c)

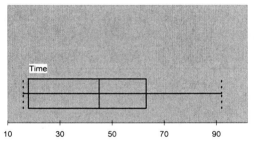

Box-and-whisker Plot

The box-and-whisker plot indicates that the distribution is not symmetrical and is skewed to the right.

(d)   The conclusion reached in (a) is consistent with the findings in Problem 3.61.

9.60   (a) $H_0 : \mu = 5.5$ $H_1 : \mu \neq 5.5$

Decision rule: Reject H_0 if $|t| > 2.680$ $d.f. = 49$

Test statistic: $t = \dfrac{\overline{X} - \mu}{S/\sqrt{n}} = \dfrac{5.5014 - 5.5}{0.1058/\sqrt{50}} = 0.0935$

Decision: Since $|t| < 2.680$, do not reject H_0. There is not enough evidence to conclude that the average amount of tea per bag is different than 5.5 grams.

(b) $\overline{X} \pm t \cdot \dfrac{s}{\sqrt{n}} = 5.5014 \pm 2.6800 \cdot \dfrac{0.1058}{\sqrt{50}}$ $5.46 < \mu < 5.54$

With 99% confidence, one can conclude that the population average amount of tea per bag is somewhere between 5.46 and 5.54 grams.

(c)   The conclusions are the same.

9.62 $p_s = \dfrac{X}{n} = \dfrac{88}{400} = 0.22$

9.64 H_0: $p = 0.20$
H_1: $p \neq 0.20$
Decision rule: If $Z < -1.96$ or $Z > 1.96$, reject H_0.
Test statistic: $Z = \dfrac{p_s - p}{\sqrt{\dfrac{p(1-p)}{n}}} = \dfrac{0.22 - 0.20}{\sqrt{\dfrac{0.20(0.80)}{400}}} = 1.00$
Decision: Since $Z_{calc} = 1.00$ is between the critical bounds of $Z = \pm 1.96$, do not reject H_0.

9.66   (a) H_0: $p = 0.50$
H_1: $p \neq 0.50$
Decision rule: If $Z < -1.96$ or $Z > 1.96$, reject H_0.
Test statistic: $Z = \dfrac{p_s - p}{\sqrt{\dfrac{p(1-p)}{n}}} = \dfrac{0.44 - 0.50}{\sqrt{\dfrac{0.50(0.50)}{811}}} = -3.4061$
Decision: Since $Z_{calc} = -3.4061$ is less than the lower critical bounds of $Z = -1.96$, reject H_0 and conclude that there is enough evidence to show that the percentage of all PC owners in the U.S. who rank sharing their credit card information as the number one concern in on-line shopping is not 50%.

(b) p-value $= P(Z < -3.4061 \text{ or } Z > 3.4061) = 0.00066$. The probability of obtaining a sample proportion further away from the hypothesized value of 0.50 is 0.00066 if the null hypothesis is true.

(c) H_0: $p \leq 0.50$
H_1: $p > 0.50$
Decision rule: If $Z > 1.645$, reject H_0.
Test statistic: $Z = \dfrac{p_s - p}{\sqrt{\dfrac{p(1-p)}{n}}} = \dfrac{0.57 - 0.50}{\sqrt{\dfrac{0.50(0.50)}{811}}} = 3.9680$

Decision: Since $Z_{calc} = 3.9680$ is greater than the critical bound of $Z = 1.645$, reject H_0 and conclude that there is enough evidence to show that the percentage of all PC owners in the U.S. who would pay an extra \$75 for a new PC delivering a more secure on-line experience is more than 50%.

(d) p-value $= P(Z > 3.9680) = 3.6260(10^{-5})$. The probability of obtaining a sample which will yield higher than 57% of all PC owners in the U.S. who would pay an extra \$75 for a new PC delivering a more secure on-line experience is essentially zero if the null hypothesis is true.

9.66   (e) $H_0: p \leq 0.55$
cont. $H_1: p > 0.55$
                 Decision rule: If $Z > 1.645$, reject H_0.

Test statistic: $Z = \dfrac{p_s - p}{\sqrt{\dfrac{p(1-p)}{n}}} = \dfrac{0.57 - 0.55}{\sqrt{\dfrac{0.55(0.45)}{811}}} = 1.1258$

Decision: Since $Z_{calc} = 1.1258$ falls below the critical bound of 1.645, do not reject H_0 and conclude that there is not enough evidence to show that the percentage of all PC owners in the U.S. who would pay an extra \$75 for a new PC delivering a more secure on-line experience is more than 55%.

(f) p-value $= P(Z > 1.1258) = 0.1301$. The probability of obtaining a sample which will yield a higher percentage than 57% of all PC owners in the U.S. who would pay an extra \$75 for a new PC delivering a more secure on-line experience is 0.1301 if the null hypothesis is true.

9.68   (a) $H_0: p \leq 0.101$
                 $H_1: p > 0.101$
                 Decision rule: If $Z > 1.645$, reject H_0.

Test statistic: $Z = \dfrac{p_s - p}{\sqrt{\dfrac{p(1-p)}{n}}} = \dfrac{0.12 - 0.101}{\sqrt{\dfrac{0.101(1 - 0.101)}{200}}} = 0.8917$

Decision: Since $Z_{calc} = 0.8917$ is below the critical bound of 1.645, do not reject H_0. There is not enough evidence to conclude that the conversion rate at llbean.com has increased.

(b) $H_0: p \leq 0.082$
        $H_1: p > 0.082$
        Decision rule: If $Z > 1.645$, reject H_0.

Test statistic: $Z = \dfrac{p_s - p}{\sqrt{\dfrac{p(1-p)}{n}}} = \dfrac{0.125 - 0.082}{\sqrt{\dfrac{0.082(1 - 0.082)}{200}}} = 2.2164$

Decision: Since $Z_{calc} = 2.2164$ is above the critical bounds of 1.645, reject H_0. There is enough evidence to conclude that the conversion rate at victoriasecret.com has increased.

9.70   (a) $H_0: p \geq 0.22$ $H_1: p < 0.22$
Decision rule: If $Z < -2.3263$, reject H_0.

Test statistic: $Z = \dfrac{p_s - p}{\sqrt{\dfrac{p(1-p)}{n}}} = \dfrac{0.18 - 0.22}{\sqrt{\dfrac{0.22(0.78)}{1189}}} = -3.3296$

Decision: Since $Z_{calc} = -3.3296$ is below the critical bound of $Z = -2.3263$, reject H_0. There is enough evidence to conclude that Home Depot ads are less successful than the typical ad.

(b) p-value = 0.00043. The probability of observing 18% or less out of the 1189 surveyed indicate that they "like the ads a lot" is 0.00043 if the population proportion is indeed no less than 0.22.

9.72   (a)   For $df = 15$ and $\alpha = 0.01$, $\chi^2 = 30.578$.
(b)   For $df = 10$ and $\alpha = 0.025$, $\chi^2 = 20.483$.
(c)   For $df = 7$ and $\alpha = 0.05$, $\chi^2 = 14.067$.
(d)   For $df = 27$ and $\alpha = 0.95$, $\chi^2 = 16.151$.
(e)   For $df = 20$ and $\alpha = 0.975$, $\chi^2 = 9.591$.
(f)   For $df = 4$ and $\alpha = 0.99$, $\chi^2 = 0.297$.

9.74   (a)   For $df = 25$ and $\alpha = 0.01$, $\chi_L^2 = 10.520$ and $\chi_U^2 = 46.928$.
(b)   For $df = 16$ and $\alpha = 0.05$, $\chi_L^2 = 6.908$ and $\chi_U^2 = 28.845$.
(c)   For $df = 13$ and $\alpha = 0.10$, $\chi_L^2 = 5.892$ and $\chi_U^2 = 22.362$.

9.76 $df = n - 1 = 16 - 1 = 15$

9.78   (a)   If $H_1 : \sigma \neq 12$, do not reject H_0 since the test statistic $\chi^2 = 10.417$ falls between the two critical bounds, $\chi_L^2 = 6.262$ and $\chi_U^2 = 27.488$.
(b)   If $H_1 : \sigma < 12$, do not reject H_0 since the test statistic $\chi^2 = 10.417$ falls above the critical bound, $\chi^2 = 7.261$.

9.80   (a) $H_0: \sigma \leq 1.2\degree F$. The standard deviation of the oven temperature has not increased above the process standard deviation, 1.2 degrees F.
$H_1: \sigma > 1.2\degree F$. The standard deviation of the oven temperature has increased above the process standard deviation, 1.2 degrees F.
Decision rule: $df = 29$. If $\chi^2 > 42.557$, reject H_0.

Test statistic: $\chi^2 = \dfrac{(n-1) \cdot S^2}{\sigma^2} = \dfrac{29 \cdot 2.1^2}{1.2^2} = 88.813$

Decision: Since the test statistic of $\chi_{calc}^2 = 88.813$ is above the critical boundary of $\chi^2 = 42.557$, reject H_0. There is sufficient evidence to conclude that the standard deviation of the oven temperature has increased above 1.2 degrees F.

(b)   We must assume that the data in the population are normally distributed to be able to use the chi-square test of a population variance or standard deviation.

9.80
cont.   (c) p value = 5.53 x 10^{-8} or 0.00000005. The p value is the probability that a sample is obtained whose standard deviation is larger than 2.1 degrees F. when the null hypothesis is true is 5.53 x 10^{-8}, a very small probability.
Note: The p value was found using Excel.

9.82   (a) H_0: σ = $12. The standard deviation of the average monthly calls within the local calling region is $12.
H_1: $\sigma \neq$ $12. The standard deviation of the average monthly calls within the local calling region differs from $12.
Decision rule: df = 14. If χ^2 < 6.571 or χ^2 > 23.685, reject H_0.
Test statistic: $\chi^2 = \dfrac{(n-1) \cdot S^2}{\sigma^2} = \dfrac{14 \cdot 9.25^2}{12^2} = 8.319$
Decision: Since the test statistic of χ^2_{calc} = 8.319 is between the critical boundaries of 6.571 and 23.685, do not reject H_0. There is insufficient evidence to conclude that the standard deviation of the average monthly calls within the local calling region differs from $12.

(b)   We must assume that the data in the population are normally distributed to be able to use the chi-square test of a population variance or standard deviation.

(c) p value = 2(1 – 0.8721) = 0.2558. The p value is the probability that a sample is obtained whose standard deviation is further away from the hypothesized value of $12 than this sample value of $9.25 when the null hypothesis is true is 0.2558.
Note: The p value was found using Excel. Because the sample standard deviation is smaller than the hypothesized value, Excel reports an upper-tail p value of 0.8721, which means (1 – 0.8721) represents the amount of area in the lower tail. It is that value that is doubled to accommodate the two-tail hypotheses.

9.84   (a) H_0: σ = 0.25 ounce. The standard deviation in the weight of raisins packaged per box is equal to 0.25 ounce.
H_1: $\sigma \neq$ 0.25 ounce. The standard deviation in the weight of raisins packaged per box differs from 0.25 ounce.
Decision rule: df = 29. If χ^2 < 16.047 or χ^2 > 45.722, reject H_0.
Test statistic: $\chi^2 = \dfrac{(n-1) \cdot S^2}{\sigma^2} = \dfrac{29 \cdot 0.40576^2}{0.25^2} = 76.395$
Decision: Since the test statistic of χ^2_{calc} = 76.395 is above the critical boundary of 45.722, reject H_0. There is sufficient evidence to conclude that the standard deviation in the weight of raisins packaged per box differs from 0.25 ounce.

(b)   We must assume that the data in the population are normally distributed to be able to use the chi-square test of a population variance or standard deviation.

(c) p value = 2(3.8538 x 10^{-6}) = 7.7076 x 10^{-6} or 0.0000077. The probability of obtaining a test statistic equal to or more extreme than the result obtained from this sample data is 0.0000077 if the population standard deviation is indeed 0.25 ounce.

9.86   The null hypothesis represents the status quo or the hypothesis that is to be disproved. The null hypothesis includes an equal sign in its definition of a parameter of interest. The alternative hypothesis is the opposite of the null hypothesis, and usually represents taking an action. The alternative hypothesis includes either a less than sign, a not equal sign, or a greater than sign in its definition of a parameter of interest.

9.88   The power of a test is the probability that the null hypothesis will be rejected when the null hypothesis is false.

9.90   The *p*-value is the probability of obtaining a test statistic equal to or more extreme than the result obtained from the sample data, given that the null hypothesis is true.

9.92   The following steps would be used in all hypothesis tests: State the null hypothesis H_0. State the alternative hypothesis H_1. Choose the level of significance α. Choose the sample size *n*. Determine the appropriate statistical technique and corresponding test statistic to use. Set up the critical values that divide the rejection and nonrejection regions. Collect the data and compute the sample value of the appropriate test statistic. Determine whether the test statistic has fallen into the rejection or the nonrejection region. The computed value of the test statistic is compared with the critical values for the appropriate sampling distribution to determine whether it falls into the rejection or nonrejection region. Make the statistical decision. If the test statistic falls into the nonrejection region, the null hypothesis H_0 cannot be rejected. If the test statistic falls into the rejection region, the null hypothesis is rejected. Express the statistical decision in terms of a particular situation.

9.94   Among the questions to be raised are: What is the goal of the experiment or research? Can it be translated into a null and alternative hypothesis? Is the hypothesis test going to be two-tailed or one-tailed? Can a random sample be drawn from the underlying population of interest? What kinds of measurements will be obtained from the sample? Are the sampled outcomes of the random variable going to be numerical or categorical? At what significance level, or risk of committing a Type I error, should the hypothesis test be conducted? Is the intended sample size large enough to achieve the desired power of the test for the level of significance chosen? What statistical test procedure is to be used on the sampled data and why? What kind of conclusions and interpretations can be drawn from the results of the hypothesis test?

9.96   (a)   La Quinta Motor Inns commits a Type I error when it purchases a site that is not profitable. If a Type I error has been committed, its cost will be the amount of lost profit the Inns could have earned by using the money to purchase another profitable site.

        (b)   Type II error occurs when La Quinta Motor Inns fails to purchase a profitable site. The cost to La Quinta Motor Inns when a Type II error is committed is the loss on the potential amount of profit the site could have generated had the Inns decided to purchase the site.

        (c)   The executives at La Quinta Motor Inns are trying to avoid a Type I error by adopting a very stringent decision criterion. Only sites that are classified as capable of generating high profit will be purchased. Sites classified as capable of generating moderate profit will have a much higher likelihood of not being profitable.

        (d)   If the executives adopt a less stringent rejection criterion by buying sites that the computer model predicts moderate or large profit, the probability of committing a Type I error will increase. Many more of the sites the computer model predicts that will generate moderate profit may end up not being profitable at all. On the other hand, the less stringent rejection criterion will lower the probability of committing a Type II error since now more potentially profitable sites will be purchased.

9.98   (a) H_0: μ = 10.0 gallons. The average gasoline purchase is equal to 10 gallons.
H_1: $\mu \neq$ 10.0 gallons. The average gasoline purchase differs from 10 gallons.
Decision rule: df = 59. If $t < -2.0010$ or $t > 2.0010$, reject H_0.

Test statistic: $t = \dfrac{\bar{X} - \mu}{S/\sqrt{n}} = \dfrac{11.3 - 10.0}{3.1/\sqrt{60}} = 3.2483$

Decision: Since the test statistic of t_{calc} = 3.2483 is above the upper critical value of t = 2.0010, reject H_0. There is enough evidence to conclude that the average gasoline purchase differs from 10 gallons.

(b) p value = 0.0019.
Note: The p value was found using Excel.

(c) H_0: $p \geq 0.20$. At least 20% of the motorists purchased super unleaded gasoline.
H_1: $p < 0.20$. Less than 20% of the motorists purchased super unleaded gasoline.
Decision rule: If $Z < -1.645$, reject H_0.

Test statistic: $Z = \dfrac{p_s - p}{\sqrt{\dfrac{p(1-p)}{n}}} = \dfrac{0.1833 - 0.20}{\sqrt{\dfrac{0.20(0.80)}{60}}} = -0.32$

Decision: Since the test statistic of Z_{calc} = -0.32 is above the critical bound of $Z = -1.645$, do not reject H_0. There is not sufficient evidence to conclude that less than 20% of the motorists purchased super unleaded gasoline.

(d) H_0: μ = 10.0 gallons. The average gasoline purchase is equal to 10 gallons.
H_1: $\mu \neq$ 10.0 gallons. The average gasoline purchase differs from 10 gallons.
Decision rule: df = 59. If $t < -2.0010$ or $t > 2.0010$, reject H_0.

Test statistic: $t = \dfrac{\bar{X} - \mu}{S/\sqrt{n}} = \dfrac{10.3 - 10.0}{3.1/\sqrt{60}} = 0.7496$

Decision: Since the test statistic of t_{calc} = 0.7496 is between the critical bounds of $t = \pm 2.0010$, do not reject H_0. There is not enough evidence to conclude that the average gasoline purchase differs from 10 gallons.

(e) H_0: $p \geq 0.20$. At least 20% of the motorists purchased super unleaded gasoline.
H_1: $p < 0.20$. Less than 20% of the motorists purchased super unleaded gasoline.
Decision rule: If $Z < -1.645$, reject H_0.

Test statistic: $Z = \dfrac{p_s - p}{\sqrt{\dfrac{p(1-p)}{n}}} = \dfrac{0.1167 - 0.20}{\sqrt{\dfrac{0.20(0.80)}{60}}} = -1.61$

Decision: Since the test statistic of Z_{calc} = -1.61 is above the critical bound of $Z = -1.645$, do not reject H_0. There is not sufficient evidence to conclude that less than 20% of the motorists purchased super unleaded gasoline.

9.100   (a) H_0: $\mu \geq 5$ minutes. The average waiting time at a bank branch in a commercial district of the city is at least 5 minutes during the 12:00 p.m. to 1 p.m. peak lunch period.
H_1: $\mu < 5$ minutes. The average waiting time at a bank branch in a commercial district of the city is less than 5 minutes during the 12:00 p.m. to 1 p.m. peak lunch period.
Decision rule: $df = 14$. If $t < -1.7613$, reject H_0.

Test statistic: $t = \dfrac{\overline{X} - \mu}{S/\sqrt{n}} = \dfrac{4.2866 - 5.0}{1.637985/\sqrt{15}} = -1.6867$

Decision: Since the test statistic of $t_{calc} = -1.6867$ is above the critical bound of $t = -1.7613$, do not reject H_0. There is not enough evidence to conclude that the average waiting time at a bank branch in a commercial district of the city is less than 5 minutes during the 12:00 p.m. to 1 p.m. peak lunch period.

(b)   To perform the t-test on the population mean, you must assume that the observed sequence in which the data were collected is random and that the data are approximately normally distributed.

(c)   Box-and-whisker plot:

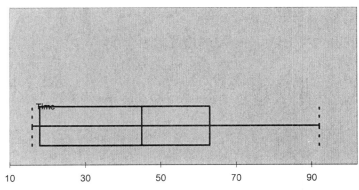

Box-and-whisker Plot

With the exception of one extreme point, the data are approximately normally distributed.

(d) p value = 0.0569. The probability of obtaining a sample whose mean is 4.2867 minutes or less when the null hypothesis is true is 0.0569.
Note: The p value was found using Excel.

9.102   (a) $H_0 : \mu = 30$ $H_1 : \mu \neq 30$
Decision rule: Reject H_0 if $|t| > 2.0555$ $d.f. = 26$

Test statistic: $t = \dfrac{\overline{X} - \mu}{S/\sqrt{n}} = \dfrac{43.8889 - 30}{25.2835/\sqrt{27}} = 2.8544$

Decision: Since $|t| > 2.0555$, reject H_0. There is enough evidence to conclude that the average processing time is different from 30 days.

(b)   In order for the t test to be valid, the data are assumed to be independently drawn from a population that is normally distributed.

9.102
cont.   (c)

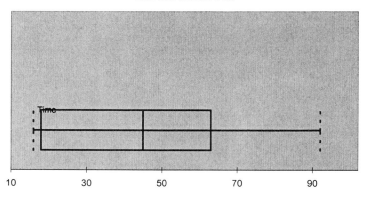

Box-and-whisker Plot

The box-and-whisker plot suggests that the distribution of the data is skewed to the right. With a sample size of just 27, the t distribution will not provide a good approximation to the sampling distribution of the sample mean.

(d)   The right skewed distribution of the data makes the t test in part (a) invalid. The manager should be very careful not to make any misleading statement and should, instead, request another test with a much larger data set to be performed in order for the central limit theorem to have a chance to operate.

9.104   (a) $H_0 : \mu \geq 0.35$ $H_1 : \mu < 0.35$

Decision rule: Reject H_0 if $t < -1.690$ $d.f. = 35$

Test statistic: $t = \dfrac{\bar{X} - \mu}{S/\sqrt{n}} = \dfrac{0.3167 - 0.35}{0.1357/\sqrt{36}} = -1.4735$

Decision: Since $t > -1.690$, do not reject H_0. There is not enough evidence to conclude that the average moisture content is less than 0.35 pounds per 100 square feet.

(b) p-value = 0.0748. The probability of observing a sample of 36 shingles that will result in a sample average moisture content of 0.3167 pounds per 100 square feet or less is 7.48% if the population average moisture content is in fact no less than 0.35 pounds per 100 square feet.

(c) $H_0 : \mu \geq 0.35$ $H_1 : \mu < 0.35$

Decision rule: Reject H_0 if $t < -1.6973$ $d.f. = 30$

Test statistic: $t = \dfrac{\bar{X} - \mu}{S/\sqrt{n}} = \dfrac{0.2735 - 0.35}{0.1373/\sqrt{31}} = -3.1003$

Decision: Since $t < -1.6973$, reject H_0. There is enough evidence to conclude that the average moisture content is less than 0.35 pounds per 100 square feet.

(d) p-value = 0.0021. The probability of observing a sample of 31 shingles that will result in a sample average moisture content of 0.2735 pounds per 100 square feet or less is 0.21% if the population average moisture content is in fact no less than 0.35 pounds per 100 square feet.

9.104
cont.   (e)   In order for the *t* test to be valid, the data are assumed to be independently drawn from a population that is normally distributed. Since the sample sizes are 36 and 31, respectively, which are considered quite large, the *t* distribution will provide a good approximation to the sampling distribution of the mean as long as the population distribution is not very skewed.

(f)

Box-and-whisker Plot (Boston)

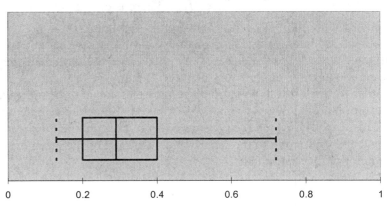

Box-and-whisker Plot (Vermont)

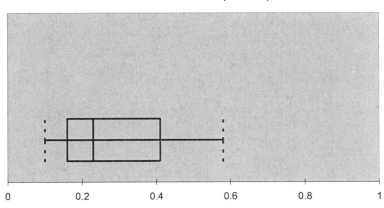

Both box-and-whisker plots suggest that the data are skewed slightly to the right, more so for the Boston shingles. To be more conservative, larger sample sizes should be used in both samples.

9.106   (a) $H_0 : \mu = 0.5$ $H_1 : \mu \neq 0.5$

Decision rule: Reject H_0 if $|t| > 1.9741$ $d.f. = 169$

Test statistic: $t = \dfrac{\overline{X} - \mu}{S / \sqrt{n}} = \dfrac{0.2641 - 0.5}{0.1424 / \sqrt{170}} = -21.6059$

Decision: Since $t < -1.9741$, reject H_0. There is enough evidence to conclude that the average granule loss is different from 0.5 grams.

(b) p-value is virtually zero. The probability of observing a sample of 170 shingles that will yield a test statistic more extreme than -21.6059 is virtually zero if the population average granule loss is in fact 0.5 grams.

(c) $H_0 : \mu = 0.5$ $H_1 : \mu \neq 0.5$

Decision rule: Reject H_0 if $|t| > 1.977$ $d.f. = 139$

Test statistic: $t = \dfrac{\overline{X} - \mu}{S / \sqrt{n}} = \dfrac{0.218 - 0.5}{0.1227 / \sqrt{140}} = -27.1940$

Decision: Since $t < -1.977$, reject H_0. There is enough evidence to conclude that the average granule loss is different from 0.5 grams.

(d) p-value is virtually zero. The probability of observing a sample of 140 shingles that will yield a test statistic more extreme than -27.1940 is virtually zero if the population average granule loss is in fact 0.5 grams.

(e)   In order for the t test to be valid, the data are assumed to be independently drawn from a population that is normally distributed. Since the sample sizes are 170 and 140, respectively, which are considered large enough, the t distribution will provide a good approximation to the sampling distribution of the mean even if the population is not normally distributed.

CHAPTER 10

OBJECTIVES

- To use hypothesis testing for two-sample tests involving numerical variables
- To use hypothesis testing for related samples
- To be familiar with nonparametric alternative tests that can be used when the assumptions of the t tests are violated

OVERVIEW AND KEY CONCEPTS

Z Test for Difference in Two Means $(\mu_1 - \mu_2)$

- **Assumptions:**
  - The two samples are randomly and independently drawn from normal distributions.
  - Population variances are known.
- **Test statistic:**
  - $$Z = \frac{(\bar{X}_1 - \bar{X}_2) - (\mu_1 - \mu_2)}{\sqrt{\dfrac{\sigma_1^2}{n_1} + \dfrac{\sigma_2^2}{n_2}}}$$
  - The alternative hypothesis can be one-tail with a right-tail rejection region, one-tail with a left-tail rejection region or two-tail with both right-tail and left-tail rejection regions.

Z Test for Difference in Two Means $(\mu_1 - \mu_2)$, Large Samples

- **Assumptions:**
  - The two samples are randomly and independently drawn.
  - Population variances are known
  - Both sample sizes are at least 30.
- **Test statistic:**
  - $$Z = \frac{(\bar{X}_1 - \bar{X}_2) - (\mu_1 - \mu_2)}{\sqrt{\dfrac{\sigma_1^2}{n_1} + \dfrac{\sigma_2^2}{n_2}}}$$ if both population variances are known.
  - The alternative hypothesis can be one-tail with a right-tail rejection region, one-tail with a left-tail rejection region or two-tail with both right-tail and left-tail rejection regions.

Pooled-Variance t Test for Difference in Two Means $(\mu_1 - \mu_2)$

- **Assumptions:**
  - The two samples are randomly and independently drawn.
  - Both populations are normally distributed.
  - Population variances are unknown but assumed equal.
  - If the two populations are not normally distributed, large sample sizes are needed.

- **Test statistic:**

  - $$t = \frac{\left(\bar{X}_1 - \bar{X}_2\right) - \left(\mu_1 - \mu_2\right)}{\sqrt{S_p^2\left(\dfrac{1}{n_1} + \dfrac{1}{n_2}\right)}} \quad \text{with } n_1 + n_2 - 2 \text{ degrees of freedom}$$

    where $S_p^2 = \dfrac{\left(n_1 - 1\right)S_1^2 + \left(n_2 - 1\right)S_2^2}{\left(n_1 - 1\right) + \left(n_2 - 1\right)}$

  - The alternative hypothesis can be one-tail with a right-tail rejection region, one-tail with a left-tail rejection region or two-tail with both right-tail and left-tail rejection regions.

- **Confidence interval estimate:** Use the $100\left(1 - \alpha\right)\%$ confidence interval for the difference in two means.

  - $$\left(\bar{X}_1 - \bar{X}_2\right) \pm t_{\alpha/2, n_1 + n_2 - 2}\sqrt{S_p^2\left(\frac{1}{n_1} + \frac{1}{n_2}\right)}$$

Separate-Variance t Test for Difference in Two Means $\left(\mu_1 - \mu_2\right)$

- **Assumptions:**
  - The two samples are randomly and independently drawn.
  - Both populations are normally distributed.
  - Both population variances are unknown and assumed not equal.
  - If the two populations are not normally distributed, large sample sizes are needed.
- **Test statistic:**

  - $$t = \frac{\left(\bar{X}_1 - \bar{X}_2\right) - \left(\mu_1 - \mu_2\right)}{\sqrt{\dfrac{S_1^2}{n_1} + \dfrac{S_2^2}{n_2}}} \quad \text{with degrees of freedom } v \text{ taken to be the integer}$$

    portion of $v = \dfrac{\left(\dfrac{S_1^2}{n_1} + \dfrac{S_2^2}{n_2}\right)^2}{\dfrac{\left(\dfrac{S_1^2}{n_1}\right)^2}{n_1 - 1} + \dfrac{\left(\dfrac{S_2^2}{n_2}\right)^2}{n_2 - 1}}$

  - The alternative hypothesis can be one-tail with a right-tail rejection region, one-tail with a left-tail rejection region or two-tail with both right-tail and left-tail rejection regions.

F Test for Difference in Two Variances $\left(\sigma_1^2 - \sigma_2^2\right)$

- **Assumptions:**
  - The two samples are randomly and independently drawn.
  - Both populations are normally distributed.
  - The test is not robust to violation of the normality assumption.

- **Test statistic:**

  - $F = \dfrac{S_1^2}{S_2^2}$ with $n_1 - 1$ numerator degrees of freedom and $n_2 - 1$ denominator degrees of freedom.

  - The upper-tail critical value has $n_1 - 1$ numerator degrees of freedom and $n_2 - 1$ denominator degrees of freedom.

  - The lower-tail critical value can be obtained using $F_L = \dfrac{1}{F_{U^*}}$ where F_{U^*} is the upper-tail critical value with $n_2 - 1$ numerator degrees of freedom and $n_1 - 1$ denominator degrees of freedom.

  - The alternative hypothesis can be one-tail with a right-tail rejection region, one-tail with a left-tail rejection region or two-tail with both right-tail and left-tail rejection regions.

Z Test for the Mean Difference $\left(\mu_D\right)$ with Known Variance

- **Assumptions:**
  - Both populations are normally distributed.
  - Observations are matched or paired.
  - Variance is known.
  - The test is robust to the normal distribution assumption as long as the sample size is not too small and the population is not highly skewed.
- **Test statistic:**

  - $Z = \dfrac{\bar{D} - \mu_D}{\dfrac{\sigma_D}{\sqrt{n}}}$ where $\bar{D} = \dfrac{\displaystyle\sum_{i=1}^{n} D_i}{n}$

  - The alternative hypothesis can be one-tail with a right-tail rejection region, one-tail with a left-tail rejection region or two-tail with both right-tail and left-tail rejection regions.

t Test for the Mean Difference $\left(\mu_D\right)$ with Unknown Variance

- **Assumptions:**
  - Both populations are normally distributed.
  - Observations are matched or paired.
  - Variance is unknown.
  - The test is robust to the normal distribution assumption as long as the sample size is not too small and the population is not highly skewed.

- **Test statistic:**
  - $t = \dfrac{\bar{D} - \mu_D}{\dfrac{S_D}{\sqrt{n}}}$ with $n-1$ degrees of freedom

    where $\bar{D} = \dfrac{\displaystyle\sum_{i=1}^{n} D_i}{n}$ and $S_D = \sqrt{\dfrac{\displaystyle\sum_{i=1}^{n} (D_i - \bar{D})^2}{n-1}}$

  - The alternative hypothesis can be one-tail with a right-tail rejection region, one-tail with a left-tail rejection region or two-tail with both right-tail and left-tail rejection regions.
- **Confidence interval estimate:** Use the $100(1-\alpha)\%$ confidence interval for the mean difference.
  - $\bar{D} \pm t_{\alpha/2,n-1} \dfrac{S_D}{\sqrt{n}}$

Wilcoxon Rank Sum Test for Difference in Two Medians $(M_1 - M_2)$

- **Assumptions:**
  - Both populations do not need to be normally distributed. It is a distribution free procedure.
  - The two samples are randomly and independently drawn.
  - The test is also appropriate when only ordinal data is available.
- **Test procedure:**
  1. Assign ranks, $R_1, R_2, \cdots, R_{n_1+n_2}$, to each of the $n_1 + n_2$ sample observations.
     - If sample sizes are not the same, let n_1 refer to the smaller sample size.
     - Assign average rank for any ties.
  2. Compute the sum of the ranks, T_1 and T_2, for each of the two samples.
  3. Test statistic: The sum of ranks of the smaller sample, T_1.
  4. Obtain the critical value(s), T_{1L}, T_{1U} or both, from a table.
  5. Compare the test statistic T_1 to the critical value(s).

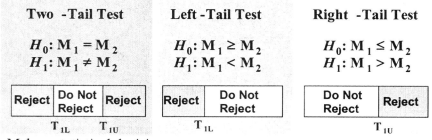

  6. Make a statistical decision.
  7. Draw a conclusion.

Wilcoxon Rank Sum Test for Difference in Two Medians $(M_1 - M_2)$, Large Sample

- **Test statistic:**
  - For large sample (at least one sample size > 10), the test statistic T_1 is approximately normally distributed with mean $\mu_{T_1} = \dfrac{n_1(n+1)}{2}$ and standard deviation

    $\sigma_{T_1} = \sqrt{\dfrac{n_1 n_2 (n+1)}{12}}$ where $n_1 \leq n_2$ and $n = n_1 + n_2$

  - $Z = \dfrac{T_1 - \mu_{T_1}}{\sigma_{T_1}}$ has a standard normal distribution.

Wilcoxon Signed-ranks Test for the Median Difference (M_D)

- **Assumptions:**
  1. The observed data either constitute a random sample of n independent items or individuals, each with two measurements, one taken before and the other taken after the presentation of some treatment or the observed data constitute a random sample of n independent pairs of items or individuals with values for each member of the match pair ($i = 1, 2, \ldots, n$).
  2. The underlying variable of interest is continuous.
  3. The observed data are measured at interval or ratio level.
  4. The distribution of the population of difference scores between repeated measurements or between matched items or individuals is approximately symmetric.

- **Test procedure:**
  1. For each item in a sample of n items obtain a difference score D_i between two measurements.
  2. Obtain a set of n absolute differences $|D_i|$.
  3. Drop any absolute difference score of zero, thereby yielding a set of $n' \leq n$.
  4. Assign ranks R_i from 1 to n' to each of the $|D_i|$ such that the smallest $|D_i|$ gets rank 1 and the largest gets rank n'. If two or more $|D_i|$ are equal, they are each assigned the average rank of the ranks they would have been assigned individually had ties in the data not occurred.
  5. Obtain the signed ranks $R_i^{(+)}$ and $R_i^{(-)}$ from each of the n' ranks R_i where the "+" or " – " sign is determined depending on whether D_i was originally positive or negative.
  6. **Test statistic:** The Wilcoxon test statistic is $W = \displaystyle\sum_{i=1}^{n'} R_i^{(+)}$ where $R_i^{(+)}$ are the positive signed ranks.
  7. If $n' \leq 20$, use Table E.9 to obtain the critical value(s) of the test statistic W. Perform the test with a one-tail (two-tail) alternative hypothesis with rejection region(s) similar to the rejection region(s) of a typical Z test.

8. If $n' > 20$, W is approximately normally distributed with mean $\mu_W = \dfrac{n'(n'+1)}{4}$ and standard deviation $\sigma_W = \sqrt{\dfrac{n'(n'+1)(2n'+1)}{24}}$. Obtain the critical value(s) from a standardized normal distribution for a one-tail (two-tail) alternative hypothesis. Perform a Z test with $Z = \dfrac{W - \mu_W}{\sigma_W}$.

SOLUTIONS TO END OF SECTION
AND CHAPTER REVIEW EVEN PROBLEMS

10.2 $H_0: \mu_1 = \mu_2$ $H_1: \mu_1 \neq \mu_2$
Decision rule: If $Z < -2.58$ or $Z > 2.58$, reject H_0.
Test statistic: $Z = \dfrac{(\overline{X}_1 - \overline{X}_2) - (\mu_1 - \mu_2)}{\sqrt{\dfrac{\sigma_1^2}{n_1} + \dfrac{\sigma_2^2}{n_2}}} = \dfrac{(72 - 66) - 0}{\sqrt{\dfrac{20^2}{40} + \dfrac{10^2}{50}}} = 1.73$

Decision: Since $Z_{calc} = 1.73$ is between the critical bounds of $Z = \pm 2.58$, do not reject H_0. There is inadequate evidence to conclude the two population means are different.

10.4   (a) $S_p^2 = \dfrac{(n_1 - 1) \cdot S_1^2 + (n_2 - 1) \cdot S_2^2}{(n_1 - 1) + (n_2 - 1)} = \dfrac{(7) \cdot 4^2 + (14) \cdot 5^2}{7 + 14} = 22$

$t = \dfrac{(\overline{X}_1 - \overline{X}_2) - (\mu_1 - \mu_2)}{\sqrt{S_p^2 \left(\dfrac{1}{n_1} + \dfrac{1}{n_2} \right)}} = \dfrac{(42 - 34) - 0}{\sqrt{22 \left(\dfrac{1}{8} + \dfrac{1}{15} \right)}} = 3.8959$

(b) $df = (n_1 - 1) + (n_2 - 1) = 7 + 14 = 21$
(c)   Decision rule: $df = 21$. If $t > 2.5177$, reject H_0.
(d)   Decision: Since $t_{calc} = 3.8959$ is above the critical bound of $t = 2.5177$, reject H_0. There is enough evidence to conclude that the first population mean is larger than the second population mean.
(e)   We are sampling from two independent normal distributions having equal variances.
(f) $(\overline{X}_1 - \overline{X}_2) \pm t \sqrt{S_p^2 \left(\dfrac{1}{n_1} + \dfrac{1}{n_2} \right)} = (42 - 34) \pm 2.0796 \sqrt{22 \left(\dfrac{1}{8} + \dfrac{1}{15} \right)}$

$3.7296 < \mu_1 - \mu_2 < 12.2704$

10.6   (a) $H_0: \mu_1 \leq \mu_2$ where Populations: 1 = new machine, 2 = old machine
The average breaking strength of parts produced by the new machine is not greater than the average breaking strength of parts produced by the old machine.
$H_1: \mu_1 > \mu_2$
The average breaking strength of parts produced by the new machine is greater than the average breaking strength of parts produced by the old machine.
Decision rule: If $Z > 2.33$, reject H_0.
Test statistic: $Z = \dfrac{(\overline{X}_1 - \overline{X}_2) - (\mu_1 - \mu_2)}{\sqrt{\dfrac{\sigma_1^2}{n_1} + \dfrac{\sigma_2^2}{n_2}}} = \dfrac{(72 - 65) - 0}{\sqrt{\dfrac{9^2}{100} + \dfrac{10^2}{100}}} = 5.20$

Decision: Since $Z_{calc} = 5.20$ is above the critical bound of 2.33, reject H_0. There is enough evidence to conclude that the average breaking strength of parts produced by the new machine is greater than the average breaking strength of parts produced by the old machine.

(b) p value = virtually zero. The probability of obtaining samples whose means differ by 7 or more units of strength when the null hypothesis is true is virtually zero.

10.8   (a) H_0: $\mu_1 \geq \mu_2$ where Populations: 1 = October 2001, 2 = October 2000

Mean credit card debt is not lower in October 2001 than in October 2000

H_1: $\mu_1 < \mu_2$

Mean credit card debt is lower in October 2001 than in October 2000

Decision rule: $df = 1998$. If $t < -1.6456$, reject H_0.

Test statistic:

$$S_p^2 = \frac{(n_1 - 1) \cdot S_1^2 + (n_2 - 1) \cdot S_2^2}{(n_1 - 1) + (n_2 - 1)} = \frac{(999) \cdot 847.43^2 + (999) \cdot 976.93^2}{999 + 999} = 836264.91$$

$$t = \frac{(\bar{X}_1 - \bar{X}_2) - (\mu_1 - \mu_2)}{\sqrt{S_p^2 \left(\frac{1}{n_1} + \frac{1}{n_2} \right)}} = \frac{(2411 - 2814) - 0}{\sqrt{836264.91 \left(\frac{1}{1000} + \frac{1}{1000} \right)}} = -9.8541$$

Decision: Since $t_{calc} = -9.8541$ is below the lower critical bound of -1.6456, reject H_0. There is enough evidence to conclude that the average credit card debt is lower in October 2001 than in October 2000.

(b) p-value is essentially zero. The probability of obtaining a sample that yields a t test statistic less than -9.8541 is essentially zero if the mean credit card debt is no lower in October 2001 than in October 2000.

(c)

$$\left(\bar{X}_1 - \bar{X}_2 \right) + t \sqrt{S_p^2 \left(\frac{1}{n_1} + \frac{1}{n_2} \right)} = (2411 - 2814) + 1.9612 \sqrt{836264.9149 \left(\frac{1}{1000} + \frac{1}{1000} \right)}$$

$$-483.2044 < \mu_1 - \mu_2 < -322.7956$$

10.10   (a) $H_0 : \mu_I = \mu_{II}$ Mean waiting time of Bank 1 and Bank 2 is the same.

  $H_1 : \mu_I \neq \mu_{II}$ Mean waiting time of Bank 1 and Bank 2 is different.

PHStat output:

t Test for Differences in Two Means	
Data	
Hypothesized Difference	0
Level of Significance	0.05
Population 1 Sample	
Sample Size	15
Sample Mean	4.286667
Sample Standard Deviation	1.637985
Population 2 Sample	
Sample Size	15
Sample Mean	7.114667
Sample Standard Deviation	2.082189
Intermediate Calculations	
Population 1 Sample Degrees of Freedom	14
Population 2 Sample Degrees of Freedom	14
Total Degrees of Freedom	28
Pooled Variance	3.509254
Difference in Sample Means	-2.828
t-Test Statistic	-4.13431
Two-Tailed Test	
Lower Critical Value	-2.04841
Upper Critical Value	2.048409
p-Value	0.000293
Reject the null hypothesis	

Since the p-value of 0.000293 is less than the 5% level of significance, reject the null hypothesis. There is enough evidence to conclude that the mean waiting time is different in the two banks.

(b) p-value = 0.000293. The probability of obtaining a sample that will yield a t test statistic more extreme than –4.13431 is 0.000293 if, in fact, the mean waiting time of Bank 1 and Bank 2 is the same.

(c)   We need to assume that the two populations are normally distributed.

(d) $$\left(\bar{X}_1 - \bar{X}_2 \right) + t \sqrt{ S_p^2 \left(\frac{1}{n_1} + \frac{1}{n_2} \right) } = \left(4.2867 - 7.1147 \right) + 2.0484 \sqrt{ 3.5093 \left(\frac{1}{15} + \frac{1}{15} \right) }$$

$$-4.2292 < \mu_1 - \mu_2 < -1.4268$$

(e)   Since the 95% confidence interval does not contain zero, the null hypothesis that the mean waiting time of Bank 1 and Bank 2 is the same can be rejected at 5% level of significance, which is the same conclusion arrived at in (a).

10.10   (f) $H_0 : \mu_I = \mu_{II}$ Mean waiting time of Bank 1 and Bank 2 are the same.

cont. $H_1 : \mu_I \neq \mu_{II}$ Mean waiting time of Bank 1 and Bank 2 is different.

Excel output:

t-Test: Two-Sample Assuming Unequal Variances

	Waiting Time (Bank 1)	Waiting Time (Bank2)
Mean	4.286667	7.114667
Variance	2.682995	4.335512
Observations	15	15
Hypothesized Mean Difference	0	
Df	27	
t Stat	-4.13431	
P(T<=t) one-tail	0.000155	
t Critical one-tail	1.703288	
P(T<=t) two-tail	0.00031	
t Critical two-tail	2.051829	

Since the *p*-value of 0.00031 is less than the 5% level of significance, reject the null hypothesis. There is enough evidence to conclude that the mean waiting time is different in the two banks.

(g)   Both *t* tests yield the same conclusion.

10.12   (a) $H_0: \mu_1 = \mu_2$ where Populations: 1 = Farmingdale, 2 = Levittown

The average appraised values for single-family homes are the same in the two   Nassau County communities.

$H_1: \mu_1 \neq \mu_2$

The average appraised values for single-family homes are not equal in the two   Nassau County communities.

Decision rule: $df = 157$. If $t < -1.9752$ or $t > 1.9752$, reject H_0.

Test statistic:

$$S_p^2 = \frac{(n_1 - 1) \cdot S_1^2 + (n_2 - 1) \cdot S_2^2}{(n_1 - 1) + (n_2 - 1)} = \frac{(59) \cdot 32.60^2 + (98) \cdot 16.92^2}{59 + 98} = 578.0822$$

$$t = \frac{(\bar{X}_1 - \bar{X}_2) - (\mu_1 - \mu_2)}{\sqrt{S_p^2 \left(\frac{1}{n_1} + \frac{1}{n_2} \right)}} = \frac{(191.33 - 172.34) - 0}{\sqrt{578.0822 \left(\frac{1}{60} + \frac{1}{99} \right)}} = 4.8275$$

Decision: Since $t_{calc} = 4.8275$ is above the upper critical bound of 1.9752, reject H_0. There is enough evidence to conclude that there is a difference in the average appraised values for single-family homes in the two Nassau County communities. The *p* value is 3.25E-06 using Excel.

(b)   The assumption of equal variances may be violated because the sample variance in Farmingdale is nearly four times the size of the sample variance in Levittown and the two sample sizes are not small. Nevertheless, the results of the test for the differences in the two means was overwhelming (i.e., the *p* value is nearly 0).

(c) $$\left(\bar{X}_1 - \bar{X}_2 \right) + t \sqrt{S_p^2 \left(\frac{1}{n_1} + \frac{1}{n_2} \right)} = (191.33 - 172.34) + 1.9752 \sqrt{578.08 \left(\frac{1}{60} + \frac{1}{99} \right)}$$

$$11.2202 < \mu_1 - \mu_2 < 26.7598$$

We are 95% confidence that the difference between the population means of Farmingdale and Levittown is between 11.2202 and 26.7598.

10.14   (a) $H_0: \mu_1 \geq \mu_2$ where Populations: 1 = unflawed, 2 = flawed

$H_1: \mu_1 < \mu_2$

Decision rule: $df = 56$. If $t < -1.6725$, reject H_0.

Test statistic:

$$S_p^{\,2} = \frac{(n_1 - 1) \cdot S_1^{\,2} + (n_2 - 1) \cdot S_2^{\,2}}{(n_1 - 1) + (n_2 - 1)} = \frac{(17) \cdot 0.0219^2 + (39) \cdot 0.0840^2}{17 + 39} = 0.0051$$

$$t = \frac{(\overline{X}_1 - \overline{X}_2) - (\mu_1 - \mu_2)}{\sqrt{S_p^{\,2}\left(\dfrac{1}{n_1} + \dfrac{1}{n_2}\right)}} = \frac{(0.0359 - 0.0946) - 0}{\sqrt{0.0051\left(\dfrac{1}{18} + \dfrac{1}{40}\right)}} = -2.9047$$

Decision: Since $t_{calc} = -2.9047$ is below the lower critical bound of -1.6725, reject H_0. There is enough evidence to conclude that the average crack size is lower for the unflawed specimens than for the flawed specimens.

(b)   (a) $H_0: \mu_1 \geq \mu_2$ where Populations: 1 = unflawed, 2 = flawed

$H_1: \mu_1 < \mu_2$

Decision rule: $df = 49$. If $t < -1.6766$, reject H_0.

t-Test: Two-Sample Assuming Unequal Variances

	Unflawed	flawed
Mean	0.035944	0.0946
Variance	0.000481	0.007059
Observations	18	40
Hypothesized Mean Difference	0	
df	49	
t Stat	-4.11472	
P(T<=t) one-tail	7.4E-05	
t Critical one-tail	1.676551	
P(T<=t) two-tail	0.000148	
t Critical two-tail	2.009574	

Since p-value is virtually zero and is smaller than 0.05, reject H_0. There is enough evidence to conclude that the average crack size is lower for the unflawed specimens than for the flawed specimens.

(c)   The conclusions in (a) and (b) are the same. Since the sample variance of the flawed sample is almost 15 times as big as that of the unflawed sample, the test in (b) is the appropriate test to perform assuming that both samples are drawn from normally distributed populations.

10.16   (a) $F_U = 2.20$, $F_L = \dfrac{1}{2.33} = 0.429$

(b) $F_U = 2.57$, $F_L = \dfrac{1}{2.76} = 0.362$

(c) $F_U = 3.09$, $F_L = \dfrac{1}{3.37} = 0.297$

(d) $F_U = 3.50$, $F_L = \dfrac{1}{3.88} = 0.258$

(e)   As α gets smaller, the rejection region gets narrower and the acceptance region gets wider. F_L gets smaller and F_U gets larger.

10.18   (a) $F_L = \dfrac{1}{2.33} = 0.429$

          (b) $F_L = \dfrac{1}{2.76} = 0.362$

          (c) $F_L = \dfrac{1}{3.37} = 0.297$

          (d) $F_L = \dfrac{1}{3.88} = 0.258$

          (e)   As α gets smaller, the rejection region gets narrower and the nonrejection region gets wider. F_L gets smaller (approaching zero).

10.20   The degrees of freedom for the numerator is 24 and for the denominator is 24.

10.22   Since $F_{calc} = 0.826$ is between the critical bounds of $F_U = 2.27$ and $F_L = 0.441$, do not reject H_0. There is not enough evidence to conclude that the two population variances are different.

10.24   (a) $H_0: \sigma_1^2 = \sigma_2^2$ The population variances are the same.
          $H_1: \sigma_1^2 \neq \sigma_2^2$ The population variances are different.
          Decision rule: If $F > 3.18$ or $F < 0.338$, reject H_0.
          Test statistic: $F = \dfrac{S_1^2}{S_2^2} = \dfrac{47.3}{36.4} = 1.299$

          Decision: Since $F_{calc} = 1.299$ is between the critical bounds of $F_U = 3.18$ and $F_L = 0.338$, do not reject H_0. There is not enough evidence to conclude that the two population variances are different.

          (b) $H_0: \sigma_1^2 \leq \sigma_2^2$ The variance for population 1 is less than or equal to the variance for population 2.
          $H_1: \sigma_1^2 > \sigma_2^2$ The variance for population 1 is greater than the variance for population 2.
          Decision rule: If $F > 2.62$, reject H_0.
          Test statistic: $F = \dfrac{S_1^2}{S_2^2} = \dfrac{47.3}{36.4} = 1.299$

          Decision: Since $F_{calc} = 1.299$ is below the critical bound of $F_U = 2.62$, do not reject H_0. There is not enough evidence to conclude that the variance for population 1 is greater than the variance for population 2.

          (c) $H_0: \sigma_1^2 \geq \sigma_2^2$ The variance for population 1 is greater than or equal to the variance for population 2.
          $H_1: \sigma_1^2 < \sigma_2^2$ The variance for population 1 is less than the variance for population 2.
          Decision rule: If $F < 0.403$, reject H_0.
          Test statistic: $F = \dfrac{S_1^2}{S_2^2} = \dfrac{47.3}{36.4} = 1.299$

          Decision: Since $F_{calc} = 1.299$ is above the critical bound of $F_L = 0.403$, do not reject H_0. There is not enough evidence to conclude that the variance for population 1 is less than the variance for population 2.

10.26 (a) H_0: $\sigma_1^2 = \sigma_2^2$ The population variances are the same.
H_1: $\sigma_1^2 \neq \sigma_2^2$ The population variances are different.
Decision rule: If $F > 1.556$ or $F < 0.653$, reject H_0.

Test statistic: $F = \dfrac{S_1^2}{S_2^2} = \dfrac{13.35^2}{9.42^2} = 2.008$

Decision: Since $F_{calc} = 2.008$ is greater than $F_U = 1.556$, reject H_0. There is enough evidence to conclude that the two population variances are different.

(b) p-value = 0.0022.

(c)   The test assumes that the two populations are each normally distributed.

(d)   Based on (a) and (b), a separate variance t test should be used.

10.28 (a) H_0: $\sigma_1^2 = \sigma_2^2$ The population variances are the same.
H_1: $\sigma_1^2 \neq \sigma_2^2$ The population variances are different.
Decision rule: If $F > 2.5264$ or $F < 0.3958$, reject H_0.

Test statistic: $F = \dfrac{S_1^2}{S_2^2} = \dfrac{1.718^2}{1.8917^2} = 0.8248$

Decision: Since $F_{calc} = 0.8248$ is between $F_L = 0.3958$ and $F_U = 2.5264$, do not reject H_0. There is not enough evidence to conclude that the two population variances are different.

(b) p-value = 0.6789. The probability of obtaining a sample that yields a test statistic more extreme than 0.8248 is 0.6789 if the null hypothesis that there is no difference in two population variances is true.

(c)   The test assumes that the two populations are each normally distributed.

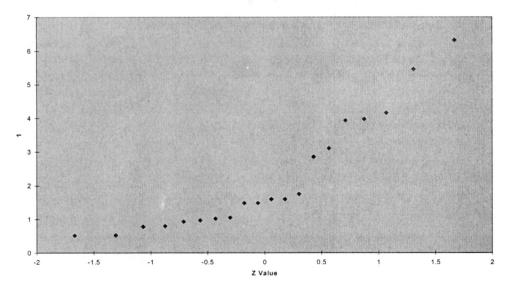

10.28   (c)
cont.

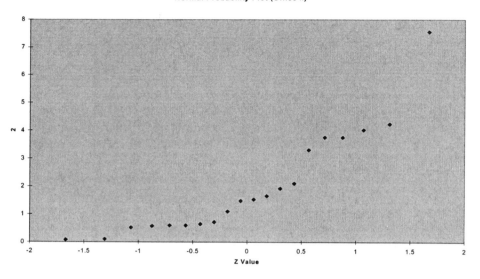

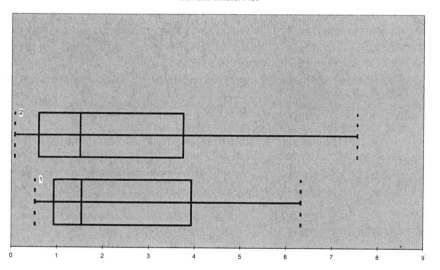

Both the normal probability plots and the box-and-whisker plot suggest that the time to clear problems in both offices does not appear to be normally distributed. Hence, the F test for the difference in variances, which is sensitive to departure from the normality assumption, should not be used to test the equality of two variances. The box-and-whisker plot and the summary statistics suggest that the two samples appear to have about the same amount of dispersion with the exception of a somewhat larger range in Office I. Hence, the pooled-variance t test is robust to departure from the normality assumption and can be used to test for the difference in the means.

(d)   Based on the results of (a), it is appropriate to use the pooled-variance t-test to compare the means of the two offices.

10.30 H_0: $\sigma_1^2 \leq \sigma_2^2$ where Populations: 1 = Line A   2 = accounting students
       H_1: $\sigma_1^2 > \sigma_2^2$

Decision rule: If $F > 2.5437$, reject H_0.

Test statistic: $F = \dfrac{S_1^2}{S_2^2} = \dfrac{0.012^2}{0.005^2} = 5.76$

Decision: Since $F_{\text{calc}} = 5.76$ is above the critical bound of $F_U = 2.5437$, reject H_0. There is enough evidence to conclude that the variance in Line A is larger than the variance in Line B.

10.32 $df = n - 1 = 15 - 1 = 14$, where n = number of pairs of data

10.34 (a) $H_0 : \mu_D = 0$ vs. $H_1 : \mu_D \neq 0$

Excel output:

t-Test: Paired Two Sample for Means

	2001	2002
Mean	286045.8	295456.2
Variance	15079913231	14076139280
Observations	10	10
Pearson Correlation	0.989765971	
Hypothesized Mean Difference	0	
df	9	
t Stat	-1.675385145	
P(T<=t) one-tail	0.064089384	
t Critical one-tail	1.383028803	
P(T<=t) two-tail	0.128178769	
t Critical two-tail	1.833113856	

Test statistic: $t = \dfrac{\bar{D} - \mu_D}{\dfrac{S_D}{\sqrt{n}}} = -1.6754$

Decision: Since $t = -1.6754$ falls in between the lower and upper critical values ± 1.8331, do not reject H_0. There is not enough evidence to conclude that there is a difference in the mean selling price for homes between 2001 and 2002.

(b)   One must assume that the distribution of the differences between the mean selling price for homes between 2001 and 2002 is approximately normally distributed.

(c) p-value = 0.1282. The probability of obtaining a mean difference in mean selling price that gives rise to a test statistic that deviates from 0 by 1.673 or more in either direction is 0.1282.

(d) $\bar{D} \pm t \dfrac{S_D}{\sqrt{n}} = -9410.4 \pm 1.8331 \dfrac{17762.0637}{\sqrt{10}}$ $-19706.7397 < \mu_D < 885.9397$

(e)   Since the 90% confidence interval estimate of the difference in the mean selling price contains zero, the null hypothesis can not be rejected and the same conclusion can be drawn in both (a) and (d).

10.36   (a) H_0: $\mu_{\bar{D}} = 0$ There is no difference in the average price of textbooks between the local bookstore and Amazon.com.

H_1: $\mu_{\bar{D}} \neq 0$ There is a difference in the average price of textbooks between the local bookstore and Amazon.com.

Decision rule: $df = 14$. If $t < -2.9768$ or $t > 2.9768$, reject H_0.

Test statistic: $t = \dfrac{\bar{D} - \mu_{\bar{D}}}{S_{\bar{D}} \big/ \sqrt{n}} = \dfrac{3.5307 - 0}{13.8493 \big/ \sqrt{15}} = 0.9874$

Decision: Since $t_{calc} = 0.9874$ is between the critical bounds of -2.9768 and 2.9768, do not reject H_0. There is not enough evidence to conclude that there is a difference in the average price of textbooks between the local bookstore and Amazon.com.

(b)   One must assume that the distribution of the differences between the average price of business textbooks between on-campus and off-campus stores is approximately normally distributed.

(c)   Excel, p value $= 0.3402$.
The probability of obtaining a mean difference that gives rise to a test statistic that deviates from 0 by 0.9874 or more when the null hypothesis is true is 0.3402.

(d) $\bar{D} \pm t \dfrac{S_D}{\sqrt{n}} = 3.5307 \pm 2.9768 \dfrac{13.8493}{\sqrt{15}}$ $-7.1141 < \mu_D < 14.1755$

We are 99% confident that the average difference between the price is somewhere between -7.1141 and 14.1755.

(e)   The results in (a) and (d) are the same. The hypothesized value of 0 for the difference in the average price for textbooks between the local bookstore and Amazon.com is inside the 99% confidence interval.

10.38   (a) H_0: $\mu_{\bar{D}} \geq 0$

H_1: $\mu_{\bar{D}} < 0$

Decision rule: $df = 39$. If $t < -2.4258$, reject H_0.

Test statistic: $t = \dfrac{\bar{D} - \mu_{\bar{D}}}{S_{\bar{D}} \big/ \sqrt{n}} = -9.372$

Decision: Since $t_{calc} = -9.372$ is below the critical bound of -2.4258, reject H_0. There is enough evidence to conclude that the average strength is less at two days than at seven days.

(b)   One must assume that the distribution of the differences between the average strength of the concrete is approximately normally distributed.

(c) p-value is virtually 0. The probability of obtaining a mean difference that gives rise to a test statistic that is -9.372 or less when the null hypothesis is true is virtually 0.

10.40   (a)   The upper critical value is 59.
(b)   The upper critical value is 61.
(c)   The upper critical value is 63.
(d)   The upper critical value is 65.
(e)   As the level of significance α gets smaller, the width of the nonrejection region gets wider.

10.42 $T_1 = 4 + 1 + 8 + 2 + 5 + 10 + 11 = 41$

10.44   Decision: Since $T_1 = 41$ is between the critical bounds of 40 and 79, do not reject H_0.

10.46   The lower critical value is 20.

10.48 H_0: $M_1 = M_2$ where Populations: 1 = traditional, 2 = experimental
There is no difference in performance between the traditional and the experimental training methods.
H_1: $M_1 \neq M_2$ There is a difference in performance between the traditional and the experimental training methods.
Decision rule: If $T_1 < 78$ or $T_1 > 132$, reject H_0.
Test statistic: $T_1 = 1 + 2 + 3 + 5 + 9 + 10 + 12 + 13 + 14 + 15 = 84$
Decision: Since $T_1 = 84$ is between the critical bounds of 78 and 132, do not reject H_0. There is not enough evidence to conclude that there is a difference in performance between the traditional and the experimental training methods.

10.50   (a) H_0: $M_1 = M_2$ where Populations: 1 = Computer-assisted individual-based
2 = Team-based program
Median assembly time in seconds is the same for employees trained in a computer-assisted, individual-based program and those trained in a team-based program.
H_1: $M_1 \neq M_2$ Median assembly time in seconds is different for employees trained in a computer-assisted, individual-based program and those trained in a team-based program.
Decision rule: If $Z < -1.96$ or $Z > 1.96$, reject H_0.
Test statistic: $T_1 = 379$ $\mu_{T_1} = \dfrac{n_1 \cdot (n+1)}{2} = \dfrac{21 \cdot (43)}{2} = 451.5,$

$$\sigma_{T_1} = \sqrt{\frac{n_1 \cdot n_2 \cdot (n+1)}{12}} = \sqrt{\frac{21 \cdot 21 \cdot 43}{12}} = 39.7524$$

$$Z = \frac{T_1 - \mu_{T_1}}{\sigma_{T_1}} = \frac{379 - 451.5}{39.7524} = -1.82$$

Decision: Since $Z_{calc} = -1.82$ is between the critical bounds of ± 1.96, do not reject H_0. There is not enough evidence to conclude that median assembly time in seconds is different for employees trained in a computer-assisted, individual-based program and those trained in a team-based program.
(b)   One must assume approximately equal variability in the two populations.
(c)   Using the pooled-variance t-test allowed us to reject the null hypothesis and conclude that average assembly time in seconds is different for the two sets of trainees in Problem 10.13. Using the separate-variance t-test in Problem 10.13, however, the test statistic fell short of the critical bound and we were unable to conclude there was any difference in the average assembly times. In this test, the test statistic using the Wilcoxon rank sum test with large-sample Z-approximation also fell short of the critical bound and we failed to reject the null hypothesis here as well.

10.52   (a) H_0: $M_1 = M_2$ where Populations: 1 = Bank 1   2 = Bank 2
                 H_1: $M_1 \neq M_2$
                 PHStat Output:

Wilcoxon Rank Sum Test	
Data	
Level of Significance	0.05
Population 1 Sample	
Sample Size	15
Sum of Ranks	153
Population 2 Sample	
Sample Size	15
Sum of Ranks	312
Intermediate Calculations	
Total Sample Size n	30
$T1$ Test Statistic	153
$T1$ Mean	232.5
Standard Error of $T1$	24.10913
Z Test Statistic	-3.29751
Two-Tailed Test	
Lower Critical Value	**-1.95996**
Upper Critical Value	**1.959961**
p-value	**0.000976**
Reject the null hypothesis	

        (a)   Decision rule: If $Z < -1.96$ or $Z > 1.96$, reject H_0.
                 Decision: Since $Z_{calc} = -3.2975$ is below the lower critical bound of -1.96, reject H_0.
                 There is enough evidence to conclude that the median waiting time between the two
                 branches is different.
        (b)   One must assume approximately equal variability in the two populations.
        (c)   Using both the pooled-variance t-test and the separate-variance t-test allowed us to
                 reject the null hypothesis and conclude in Problem 10.10 that the mean waiting time
                 between the two branches is different. In this test, using the Wilcoxon rank sum test
                 with large-sample Z-approximation also allowed us to reject the null hypothesis and
                 conclude that the median waiting time between the two branches is different.

10.54   (a) $W_L = 13$, $W_U = 53$ (b) $W_L = 10$, $W_U = 56$ (c) $W_L = 7$, $W_U = 59$
        (d) $W_L = 5$, $W_U = 61$
        (e)   As the level of significance gets smaller, the nonrejection region becomes wider.

10.56   (a) $W_L = 13$ (b) $W_L = 10$ (c) $W_L = 7$
        (d) $W_L = 5$
        (e)   As the level of significance gets smaller, the nonrejection region becomes wider.

10.58 $n' = 10$, $\alpha = 0.05$, $W_L = 8$, $W_U = 47$

10.60 $W = \Sigma_{i=1}^{n'} R_i^{(+)} = 67.5$

10.62   Since $W = 67.5 > W_U = 61$, reject H_0.

10.64   (a) H_0: $M_1 = M_2$ where Populations: $1 = 2001$ $2 = 2002$
                 H_1: $M_1 \neq M_2$
                 Minitab Output:
                 Wilcoxon Signed Rank Test: Di

```
Test of median = 0.000000 versus median not = 0.000000

              N for   Wilcoxon               Estimated
         N    Test    Statistic        P      Median
Di       10    10        13.0      0.154      -8378
```

Since the p-value = 0.154 is greater than the 0.10 level of significance, do not reject H_0. There is insufficient evidence of a difference in the median selling price for homes between 2001 and 2002.

(b)   Using the paired-sample t-test, we do not reject the null hypothesis and conclude that there is not enough evidence of a difference in the mean selling price for homes between 2001 and 2002 in Problem 10.34. Using the Wilcoxon signed rank test, we do not reject the null hypothesis and conclude that there is not enough evidence of a difference in the median selling price for homes between 2001 and 2002.

10.66   (a) H_0: $M_1 = M_2$ where Populations: $1 = $ Book Store $2 = $ Amazon
                 H_1: $M_1 \neq M_2$
                 Minitab Output:
                 Wilcoxon Signed Rank Test: Di

```
Test of median = 0.000000 versus median not = 0.000000

              N for   Wilcoxon               Estimated
         N    Test    Statistic        P      Median
Di       15    15        54.0      0.755      -1.500
```

Since the p-value = 0.755 is greater than the 0.01 level of significance, do not reject H_0. There is insufficient evidence of a difference in the median price of textbooks between the local bookstore and Amazon.com.

(b)   Using the paired-sample t-test, we do not reject the null hypothesis and conclude that there is not enough evidence of a difference in the mean price of textbooks between the local bookstore and Amazon.com in Problem 10.36. Using the Wilcoxon signed rank test, we do not reject the null hypothesis and conclude that there is not enough evidence of a difference in the median price of textbooks between the local bookstore and Amazon.com.

10.68 (a) $H_0: M_1 \geq M_2$ where Populations: 1 = two days   2 = seven days
             $H_1: M_1 < M_2$
             Minitab Output:
             Wilcoxon Signed Rank Test: Di

```
Test of median = 0.000000 versus median < 0.000000

                 N for    Wilcoxon                Estimated
           N     Test     Statistic        P       Median
Di         40    40           0.0      0.000      -0.5100
```

Since the p-value = 0.000 is smaller than the 0.01 level of significance, reject H_0.

There is sufficient evidence that the median strength is less at two days than at seven days.

       (b) Using the paired-sample t-test, we reject the null hypothesis and conclude that there is enough evidence that the mean strength is less at two days than at seven days in Problem 10.38. Using the Wilcoxon signed rank test, we reject the null hypothesis and conclude that there is enough evidence that the median strength is less at two days than at seven days.

10.70 The pooled variance t-test should be used when the populations are approximately normally distributed and the variances of the two populations are equal.

10.72 The F test can be used to examine differences in two variances when each of the two populations is assumed to be normally distributed.

10.74 Repeated measurements represent two measurements on the same items or individuals, while paired measurements involve matching items according to a characteristic of interest.

10.76 They are two different ways of investigating the concern of whether there is any difference between the means of two independent populations. If the hypothesized value of 0 for the difference in two population means does not fall into the confidence interval, then, assuming a two-tailed test is used, the null hypothesis of no difference in two population means can be rejected.

10.78 (a) The new drug Anafranil can be said to have a statistically significant effect on reducing the anxiety condition if it can be concluded that the average level of anxiety level of dogs that are treated with the drug is lower than the average anxiety level of the dogs that are given a placebo at some pre-chosen level of significance.

       (b) One of the symptoms of anxiety is loss of appetite. Suppose X_1 measures the increase in food intake after taking Anafranil and X_2 measures the increase in food intake after being given a placebo. An increase in food intake after taken the drug is translated into effectiveness of the drug in reducing anxiety level.

       (c) $H_0 : \mu_A \leq \mu_P$ The average increase in food intake after taken Anafranil is no higher than the average increase in food intake after taken a placebo
            $H_1 : \mu_A > \mu_P$ The average increase in food intake after taken Anafranil is higher than the average increase in food intake after taken a placebo

10.80 I = the public universities, II = the private universities.
       First quartile of SAT scores:

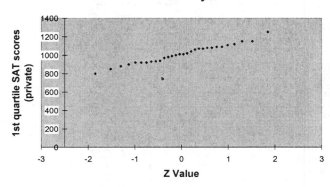

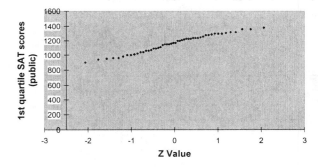

The two normal probability plots do not suggest any departure from the normality assumption. We can perform an F test on the difference of variances.

$$H_0 : \sigma_I^2 = \sigma_{II}^2 \quad \text{vs.} \quad H_1 : \sigma_I^2 \neq \sigma_{II}^2$$

10.80
cont.

PHStat output:

F Test for Differences in Two Variances	
Data	
Level of Significance	0.05
Population 1 Sample	
Sample Size	30
Sample Standard Deviation	100.8728
Population 2 Sample	
Sample Size	50
Sample Standard Deviation	128.3643
Intermediate Calculations	
F-Test Statistic	0.617532
Population 1 Sample Degrees of Freedom	29
Population 2 Sample Degrees of Freedom	49
Two-Tailed Test	
Lower Critical Value	0.502423
Upper Critical Value	1.881418
p-Value	0.167042
Do not reject the null hypothesis	

Since the p-value = 0.167 > 0.05, do not reject the null hypothesis. There is not sufficient evidence to conclude that the two variances are different. We can perform a pooled-variance t test for the difference in means.

$$H_0 : \mu_I = \mu_{II} \quad \text{vs.} \quad H_1 : \mu_I \neq \mu_{II}$$

PHStat output:

t Test for Differences in Two Means	
Data	
Hypothesized Difference	0
Level of Significance	0.05
Population 1 Sample	
Sample Size	30
Sample Mean	1011.167
Sample Standard Deviation	100.8728
Population 2 Sample	
Sample Size	50
Sample Mean	1160.4
Sample Standard Deviation	128.3643
Intermediate Calculations	
Population 1 Sample Degrees of Freedom	29
Population 2 Sample Degrees of Freedom	49
Total Degrees of Freedom	78
Pooled Variance	14134.32
Difference in Sample Means	-149.233
t-Test Statistic	-5.43537
Two-Tailed Test	
Lower Critical Value	-1.99085
Upper Critical Value	1.990848
p-Value	6.05E-07
Reject the null hypothesis	

Since the p-value is essentially zero. Reject the null hypothesis. There is sufficient evidence to conclude that the averages of the 1st quartile of SAT scores are different between public and private universities.

10.80   **Third quartile of SAT scores:**
cont.

Normal Probability Plot

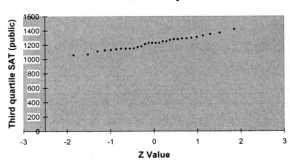

Normal Probability Plot

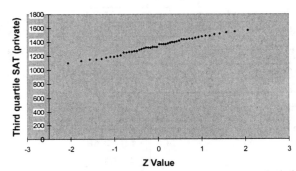

The two normal probability plots do not suggest any departure from the normality assumption. We can perform an F test on the difference of variances.

$$H_0 : \sigma_I^2 = \sigma_{II}^2 \quad \text{vs.} \quad H_1 : \sigma_I^2 \neq \sigma_{II}^2$$

PHStat output:

F Test for Differences in Two Variances	
Data	
Level of Significance	0.05
Population 1 Sample	
Sample Size	30
Sample Standard Deviation	89.9363
Population 2 Sample	
Sample Size	50
Sample Standard Deviation	122.2285
Intermediate Calculations	
F-Test Statistic	0.541408
Population 1 Sample Degrees of Freedom	29
Population 2 Sample Degrees of Freedom	49
Two-Tailed Test	
Lower Critical Value	0.502423
Upper Critical Value	1.881418
p-Value	0.079695
Do not reject the null hypothesis	

Since the p-value $= 0.08 > 0.05$, do not reject the null hypothesis. There is not sufficient evidence to conclude that the two variances are different. We can perform a pooled-variance t test for the difference in means.

10.80
cont.

$H_0 : \mu_I = \mu_{II}$ vs. $H_1 : \mu_I \neq \mu_{II}$

PHStat output:

t Test for Differences in Two Means	
Data	
Hypothesized Difference	0
Level of Significance	0.05
Population 1 Sample	
Sample Size	30
Sample Mean	1223.567
Sample Standard Deviation	89.9353
Population 2 Sample	
Sample Size	50
Sample Mean	1345
Sample Standard Deviation	122.2285
Intermediate Calculations	
Population 1 Sample Degrees of Freedom	29
Population 2 Sample Degrees of Freedom	49
Total Degrees of Freedom	78
Pooled Variance	12392.47
Difference in Sample Means	-121.433
t-Test Statistic	-4.72345
Two-Tailed Test	
Lower Critical Value	-1.99085
Upper Critical Value	1.990848
p-Value	1.01E-05
Reject the null hypothesis	

Since the *p*-value is essentially zero. Reject the null hypothesis. There is sufficient evidence to conclude that the averages of the 3rd quartile of SAT scores are different between public and private universities.

Total cost:

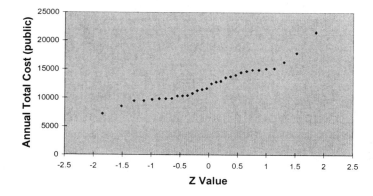

10.80
cont.

Normal Probability Plot

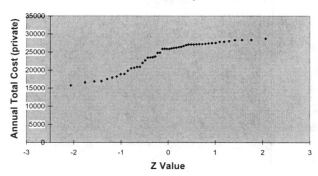

Both normal probability plots suggest that both distributions are not normal. It is inappropriate to perform an F test on the difference in variances. Values of the sample variances, $S_I^2 = 9410128.179$ and $S_{II}^2 = 15180521.27$, suggest that a separate-variance t test is more appropriate.

$H_0 : \mu_I = \mu_{II}$ vs. $H_1 : \mu_I \neq \mu_{II}$

Excel output:

t-Test: Two-Sample Assuming
Unequal Variances

	Annual Total Cost	Annual Total Cost
Mean	12478.4	24124.44
Variance	9410128.179	15180521.27
Observations	30	50
Hypothesized Mean Difference	0	
df	72	
t Stat	-14.82301999	
P(T<=t) one-tail	7.16909E-24	
t Critical one-tail	1.666294338	
P(T<=t) two-tail	1.43382E-23	
t Critical two-tail	1.99346232	

Since the p-value is essentially zero. Reject the null hypothesis. There is sufficient evidence to conclude that the averages of the total cost are different between public and private universities.

10.80   **Room and board cost:**
cont.

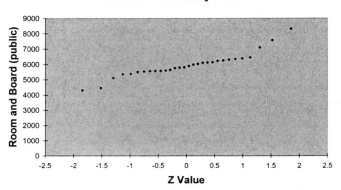

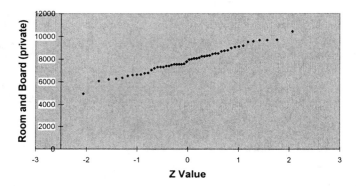

Both normal probability plots suggest that both distributions are not normal. It is inappropriate to perform an F test on the difference in variances. Values of the sample variances, $S_I^2 = 617974.0103$ and $S_{II}^2 = 1306292.396$, suggest that a separate-variance t test is more appropriate.

$H_0 : \mu_I = \mu_{II}$ vs. $H_1 : \mu_I \neq \mu_{II}$

Excel output:

t-Test: Two-Sample Assuming Unequal Variances

	Room and Board	Room and Board
Mean	5936.7	7867.18
Variance	617974	1306292
Observations	30	50
Hypothesized Mean Difference	0	
df	76	
t Stat	-8.93081	
P(T<=t) one-tail	9.06E-14	
t Critical one-tail	1.665151	
P(T<=t) two-tail	1.81E-13	
t Critical two-tail	1.991675	

10.80
cont.

Since the *p*-value is essentially zero. Reject the null hypothesis. There is sufficient evidence to conclude that the averages of the room and board cost are different between public and private universities.

Total indebtedness at graduation:

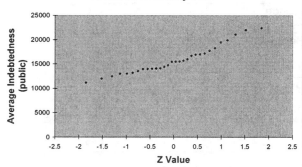

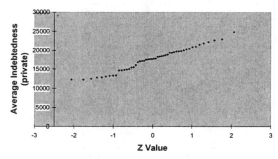

The two normal probability plots do not suggest severe departures from the normality assumption. We can perform an F test on the difference of variances.

$$H_0 : \sigma_I^2 = \sigma_{II}^2 \quad \text{vs.} \quad H_1 : \sigma_I^2 \neq \sigma_{II}^2$$

PHStat output:

F Test for Differences in Two Variances	
Data	
Level of Significance	0.05
Population 1 Sample	
Sample Size	30
Sample Standard Deviation	2940.172
Population 2 Sample	
Sample Size	50
Sample Standard Deviation	3183.556
Intermediate Calculations	
F-Test Statistic	0.852944
Population 1 Sample Degrees of Freedom	29
Population 2 Sample Degrees of Freedom	49
Two-Tailed Test	
Lower Critical Value	0.502423
Upper Critical Value	1.881418
p-Value	0.656293
Do not reject the null hypothesis	

**10.80
cont.**   Since the p-value = 0.66 > 0.05, do not reject the null hypothesis. There is not sufficient evidence to conclude that the two variances are different. We can perform a pooled-variance t test for the difference in means.
PHStat output:

t Test for Differences in Two Means	
Data	
Hypothesized Difference	0
Level of Significance	0.05
Population 1 Sample	
Sample Size	30
Sample Mean	15822.03
Sample Standard Deviation	2940.172
Population 2 Sample	
Sample Size	50
Sample Mean	17585.64
Sample Standard Deviation	3183.556
Intermediate Calculations	
Population 1 Sample Degrees of Freedom	29
Population 2 Sample Degrees of Freedom	49
Total Degrees of Freedom	78
Pooled Variance	9580901
Difference in Sample Means	-1763.61
t-Test Statistic	-2.46717
Two-Tailed Test	
Lower Critical Value	-1.99085
Upper Critical Value	1.990848
p-Value	0.01581
Reject the null hypothesis	

Since the p-value = 0.01581 < 0.05, reject the null hypothesis. There is sufficient evidence to conclude that the average total indebtedness at graduation are different between public and private universities.

10.82   (a) $\bar{X} \pm t \cdot \dfrac{S}{\sqrt{n}} = 7.8 \pm 2.7765 \cdot \dfrac{3.2711}{\sqrt{5}}$ $3.74 < \mu_{X_A} < 11.86$

(b) H_0: $\mu_R \le 6$ seconds. The average processing time in the Research Department is no more than 6 seconds.
H_1: $\mu_R > 6$ seconds. The average processing time in the Research Department is greater than 6 seconds.
Decision rule: $df = 5$. If $t > 2.0150$, reject H_0.

Test statistic: $t = \dfrac{\bar{X} - \mu}{S/\sqrt{n}} = \dfrac{8.5 - 6}{3.1464/\sqrt{6}} = 1.9463$

Decision: Since $t_{\text{calc}} = 1.9463$ is below the critical bound of 2.0150, do not reject H_0. There is insufficient evidence to conclude that the average processing time in the Research Department is greater than 6 seconds.

10.82 (c)
cont.

H_0: $\sigma_A^{\,2} = \sigma_R^{\,2}$ The population variances for processing times are the same for the Accounting Department and the Research Department.

H_1: $\sigma_A^{\,2} \neq \sigma_R^{\,2}$ The population variances for processing times are different for the Accounting Department and the Research Department.

Decision rule: If $F < 0.107$ or $F > 7.39$, reject H_0.

Test statistic: $F = \dfrac{S_A^{\,2}}{S_R^{\,2}} = \dfrac{3.2711^2}{3.1464^2} = 1.08$

Decision: Since $F_{calc} = 1.08$ is between the critical bounds of 0.107 and 7.39, do not reject H_0. There is not enough evidence to conclude that the population variances for processing times are different for the Accounting Department and the Research Department.

(d) One must assume the two populations are each normally distributed.

(e) H_0: $\mu_A = \mu_R$ The two departments have the same average processing time.

H_1: $\mu_A \neq \mu_R$ The two departments have different average processing times.

Decision rule: $df = 9$. If $t < -2.2622$ or $t > 2.2622$, reject H_0.

Test statistic:

$S_p^{\,2} = \dfrac{(n_A - 1) \cdot S_A^{\,2} + (n_R - 1) \cdot S_R^{\,2}}{(n_A - 1) + (n_R - 1)} = \dfrac{4 \cdot 3.2711^2 + 5 \cdot 3.1464^2}{4 + 5} = 10.2556$

$t = \dfrac{(\overline{X}_A - \overline{X}_R) - (\mu_A - \mu_R)}{\sqrt{S_p^{\,2}\left(\dfrac{1}{n_A} + \dfrac{1}{n_R}\right)}} = \dfrac{7.8 - 8.5}{\sqrt{10.2556\left(\dfrac{1}{5} + \dfrac{1}{6}\right)}} = -0.3610$

Decision: Since $t_{calc} = -0.3610$ is between the critical bounds of ± 2.2622, do not reject H_0. There is not enough evidence to support a conclusion that the two departments have different average processing times.

(f) One must assume that each of the two populations is normally distributed and the population variances are equal.

(g) (b) Given $t_{calc} = 1.9463$, $df = 5$ for a one-tailed hypothesis test, using Excel, we find the p value $= 0.0546$.

(c) Given $F_{calc} = 1.08$, numerator $df = 4$ and denominator $df = 5$, using Excel for a two-tailed hypothesis test:

$P(F_{4,5} > 1.08) = 0.4551$

$P\left(\dfrac{1}{F_{5,4}} < \dfrac{1}{1.08}\right) = 0.4551$

$p - \text{value} = P(F_{4,5} > 1.08) + P\left(\dfrac{1}{F_{5,4}} < \dfrac{1}{1.08}\right)$

$= 0.4551 + 0.4551 = 0.9102$

(e) Given $t_{calc} = 0.3610$, $df = 9$ for a two-tailed hypothesis test, using Excel, we find the p value $= 0.7264$.

(h) $(\overline{X}_A - \overline{X}_B) \pm t \sqrt{S_p^{\,2}\left(\dfrac{1}{n_1} + \dfrac{1}{n_2}\right)} = -0.7 \pm 2.2622\sqrt{10.2556\left(\dfrac{1}{5} + \dfrac{1}{6}\right)}$

$-5.0867 < \mu_A - \mu_B < 3.6867$

10.82   (i) There is not enough evidence to conclude that there is a difference in mean
cont.   processing time between the accounting department and the research department.
              With 95% confidence, the mean processing time in the accounting department is
              between 3.74 and 11.86 seconds. There is insufficient evidence to conclude that the
              average processing time in the research department is greater than 6 seconds. There
              is also not enough evidence to conclude that the population variances are different
              between the two departments.

10.84   (a) $\bar{X} \pm t \dfrac{S_X}{\sqrt{n}} = 372 \pm 1.9842 \dfrac{120}{\sqrt{100}}$ $348.19 < \mu < 395.81$

         (b) $\bar{X} \pm t \dfrac{S_X}{\sqrt{n}} = 510 \pm 1.9842 \dfrac{150}{\sqrt{100}}$ $480.24 < \mu < 539.76$

         (c) Excel output for $H_0 : \mu_M = \mu_W$ vs. $H_1 : \mu_M \neq \mu_W$ on cell phones:

t Test for Differences in Two Means	
Data	
Hypothesized Difference	0
Level of Significance	0.05
Population 1 Sample	
Sample Size	100
Sample Mean	372
Sample Standard Deviation	120
Population 2 Sample	
Sample Size	100
Sample Mean	275
Sample Standard Deviation	100
Intermediate Calculations	
Population 1 Sample Degrees of Freedom	99
Population 2 Sample Degrees of Freedom	99
Total Degrees of Freedom	198
Pooled Variance	12200
Difference in Sample Means	97
t-Test Statistic	6.209789
Two-Tailed Test	
Lower Critical Value	-1.97202
Upper Critical Value	1.972016
p-Value	3.06E-09
Reject the null hypothesis	

         (c) At 5% level of significance, reject the null hypothesis. There is enough evidence to
              show that the mean monthly talking time on cell home phones for men and women is
              different.

10.84   (d)   Excel output for $H_0: \mu_M = \mu_W$ vs. $H_1: \mu_M \neq \mu_W$ on traditional phones:

cont.

t Test for Differences in Two Means	
Data	
Hypothesized Difference	0
Level of Significance	0.05
Population 1 Sample	
Sample Size	100
Sample Mean	334
Sample Standard Deviation	100
Population 2 Sample	
Sample Size	100
Sample Mean	510
Sample Standard Deviation	150
Intermediate Calculations	
Population 1 Sample Degrees of Freedom	99
Population 2 Sample Degrees of Freedom	99
Total Degrees of Freedom	198
Pooled Variance	16250
Difference in Sample Means	-176
t-Test Statistic	-9.76272
Two-Tailed Test	
Lower Critical Value	-1.97202
Upper Critical Value	1.972016
p-Value	1.25E-18
Reject the null hypothesis	

(d)   At 5% level of significance, reject the null hypothesis. There is enough evidence to show that the mean monthly talking time on traditional home phones for men and women is different.

(e)   The assumptions needed are (1) both samples are randomly and independently drawn, and (2) population variances are assumed equal. Since both sample sizes are larger than 30, we do not need to assume that both populations are normally distributed.

(f) $\left(\bar{X}_M - \bar{X}_W\right) \pm t\sqrt{S_p^2\left(\dfrac{1}{n_M} + \dfrac{1}{n_W}\right)}$ $66.1961 < \mu_M - \mu_W < 127.8039$

(g) $\left(\bar{X}_M - \bar{X}_W\right) \pm t\sqrt{S_p^2\left(\dfrac{1}{n_M} + \dfrac{1}{n_W}\right)}$ $-211.551 < \mu_M - \mu_W < -140.449$

10.84   (h)   Excel output for $H_0 : \sigma_M^2 = \sigma_W^2$ vs. $H_1 : \sigma_M^2 \neq \sigma_W^2$ on cell phones:

cont.

F Test for Differences in Two Variances	
Data	
Level of Significance	0.05
Population 1 Sample	
Sample Size	100
Sample Standard Deviation	120
Population 2 Sample	
Sample Size	100
Sample Standard Deviation	100
Intermediate Calculations	
F-Test Statistic	1.44
Population 1 Sample Degrees of Freedom	99
Population 2 Sample Degrees of Freedom	99
Two-Tailed Test	
Lower Critical Value	0.672841
Upper Critical Value	1.486235
p-Value	0.071147
Do not reject the null hypothesis	

At 5% level of significance, do not reject the null hypothesis. There is not enough evidence to show that there is any difference in the variance of the monthly talking time on cell phones for men and women.

(i)   Excel output for $H_0 : \sigma_M^2 = \sigma_W^2$ vs. $H_1 : \sigma_M^2 \neq \sigma_W^2$ on traditional phones:

F Test for Differences in Two Variances	
Data	
Level of Significance	0.05
Population 1 Sample	
Sample Size	100
Sample Standard Deviation	100
Population 2 Sample	
Sample Size	100
Sample Standard Deviation	150
Intermediate Calculations	
F-Test Statistic	0.444444
Population 1 Sample Degrees of Freedom	99
Population 2 Sample Degrees of Freedom	99
Two-Tailed Test	
Lower Critical Value	0.672841
Upper Critical Value	1.486235
p-Value	7.15E-05
Reject the null hypothesis	

At 5% level of significance, reject the null hypothesis. There is enough evidence to show that there is some difference in the variance of the monthly talking time on traditional phones for men and women.

(j)   Since both sample sizes are greater than 30, the only assumption needed is that both samples are randomly and independently drawn.

(k)   Based on the results of (a) – (j), there is sufficient evidence to conclude that the average monthly talking time on cell phones and traditional phones are different between men and women.

10.86 (a) $H_0 : \mu_1 = \mu_2$ where 1 is for current ad pages and 2 for last year ad pages

$H_1 : \mu_1 \neq \mu_2$

Decision rule: $df = 18$. If $t > 2.1009$ or $t < -2.1009$, reject H_0.

Test statistic: $t = \dfrac{\bar{D} - \mu_{\bar{D}}}{S_{\bar{D}}/\sqrt{n}} = -1.8536$

Decision: Since $t_{calc} = -1.8536$ is between the critical bounds of -2.109 and 2.109, do not reject H_0. There is not enough evidence to conclude that the mean number of advertising pages in the current issues is different from that of the previous year.

Excel output:

t-Test: Paired Two Sample for Means

	Current Ad Pages	Ad Pages Last Year
Mean	32.09894737	42.13842105
Variance	570.5288655	1057.623614
Observations	19	19
Pearson Correlation	0.689220948	
Hypothesized Mean Difference	0	
df	18	
t Stat	-1.853565221	
P(T<=t) one-tail	0.040132628	
t Critical one-tail	1.734063062	
P(T<=t) two-tail	0.080265256	
t Critical two-tail	2.100923666	

(b)   From the Excel output, the p-value = 0.0803. The probability of observing a test statistic that is further away from 0 than the current value is 0.0803.

(c) $\bar{D} \pm t \dfrac{S_D}{\sqrt{n}} = -10.0395 \pm 2.1009 \dfrac{23.6091}{\sqrt{19}}$ $-21.4187 < \mu_D < 1.3398$

(d) $H_0 : M_1 = M_2$ where 1 is for current ad pages and 2 for last year ad pages

$H_1 : M_1 \neq M_2$

Minitab output:

Wilcoxon Signed Rank Test: Difference

```
Test of median = 0.000000 versus median not = 0.000000

                    N for   Wilcoxon                Estimated
             N      Test    Statistic        P        Median
Differen     19      19         51.0    0.080        -10.74
```

Since the p-value = 0.08 > 0.05, do not reject H_0. There is not enough evidence to conclude that the median number of advertising pages in the current issues is different from that of the previous year.

(e)   Since 0 is contained in the 95% confidence interval for the difference in the mean number of advertising pages in the current issues compared to the previous year, the null hypothesis in (a) cannot be rejected. The conclusion drawn using the confidence interval is identical to that in (a). The t test for the mean difference concludes that there is not enough evidence that the mean number of advertising pages in the current issues is different from that of the previous year and the Wilcoxon signed-ranks test concludes that there is not enough evidence that the median number of advertising pages in the current issues is different from that of the previous year.

10.88   First, the normal probability plots of cost per serving, protein in grams and fat in grams of the four different kinds of pet food are presented.

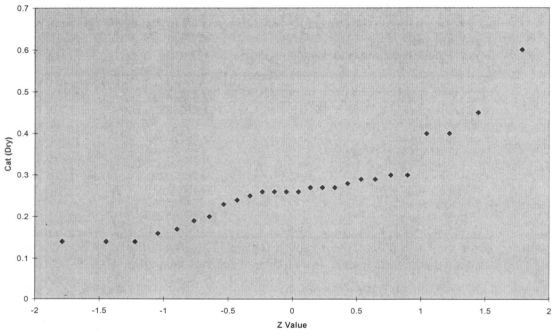

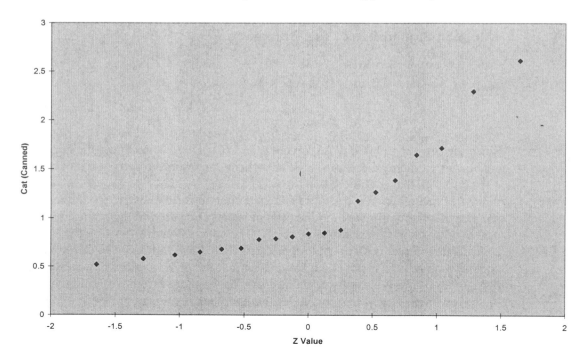

10.88
cont.

Normal Probability of Cost Per Serving (Dog/Dry)

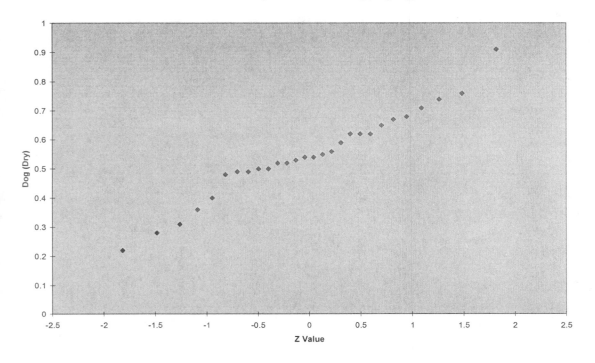

Normal Probability Plot of Cost Per Serving (Dog/Canned)

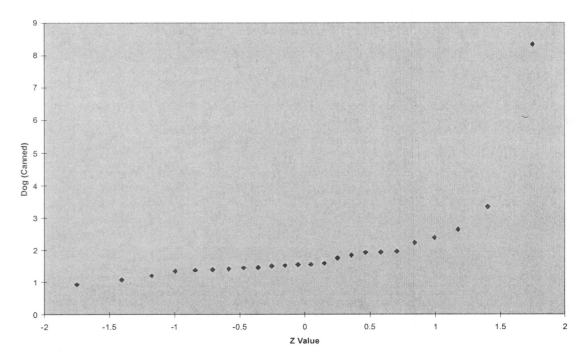

10.88
cont.

Normal Probability Plot of Protein (Cat/Dry)

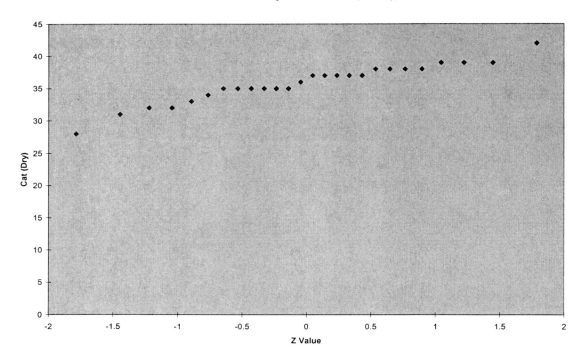

Normal Probability Plot of Protein (Cat/Canned)

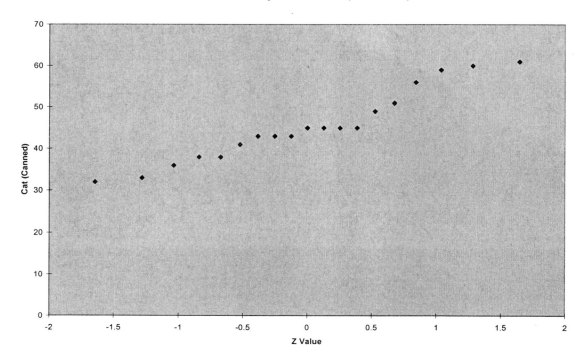

10.88
cont.

Normal Probability Plot of Protein (Dog/Dry)

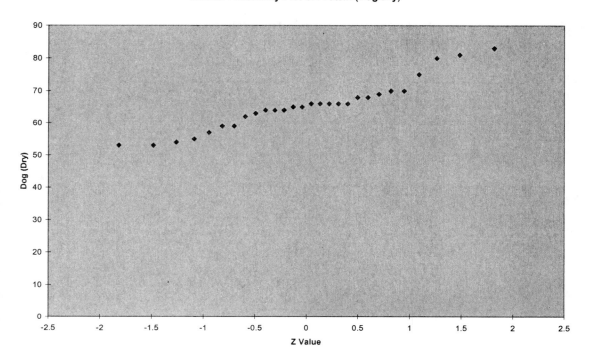

Normal Probability Plot of Protein (Dog/Canned)

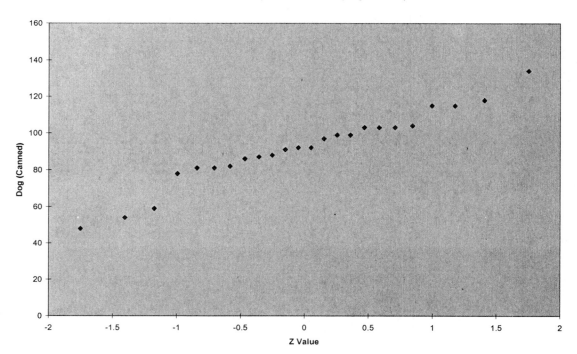

10.88
cont.

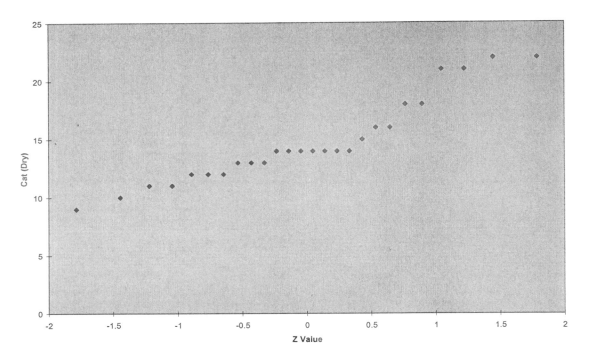

Normal Probability Plot of Fat (Cat/Dry)

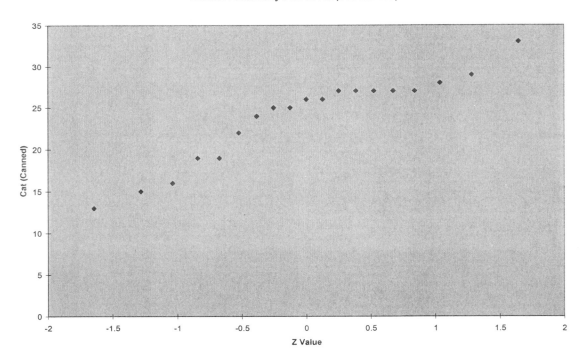

Normal Probability Plot of Fat (Cat/Canned)

10.88
cont.

Normal Probability Plot of Fat (Dog/Dry)

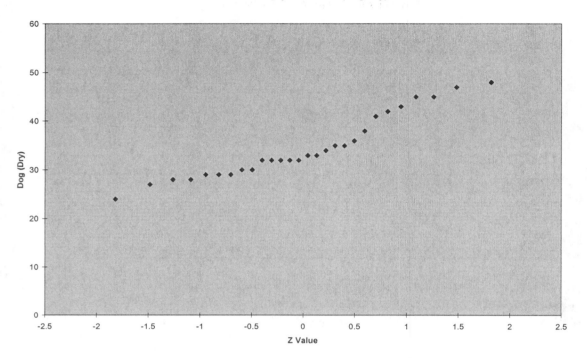

Normal Probability Plot of Fat (Dog/Canned)

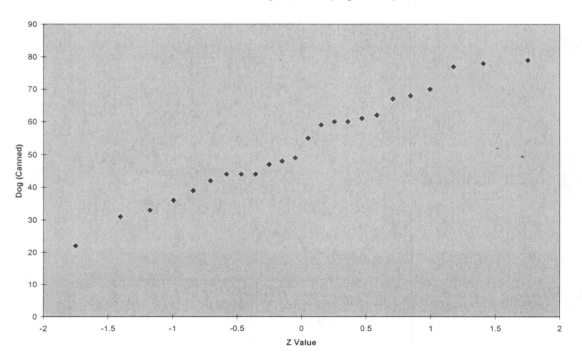

10.88   Next we present the box-and-whisker plots of cost of serving, protein in grams and fat in
cont.   grams of the four different types of pet food.

Box-and-whisker Plot of Cost Per Serving

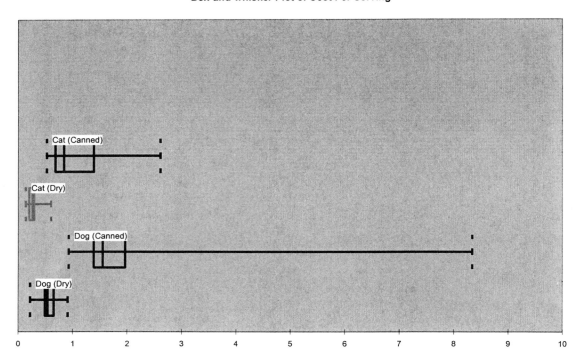

Box-and-whisker Plot of Protein in Grams

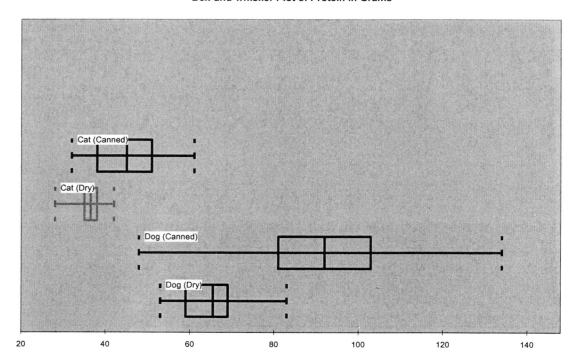

10.88
cont.

Box-and-whisker Plot of Fat in Grams

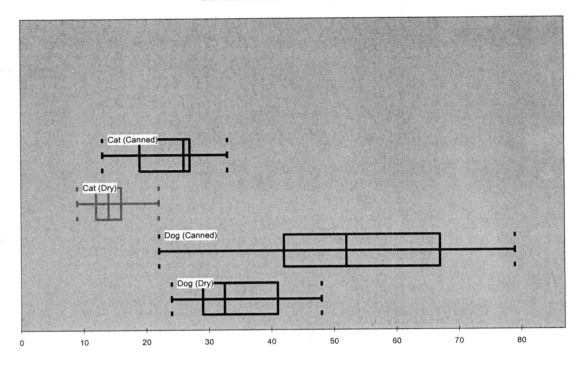

Dry and Canned Cat Food (Cost Per Serving):

The normal probability plots suggest that the data on cost per serving for dry and canned cat food do not appear to have been drawn from populations that are normally distributed. Hence, it is inappropriate to perform the F test on the difference of population variances, which is highly sensitive to the violation of the normal distribution assumption, to see whether the two population variances are equal.

The box-and-whisker plots show that the dispersions in the two samples are quite different. Since both sample sizes are not very large, both the separate-variance t test and the pooled-variance t test for the difference in two means will be quite sensitive to the violation of the normal distribution assumption. If any test was to be performed, the separate variance t test would be preferred over the pooled-variance t test.

$H_0 : \mu_I = \mu_{II}$ Mean cost per serving of dry cat food and canned cat food are the same.

$H_1 : \mu_I \neq \mu_{II}$ Mean cost per serving of dry cat food and canned cat food are different.

10.88
cont.   PHStat output for the separate variance t test:

Separate Variance t test	
Significance Level	0.05
Population 1 Sample	
Sample Size	26
Sample Mean	0.27
Sample Standard Deviation	0.103
Sample Variance	0.010609
Population 2 Sample	
Sample Size	19
Sample Mean	1.09526
Sample Standard Deviation	0.594945
Sample Variance	0.35396
nu	18.79065
Difference in Sample Means	-0.82526
Hypothesized Difference	0
Degrees of Freedom	18
Standard Error	0.137976
t Test Staistic	-5.98117
Two-tail Critical Value	2.100924
Two-tail p-value	1.17E-05
Two-tail Test	
Reject the Null Hypothesis	

Since the p-value is essentially zero, the separate variance t test overwhelmingly rejects the null hypothesis of no difference in the mean cost per serving between canned cat food and dry cat.

Dry and Canned Cat Food (Protein in grams):

The normal probability plots suggest that the data on protein in grams of dry cat food and canned cat food appear to be approximately normally distributed. So it is appropriate to perform an F test for the difference in population variances.

$H_0 : \sigma_I^2 = \sigma_{II}^2$ Variance of protein in grams of dry cat food and canned cat food are the same.

$H_1 : \sigma_I^2 \neq \sigma_{II}^2$ Variance of protein in grams of dry cat food and canned cat food are different.

10.88
cont.   PHStat output:

F Test for Differences in Two Variances	
Data	
Level of Significance	0.05
Population 1 Sample	
Sample Size	26
Sample Standard Deviation	2.989211
Population 2 Sample	
Sample Size	19
Sample Standard Deviation	8.713437
Intermediate Calculations	
F-Test Statistic	0.117689
Population 1 Sample Degrees of Freedom	25
Population 2 Sample Degrees of Freedom	18
Two-Tailed Test	
Lower Critical Value	0.427695
Upper Critical Value	2.49122
p-Value	2.34E-06
Reject the null hypothesis	

Since the p-value is essentially zero, reject the null hypothesis. There is enough evidence to conclude that the variances are not the same.

The separate variance t test should be preferred over the pooled-variance t test.

$H_0 : \mu_I = \mu_{II}$ Mean protein in grams of dry cat food and canned cat food are the
same.

$H_1 : \mu_I \neq \mu_{II}$ Mean protein in grams of dry cat food and canned cat food are
different.

Excel output:

t-Test: Two-Sample Assuming Unequal Variances

	Cat (Dry)	Cat (Canned)
Mean	0.27	1.095263
Variance	0.010608	0.35396
Observations	26	19
Hypothesized Mean Difference	0	
df	19	
t Stat	-5.9812	
P(T<=t) one-tail	4.67E-06	
t Critical one-tail	1.729131	
P(T<=t) two-tail	9.35E-06	
t Critical two-tail	2.093025	

Since the p-value is essentially zero, there is enough evidence to conclude that the mean protein in grams of dry cat food and canned cat food are different at 5% level of significance.

10.88   **Dry and Canned Cat Food (Fat in grams):**
cont.

The normal probability plots suggest that both data appear to be approximately normally distributed. So it is appropriate to perform an F test for the difference in population variances.

$H_0 : \sigma_I^2 = \sigma_{II}^2$ Variance of fat in grams of dry cat food and canned cat food are the same.

$H_1 : \sigma_I^2 \neq \sigma_{II}^2$ Variance of fat in grams of dry cat food and canned cat food are different.

PHStat output:

F Test for Differences in Two Variances	
Level of Significance	0.05
Population 1 Sample	
Sample Size	26
Sample Standard Deviation	3.617266
Population 2 Sample	
Sample Size	19
Sample Standard Deviation	5.254349
Intermediate Calculations	
F-Test Statistic	0.47394
Population 1 Sample Degrees of Freedom	25
Population 2 Sample Degrees of Freedom	18
Two-Tailed Test	
Lower Critical Value	0.427695
Upper Critical Value	2.49122
p-Value	0.084188
Do not reject the null hypothesis	

Since the p-value of 0.0842 is greater than the 5% level of significance, do not reject the null hypothesis. There is not enough evidence to conclude that the two population variances are different. Hence, a pooled-variance t test for the difference in two means is appropriate.

$H_0 : \mu_I = \mu_{II}$ Mean fat in grams of dry cat food and canned cat food are the same.

$H_1 : \mu_I \neq \mu_{II}$ Mean fat in grams of dry cat food and canned cat food are different.

10.88 PHStat output:
cont.

t Test for Differences in Two Means	
Data	
Hypothesized Difference	0
Level of Significance	0.05
Population 1 Sample	
Sample Size	26
Sample Mean	14.73077
Sample Standard Deviation	3.617266
Population 2 Sample	
Sample Size	19
Sample Mean	23.94737
Sample Standard Deviation	5.254349
Intermediate Calculations	
Population 1 Sample Degrees of Freedom	25
Population 2 Sample Degrees of Freedom	18
Total Degrees of Freedom	43
Pooled Variance	19.16425
Difference in Sample Means	-9.2166
t-Test Statistic	-6.97561
Two-Tailed Test	
Lower Critical Value	-2.01669
Upper Critical Value	2.016691
p-Value	1.4E-08
Reject the null hypothesis	

Since the p-value is essentially zero, reject the null hypothesis. There is enough evidence to conclude that the mean fat in grams of dry cat food and canned cat food are different at 5% level of significance.

Dry Cat Food and Dry Dog Food (Cost Per Serving):

The normal probability plots suggest that the data for cost per serving of dry cat food and dry dog food do not appear to have been drawn from populations that are normally distributed. Hence, it is inappropriate to perform the F test on the difference of population variances, which is highly sensitive to the violation of the normal distribution assumption, to see whether the two population variances are equal.

The box-and-whisker plots show that the dispersions in the two samples are quite different. Since both sample sizes are not very large, both the separate-variance t test and the pooled-variance t test for the difference in two means will be quite sensitive to the violation of the normal distribution assumption. If any test was to be performed, the separate variance t test would be preferred over the pooled-variance t test.

10.88 $H_0 : \mu_I = \mu_{II}$ Mean cost per serving of dry cat food and dry dog food are the same.

cont. $H_1 : \mu_I \neq \mu_{II}$ Mean cost per serving of dry cat food and dry dog food are different.

Excel output:

t-Test: Two-Sample Assuming Unequal Variances

	Cat (Dry)	Dog (Dry)
Mean	0.27	0.548571
Variance	0.010608	0.022613
Observations	26	28
Hypothesized Mean Difference	0	
df	48	
t Stat	-7.98991	
P(T<=t) one-tail	1.14E-10	
t Critical one-tail	1.677224	
P(T<=t) two-tail	2.28E-10	
t Critical two-tail	2.010634	

Since the *p*-value is essentially zero, reject the null hypothesis at 5% level of significance. There is enough evidence to conclude that the mean cost per serving of dry cat food is different from that of dry dog food.

Dry Cat Food and Dry Dog Food (Protein in grams):

The normal probability plots suggest that the data on protein in grams for dry cat food and dry dog food appear to be approximately normally distributed. So it is appropriate to perform an *F* test for the difference in population variances.

$H_0 : \sigma_I^2 = \sigma_{II}^2$ Variance of protein in grams of dry cat food and dry dog food are the same.

$H_1 : \sigma_I^2 \neq \sigma_{II}^2$ Variance of protein in grams of dry cat food and dry dog food are different.

PHStat output:

F Test for Differences in Two Variances	
Data	
Level of Significance	0.05
Population 1 Sample	
Sample Size	26
Sample Standard Deviation	2.989211
Population 2 Sample	
Sample Size	28
Sample Standard Deviation	7.818967
Intermediate Calculations	
F-Test Statistic	0.146155
Population 1 Sample Degrees of Freedom	25
Population 2 Sample Degrees of Freedom	27
Two-Tailed Test	
Lower Critical Value	0.452721
Upper Critical Value	2.182574
p-Value	7.03E-06
Reject the null hypothesis	

10.88 Since the p-value is essentially zero, reject the null hypothesis. There is enough evidence to
cont.   conclude that the two population variances are different. Hence a separate variance t test for
the difference in two means should be used.

$H_0 : \mu_I = \mu_{II}$ Mean protein in grams of dry cat food and dry dog food are the same.

$H_1 : \mu_I \neq \mu_{II}$ Mean protein in grams of dry cat food and dry dog food are different.

Excel output:

t-Test: Two-Sample Assuming Unequal Variances

	Cat (Dry)	Dog (Dry)
Mean	35.84615	65.39286
Variance	8.935385	61.13624
Observations	26	28
Hypothesized Mean Difference	0	
Df	35	
t Stat	-18.5865	
P(T<=t) one-tail	5.14E-20	
t Critical one-tail	1.689573	
P(T<=t) two-tail	1.03E-19	
t Critical two-tail	2.03011	

Since the p-value is essentially zero, reject the null hypothesis. There is enough evidence to
conclude that the mean protein in grams between dry cat food and dry dog food are different.

Dry Cat Food and Dry Dog Food (Fat in grams):
The normal probability plots suggest that both data appear to be approximately normally
distributed. So it is appropriate to perform an F test for the difference in population
variances.

$H_0 : \sigma_I^2 = \sigma_{II}^2$ Variance of fat in grams of dry cat food and dry dog food are the same.

$H_1 : \sigma_I^2 \neq \sigma_{II}^2$ Variance of fat in grams of dry cat food and dry dog food are different.

PHStat output:

F Test for Differences in Two Variances	
Level of Significance	0.05
Population 1 Sample	
Sample Size	26
Sample Standard Deviation	3.617266
Population 2 Sample	
Sample Size	28
Sample Standard Deviation	6.562177
Intermediate Calculations	
F-Test Statistic	0.303854
Population 1 Sample Degrees of Freedom	25
Population 2 Sample Degrees of Freedom	27
Two-Tailed Test	
Lower Critical Value	0.452721
Upper Critical Value	2.182574
p-Value	0.003747
Reject the null hypothesis	

10.88   Since the *p*-value of 0.003747 is less than the 5% level of significance, reject the null
cont.   hypothesis. There is enough evidence to conclude that the population variances are different.
So the separate variance *t* test should be used.

$H_0 : \mu_I = \mu_{II}$ Mean fat in grams of dry cat food and dry dog food are the same.

$H_1 : \mu_I \neq \mu_{II}$ Mean fat in grams of dry cat food and dry dog food are different.

Excel output:

t-Test: Two-Sample Assuming Unequal Variances

	Cat (Dry)	Dog (Dry)
Mean	14.73077	34.60714
Variance	13.08462	43.06217
Observations	26	28
Hypothesized Mean Difference	0	
df	43	
t Stat	-13.9122	
P(T<=t) one-tail	8.01E-18	
t Critical one-tail	1.681071	
P(T<=t) two-tail	1.6E-17	
t Critical two-tail	2.016691	

Since the *p*-value is essentially zero, reject the null hypothesis. There is enough evidence to
conclude that the mean fat in grams are different between dry cat food and dry dog food.

Canned Dog Food and Canned Cat Food (Cost Per Serving):
The normal probability plots suggest that the data on cost per serving for canned dog food
and canned cat food do not appear to have been drawn from populations that are normally
distributed. Hence, it is inappropriate to perform the *F* test on the difference of population
variances, which is highly sensitive to the violation of the normal distribution assumption, to
see whether the two population variances are equal.

The box-and-whisker plots show that the dispersions in the two samples are quite different.
Since both sample sizes are not very large, both the separate-variance *t* test and the pooled-
variance *t* test for the difference in two means will be quite sensitive to the violation of the
normal distribution assumption. If any test was to be performed, the separate variance *t* test
would be preferred over the pooled-variance *t* test.

$H_0 : \mu_I = \mu_{II}$ Mean cost per serving of canned dog food and canned cat food are
the same.

$H_1 : \mu_I \neq \mu_{II}$ Mean cost per serving of canned dog food and canned cat food are
different.

10.88
cont.

Excel output:

t-Test: Two-Sample Assuming Unequal Variances

	Dog (Canned)	Cat (Canned)
Mean	1.989583	1.095263
Variance	2.108282	0.35396
Observations	24	19
Hypothesized Mean Difference	0	
Df	32	
t Stat	2.740754	
P(T<=t) one-tail	0.004972	
t Critical one-tail	1.693888	
P(T<=t) two-tail	0.009944	
t Critical two-tail	2.036932	

Since the p-value of 0.00994 is less than the 5% level of significance, reject the null hypothesis. There is enough evidence to conclude that the mean cost per serving between canned dog food and canned cat food are different.

Canned Dog Food and Canned Cat Food (Protein in grams):

The normal probability plots suggest that the data on protein in grams for canned dog food and canned cat food appear to be approximately normally distributed. So it is appropriate to perform an F test for the difference in population variances.

$H_0 : \sigma_I^2 = \sigma_{II}^2$ Variance of protein in grams of canned dog food and canned cat food are the same.

$H_1 : \sigma_I^2 \neq \sigma_{II}^2$ Variance of protein in grams of canned dog food and canned cat food are different.

PHStat output:

F Test for Differences in Two Variances	
Level of Significance	0.05
Population 1 Sample	
Sample Size	24
Sample Standard Deviation	20.01408
Population 2 Sample	
Sample Size	19
Sample Standard Deviation	8.713437
Intermediate Calculations	
F-Test Statistic	5.275848
Population 1 Sample Degrees of Freedom	23
Population 2 Sample Degrees of Freedom	18
Two-Tailed Test	
Lower Critical Value	0.417703
Upper Critical Value	2.515094
p-Value	0.000691
Reject the null hypothesis	

10.88   Since the *p*-value of 0.000691 is less than the 5% level of significance, reject the null
cont.   hypothesis. There is enough evidence to conclude that the two population variances are
different. Hence, a separate variance *t* test should be used.

$H_0 : \mu_I = \mu_{II}$ Mean protein in grams of canned dog food and canned cat food are
the same.

$H_1 : \mu_I \neq \mu_{II}$ Mean protein in grams of canned dog food and canned cat food are
different.

Excel output:
t-Test: Two-Sample Assuming Unequal Variances

	Dog (Canned)	Cat (Canned)
Mean	92.04167	45.42105
Variance	400.5634	75.92398
Observations	24	19
Hypothesized Mean Difference	0	
Df	33	
t Stat	10.25034	
P(T<=t) one-tail	4.34E-12	
t Critical one-tail	1.69236	
P(T<=t) two-tail	8.68E-12	
t Critical two-tail	2.034517	

Since the *p*-value is essentially zero, reject the null hypothesis. There is enough evidence to
conclude that the mean protein in grams of canned dog food and canned cat food are
different.

Canned Dog Food and Canned Cat Food (Fat in grams):
The normal probability plots suggest that both data appear to be approximately normally
distributed. So it is appropriate to perform an *F* test for the difference in population
variances.

$H_0 : \sigma_I^2 = \sigma_{II}^2$ Variance of fat in grams of canned dog food and canned cat food are the
same.

$H_1 : \sigma_I^2 \neq \sigma_{II}^2$ Variance of fat in grams of canned dog food and canned cat food are
different.

10.88   PHStat output:
cont.

F Test for Differences in Two Variances	
Level of Significance	0.05
Population 1 Sample	
Sample Size	24
Sample Standard Deviation	15.66029
Population 2 Sample	
Sample Size	19
Sample Standard Deviation	5.254349
Intermediate Calculations	
F-Test Statistic	8.883043
Population 1 Sample Degrees of Freedom	23
Population 2 Sample Degrees of Freedom	18
Two-Tailed Test	
Lower Critical Value	0.417703
Upper Critical Value	2.515094
p-Value	1.7E-05
Reject the null hypothesis	

Since the p-value is essentially zero, reject the null hypothesis. There is evidence to conclude that the two population variances are different. So a separate variance t test should be used.

$H_0 : \mu_I = \mu_{II}$ Mean fat in grams of canned dog food and canned cat food are the same.

$H_1 : \mu_I \neq \mu_{II}$ Mean fat in grams of canned dog food and canned cat food are different.

Excel output:

t-Test: Two-Sample Assuming Unequal Variances

	Dog (Canned)	Cat (Canned)
Mean	53.125	23.94737
Variance	245.2446	27.60819
Observations	24	19
Hypothesized Mean Difference	0	
Df	29	
t Stat	8.540535	
P(T<=t) one-tail	1.04E-09	
t Critical one-tail	1.699127	
P(T<=t) two-tail	2.08E-09	
t Critical two-tail	2.045231	

Since the p-value is essentially zero, reject the null hypothesis. There is enough evidence to conclude that mean fat in grams of caned dog food and canned cat food are different.

10.90   From Problem 3.76, we saw that the distribution of all the variables was quite symmetrical and not too far away from normal with the exception of the price in Long Island. Hence, we perform the F test on the difference in variances to determine whether the pooled-variance t test or separate variance t test is more appropriate for the difference in means.

Food:

$$H_0 : \sigma_1^2 = \sigma_2^2 \quad \text{vs.} \quad H_1 : \sigma_1^2 \neq \sigma_2^2$$

F Test for Differences in Two Variances	
Data	
Level of Significance	0.05
Population 1 Sample	
Sample Size	50
Sample Standard Deviation	2.082483
Population 2 Sample	
Sample Size	50
Sample Standard Deviation	2.858642
Intermediate Calculations	
F-Test Statistic	0.530693
Population 1 Sample Degrees of Freedom	49
Population 2 Sample Degrees of Freedom	49
Two-Tailed Test	
Lower Critical Value	0.567477
Upper Critical Value	1.762189
p-Value	0.02865
Reject the null hypothesis	

At 5% level of significance, there is sufficient evidence to conclude that the two variances are not the same. Hence, a separate variance t test is more appropriate.

$$H_0 : \mu_1 = \mu_2 \quad \text{vs.} \quad H_1 : \mu_1 \neq \mu_2$$

t-Test: Two-Sample Assuming Unequal Variances

	Food	*Food*
Mean	20.1	20.54
Variance	4.336734694	8.171836735
Observations	50	50
Hypothesized Mean Difference	0	
df	90	
t Stat	-0.879698441	
P(T<=t) one-tail	0.190682783	
t Critical one-tail	1.661960596	
P(T<=t) two-tail	0.381365566	
t Critical two-tail	1.986672942	

Since the p-value = 0.38 is greater than the 5% level of significance, do not reject H_0. There is not enough evidence to conclude that the average food rating between N.Y.C. and L.I. is different.

10.90 **Décor:**
cont.

$$H_0 : \sigma_1^2 = \sigma_2^2 \quad \text{vs.} \quad H_1 : \sigma_1^2 \neq \sigma_2^2$$

F Test for Differences in Two Variances	
Data	
Level of Significance	0.05
Population 1 Sample	
Sample Size	50
Sample Standard Deviation	2.6927
Population 2 Sample	
Sample Size	50
Sample Standard Deviation	3.4862
Intermediate Calculations	
F-Test Statistic	0.596588
Population 1 Sample Degrees of Freedom	49
Population 2 Sample Degrees of Freedom	49
Two-Tailed Test	
Lower Critical Value	0.567477
Upper Critical Value	1.762189
p-Value	0.073639
Do not reject the null hypothesis	

There is not enough evidence to conclude that the variances are different. Hence, a pooled-variance t test is appropriate.

$$H_0 : \mu_1 = \mu_2 \quad \text{vs.} \quad H_1 : \mu_1 \neq \mu_2$$

t-Test: Two-Sample Assuming Equal Variances

	Décor	Décor
Mean	17.12	17.64
Variance	7.250612245	12.15346939
Observations	50	50
Pooled Variance	9.702040816	
Hypothesized Mean Difference	0	
df	98	
t Stat	-0.834721883	
P(T<=t) one-tail	0.202952279	
t Critical one-tail	1.660550879	
P(T<=t) two-tail	0.405904557	
t Critical two-tail	1.984467417	

Since the p-value = 0.406 is greater than the 5% level of significance, do not reject H_0. There is not enough evidence to conclude that the average décor rating between N.Y.C. and L.I. is different.

10.90
cont.

Services:

$$H_0 : \sigma_1^2 = \sigma_2^2 \quad \text{vs.} \quad H_1 : \sigma_1^2 \neq \sigma_2^2$$

F Test for Differences in Two Variances	
Data	
Level of Significance	0.05
Population 1 Sample	
Sample Size	50
Sample Standard Deviation	2.3123
Population 2 Sample	
Sample Size	50
Sample Standard Deviation	2.373
Intermediate Calculations	
F-Test Statistic	0.949495
Population 1 Sample Degrees of Freedom	49
Population 2 Sample Degrees of Freedom	49
Two-Tailed Test	
Lower Critical Value	0.567477
Upper Critical Value	1.762189
p-Value	0.856797
Do not reject the null hypothesis	

There is not enough evidence to conclude that the two variances are different. So we can use a pooled-variance t test.

$$H_0 : \mu_1 = \mu_2 \quad \text{vs.} \quad H_1 : \mu_1 \neq \mu_2$$

t-Test: Two-Sample Assuming Equal Variances

	Service	Service
Mean	18.4	19.04
Variance	5.346939	5.631020408
Observations	50	50
Pooled Variance	5.48898	
Hypothesized Mean Difference	0	
df	98	
t Stat	-1.36585	
P(T<=t) one-tail	0.087556	
t Critical one-tail	1.660551	
P(T<=t) two-tail	0.175111	
t Critical two-tail	1.984467	

Since the p-value = 0.175 is greater than the 5% level of significance, do not reject H_0.
There is not enough evidence to conclude that the average service rating between N.Y.C. and L.I. is different.

10.90
cont.

Price:

$$H_0 : \sigma_1^2 = \sigma_2^2 \quad \text{vs.} \quad H_1 : \sigma_1^2 \neq \sigma_2^2$$

F Test for Differences in Two Variances	
Data	
Level of Significance	0.05
Population 1 Sample	
Sample Size	50
Sample Standard Deviation	9.6528
Population 2 Sample	
Sample Size	50
Sample Standard Deviation	7.7191
Intermediate Calculations	
F-Test Statistic	1.563771
Population 1 Sample Degrees of Freedom	49
Population 2 Sample Degrees of Freedom	49
Two-Tailed Test	
Lower Critical Value	0.567477
Upper Critical Value	1.762189
p-Value	0.121019
Do not reject the null hypothesis	

There is not enough evidence to conclude that the two variances are different. So we can use a pooled-variance t test.

$$H_0 : \mu_1 = \mu_2 \quad \text{vs.} \quad H_1 : \mu_1 \neq \mu_2$$

t-Test: Two-Sample Assuming Equal Variances

	Price	Price
Mean	39.7400	33.7400
Variance	93.1759	59.5841
Observations	50.0000	50.0000
Pooled Variance	76.3800	
Hypothesized Mean Difference	0.0000	
df	98.0000	
t Stat	3.4327	
P(T<=t) one-tail	0.0004	
t Critical one-tail	1.6606	
P(T<=t) two-tail	0.0009	
t Critical two-tail	1.9845	

Since the p-value $= 0.0009$ is smaller than the 5% level of significance, reject H_0. There is sufficient evidence to conclude that the average price is different between N.Y.C. and L.I.

10.92

Normal Probability Plot of Processing Time (Plant A)

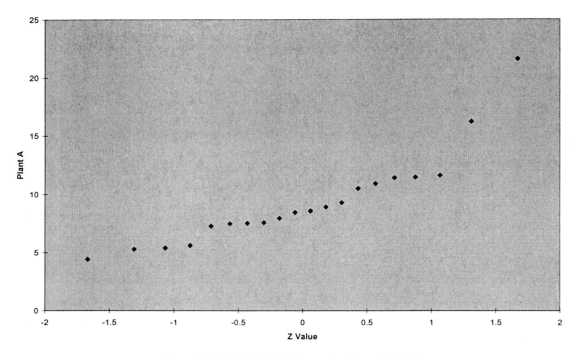

Normal Probability Plot of Processing Time (Plant B)

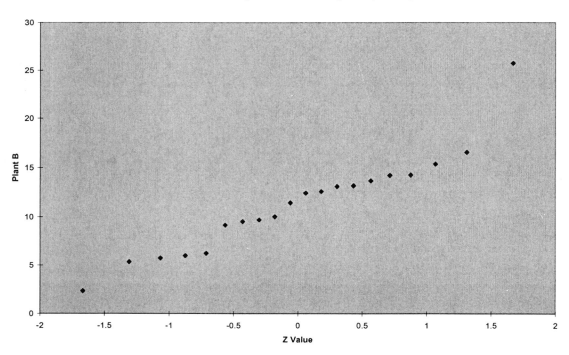

10.92
cont.

Box-and-whisker Plot

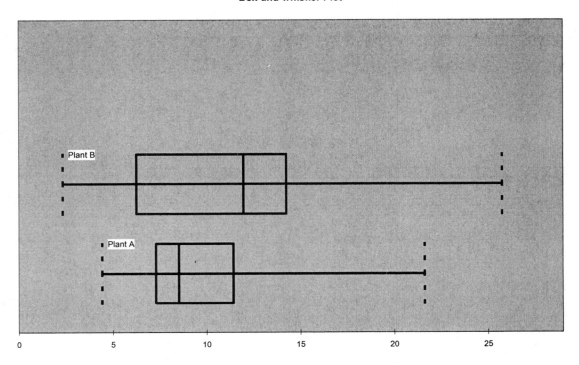

	Plant A	Plant B
Mean	9.382	11.3535
Standard Error	0.893902	1.146243
Median	8.515	11.96
Mode	#N/A	#N/A
Standard Deviation	3.997653	5.126156
Sample Variance	15.98123	26.27748
Kurtosis	3.848392	2.177018
Skewness	1.694951	0.798989
Range	17.2	23.42
Minimum	4.42	2.33
Maximum	21.62	25.75
Sum	187.64	227.07
Count	20	20
Minimum	4.42	2.33
First Quartile	7.29	6.25
Median	8.515	11.96
Third Quartile	11.42	14.25
Maximum	21.62	25.75

Both the normal probability plots and the box-and-whisker plot suggest that the processing times for the two plants do not appear to be normally distributed. Hence, the F test for the difference in variances, which is sensitive to departure from the normality assumption, should not be used to test the equality of two variances. The box-and-whisker plot and the summary statistics suggest that the two samples appear to have different amount of dispersions. Hence, the separate variance t test should be used.

10.92
cont.

$H_0 : \mu_I = \mu_{II}$ Mean processing times at Plant A and Plant B are the same.

$H_1 : \mu_I \neq \mu_{II}$ Mean processing times at Plant A and Plant B are different.

Excel output:

t-Test: Two-Sample Assuming Unequal Variances

	Plant A	Plant B
Mean	9.382	11.3535
Variance	15.98123	26.27748
Observations	20	20
Hypothesized Mean Difference	0	
df	36	
t Stat	-1.35629	
P(T<=t) one-tail	0.091726	
t Critical one-tail	1.688297	
P(T<=t) two-tail	0.183452	
t Critical two-tail	2.028091	

Since the *p*-value of 0.183452 is greater than the 5% level of significance, do not reject the null hypothesis. There is not enough evidence to conclude that the processing times at the two plants are different.

10.94   **Consultants in the United States:**

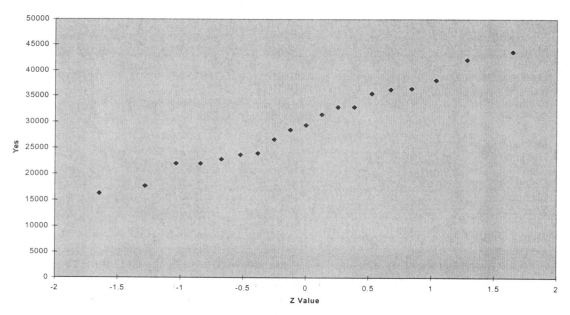

Normal Probability Plot of Attendance (With Promotion)

Assuming that the hourly rates are normally distributed for both the part-time and full-time consultants, we can perform an F-test on the difference in two variances.

10.94 $H_0 : \sigma_I^2 = \sigma_{II}^2$ Variance of hourly rates are the same for part-time and full-time consultants.

cont. $H_1 : \sigma_I^2 \neq \sigma_{II}^2$ Variance of hourly rates are different for part-time and full-time consultants.

PHStat output:

F Test for Differences in Two Variances	
Level of Significance	0.05
Population 1 Sample	
Sample Size	28
Sample Standard Deviation	43
Population 2 Sample	
Sample Size	25
Sample Standard Deviation	58
Intermediate Calculations	
F-Test Statistic	0.549643
Population 1 Sample Degrees of Freedom	27
Population 2 Sample Degrees of Freedom	24
Two-Tailed Test	
Lower Critical Value	0.455666
Upper Critical Value	2.236078
p-Value	0.133788
Do not reject the null hypothesis	

Since the p-value of 0.1337 is greater than the 5% level of significance, do not reject the null hypothesis. There is not enough evidence to conclude that the variances are different. Hence, the pooled-variance t test can be used.

$H_0 : \mu_I = \mu_{II}$ Mean hourly rates of part-time and full-time consultants are the same.

$H_1 : \mu_I \neq \mu_{II}$ Mean hourly rates of part-time and full-time consultants are different.

PHStat output:

t Test for Differences in Two Means	
Hypothesized Difference	0
Level of Significance	0.05
Population 1 Sample	
Sample Size	28
Sample Mean	79
Sample Standard Deviation	43
Population 2 Sample	
Sample Size	25
Sample Mean	102
Sample Standard Deviation	58
Intermediate Calculations	
Population 1 Sample Degrees of Freedom	27
Population 2 Sample Degrees of Freedom	24
Total Degrees of Freedom	51
hPooled Variance	2561.941
Difference in Sample Means	-23
t-Test Statistic	-1.65141
Two-Tailed Test	
Lower Critical Value	-2.00758
Upper Critical Value	2.007582
p-Value	0.1048
Do not reject the null hypothesis	

10.94   Since the *p*-value of 0.1048 is greater than the 5% level of significance, do not reject the null
cont.   hypothesis. There is insufficient evidence to conclude that the hourly rates are different
between part-time and full-time consultants.

Consultants in Canada
Assuming that the hourly rates are normally distributed for both the part-time and full-time
consultants, we can perform an F-test on the difference in two variances.

$H_0 : \sigma_I^2 = \sigma_{II}^2$ Variance of hourly rates are the same for part-time and full-time consultants.

$H_1 : \sigma_I^2 \neq \sigma_{II}^2$ Variance of hourly rates are different for part-time and full-time consultants.

PHStat output:

F Test for Differences in Two Variances	
Level of Significance	0.05
Population 1 Sample	
Sample Size	12
Sample Standard Deviation	28
Population 2 Sample	
Sample Size	15
Sample Standard Deviation	34
Intermediate Calculations	
F-Test Statistic	0.678201
Population 1 Sample Degrees of Freedom	11
Population 2 Sample Degrees of Freedom	14
Two-Tailed Test	
Lower Critical Value	0.297725
Upper Critical Value	3.094584
p-Value	0.523581
Do not reject the null hypothesis	

Since the *p*-value of 0.5236 is greater than the 5% level of significance, do not reject the null
hypothesis. There is not enough evidence to conclude that the variances are different.
Hence, the pooled-variance *t* test can be used.

$H_0 : \mu_I = \mu_{II}$ Mean hourly rates of part-time and full-time consultants are the
same.

$H_1 : \mu_I \neq \mu_{II}$ Mean hourly rates of part-time and full-time consultants are
different.

10.94 PHStat output:
cont.

t Test for Differences in Two Means	
Hypothesized Difference	0
Level of Significance	0.05
Population 1 Sample	
Sample Size	12
Sample Mean	53
Sample Standard Deviation	28
Population 2 Sample	
Sample Size	15
Sample Mean	76
Sample Standard Deviation	34
Intermediate Calculations	
Population 1 Sample Degrees of Freedom	11
Population 2 Sample Degrees of Freedom	14
Total Degrees of Freedom	25
Pooled Variance	992.32
Difference in Sample Means	-23
t-Test Statistic	-1.8852
Two-Tailed Test	
Lower Critical Value	-2.05954
Upper Critical Value	2.059537
p-Value	0.071078
Do not reject the null hypothesis	

Since the p-value of 0.07108 is greater than the 5% level of significance, do not reject the null hypothesis. There is insufficient evidence to conclude that the hourly rates are different between part-time and full-time consultants.

10.96

Normal Probability Plot

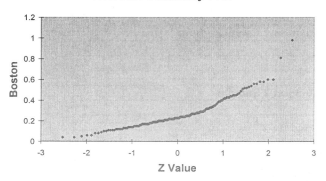

Normal Probability Plot

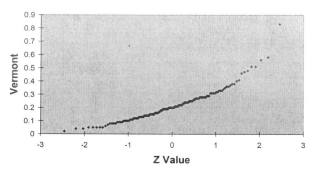

The normal probability plots suggest that the two populations are not normally distributed. An F test is inappropriate for testing the difference in two variances. The sample variances for Boston and Vermont shingles are 0.0203 and 0.015, respectively, which are not very different. It appears that a pooled-variance t test is appropriate for testing the difference in means.

$H_0 : \mu_I = \mu_{II}$ Mean granule loss of Boston and Vermont shingles are the same.

$H_1 : \mu_I \neq \mu_{II}$ Mean granule loss of Boston and Vermont shingles are different.

t-Test: Two-Sample Assuming Equal Variances

	Boston	Vermont
Mean	0.264059	0.218
Variance	0.020273	0.015055
Observations	170	140
Pooled Variance	0.017918	
Hypothesized Mean Difference	0	
df	308	
t Stat	3.014921	
P(T<=t) one-tail	0.001392	
t Critical one-tail	1.649817	
P(T<=t) two-tail	0.002784	
t Critical two-tail	1.967696	

Since the p-value = 0.0028 is less than the 5% level of significance, reject H_0. There is sufficient evidence to conclude that there is a difference in the mean granule loss of Boston and Vermont shingles.

CHAPTER 11

OBJECTIVES

- To understand the concepts of experimental design
- To be able to use the one-way ANOVA procedure to test for differences among the means of several groups
- To understand when to use a randomized block design
- To understand the factorial design and the concept of interaction

OVERVIEW AND KEY CONCEPTS

General Experimental Setting

- Investigators have control over one or more independent variables called treatment variables or factors.
- Each treatment factor has two or more levels.
- Investigators observe the effects on the dependent variable, i.e., the response to the levels of the independent variable(s).
- **Experimental Design:** The plan used to test a hypothesis.

The Completely Randomized Design

- The experimental units (subjects) are assigned randomly to treatments.
- The subjects are assumed to be homogenous.
- There is only one factor or independent variable with two or more treatment levels.
- The completely randomized design will be analyzed by one-way ANOVA.

Some Important Identities in the Completely Randomized Design

- $SST = SSA + SSW$

- $SST = \sum_{j=1}^{c} \sum_{i=1}^{n_j} (X_{ij} - \bar{\bar{X}})^2$

- $SSA = \sum_{j=1}^{c} n_j (\bar{X}_j - \bar{\bar{X}})^2$

- $SSW = \sum_{j=1}^{c} \sum_{i=1}^{n_j} (X_{ij} - \bar{X}_j)^2$

- $MSA = \dfrac{SSA}{c-1}$

- $MSW = \dfrac{SSW}{n-c}$

where n: the total number of observations in the sample

c: the number of groups

n_j: the number of observations in group j

X_{ij} : the ith observation in group j

$$\overline{\overline{X}} = \frac{\displaystyle\sum_{j=1}^{c}\sum_{i=1}^{n_j} X_{ij}}{c} : \text{the overall or grand mean}$$

$\overline{X}_j$: the sample mean of group j

F Test for Differences in More than Two Means

- **Assumptions:**
  - Samples are randomly and independently drawn.
  - Populations are normally distributed. The F test is robust to violation of this assumption.
  - Populations have equal variances. The F test is less sensitive to violation of this assumption when samples are of equal size from each population.
- **The null and alternative hypotheses:**
  - $H_0 : \mu_1 = \mu_2 = \cdots = \mu_c$ There is no treatment effect
  - H_1 : Not all μ_j are the same. There is some treatment effect.
- **Test statistic:**
  - $F = \dfrac{MSA}{MSW}$ with $(c-1)$ numerator degrees of freedom and $(n-c)$ denominator degrees of freedom
  - The F test always has the rejection region in the right tail.

One-way ANOVA Summary Table

Source of Variation	Degrees of Freedom	Sum of Squares	Mean Squares (Variance)	F Statistic
Among (Factor)	$c-1$	SSA	$MSA = SSA/(c-1)$	MSA/MSW
Within (Error)	$n-c$	SSW	$MSW = SSW/(n-c)$	
Total	$n-1$	$SST = SSA + SSW$		

The Tukey-Kramer Procedure for the Completely Randomized Design

- A post hoc (a posteriori) procedure performed after rejection of the null hypothesis of equal means.
- Enables pair-wise comparison to see which pair of means is significantly different.
- **The Tukey-Kramer procedure:**
  1. Compute the absolute difference between any pair of sample means $\left| \bar{X}_j - \bar{X}_{j'} \right|$
  2. Compute the critical range for that pair of sample means using

$$\text{Critical Range} = Q_{U(c,n-c)} \sqrt{\frac{MSW}{2} \left(\frac{1}{n_j} + \frac{1}{n_{j'}} \right)} \text{ where } Q_{U(c,n-c)} \text{ is the upper-tail critical}$$

  value from the Studentized range distribution with c numerator degrees of freedom and $(n-c)$ denominator degrees of freedom, and n_j and $n_{j'}$ are the two sample sizes for the pair of samples.

  3. The population means of a specific pair are declared significantly different if $\left| \bar{X}_j - \bar{X}_{j'} \right|$ is greater than the critical range.

Levene's Test for Homogeneity of Variance

- Used to test the assumption of equal group variances required in the F test for difference in more than two means.
- **The null and alternative hypotheses:**
  - $H_0 : \sigma_1^2 = \sigma_2^2 = \cdots = \sigma_c^2$ All group variances are the same.
  - H_1 : Not all σ_j^2 are the same. Not all group variances are the same.
- **The Levene's test procedure:**
  - For each observation in each group, obtain the absolute value of the difference between each observation and the median of the group.
  - Carry out a one-way analysis of variance on these absolute differences.

The Randomized Block Design

- Items are divided into blocks by matching individual items in different samples or taking repeated measurement of the same individuals to reduce within group variation (i.e. remove the effect of block before testing).
- Response of each treatment group is obtained.
- **Assumptions:**
  - Samples are randomly and independently drawn.
  - Populations are normally distributed. The F test is robust to violation of this assumption.
  - Populations have equal variances. The F test is less sensitive to violation of this assumption when samples are of equal size from each population.
  - There is no interaction between the levels of treatment and block.

Some Important Identities in the Randomized Block Design

- $SST = SSA + SSBL + SSE$

- $SST = \sum_{j=1}^{c} \sum_{i=1}^{r} \left(X_{ij} - \bar{\bar{X}} \right)^2$

- $SSA = r \sum_{j=1}^{c} \left(\bar{X}_{\bullet j} - \bar{\bar{X}} \right)^2$

- $SSBL = c \sum_{i=1}^{r} \left(\bar{X}_{i \bullet} - \bar{\bar{X}} \right)^2$

- $SSE = \sum_{j=1}^{c} \sum_{i=1}^{r} \left(X_{ij} - \bar{X}_{i \bullet} - \bar{X}_{\bullet j} + \bar{\bar{X}} \right)^2$

- $MSA = \dfrac{SSA}{c-1}$

- $MSBL = \dfrac{SSBL}{r-1}$

- $MSE = \dfrac{SSE}{(r-1)(c-1)}$

    where n: total number of observations ($n = rc$)
    r: the number of blocks
    c: the number of groups or levels
    X_{ij} : the value of the ith block for the jth treatment

$$\bar{X}_{i \bullet} = \frac{\sum_{j=1}^{c} X_{ij}}{c} \quad : \text{ the mean of all values in block } i$$

$$\bar{X}_{\bullet j} = \frac{\sum_{i=1}^{r} X_{ij}}{r} : \text{ the mean of all values for treatment level } j$$

$$\bar{\bar{X}} = \frac{\sum_{j=1}^{c} \sum_{i=1}^{r} X_{ij}}{rc} : \text{ the overall or grand mean}$$

The Randomized Block F Test for Differences in c Means

- **The null and alternative hypotheses:**
    - $H_0 : \mu_{\bullet 1} = \mu_{\bullet 2} = \cdots = \mu_{\bullet c}$ No treatment effect
    - H_1 : Not all $\mu_{\bullet j}$ are equal   There is some treatment effect

- **Test statistic:**
    - $F = \dfrac{MSA}{MSE}$ with $(c-1)$ numerator degrees of freedom and $(r-1)(c-1)$
    denominator degrees of freedom.
    - The rejection region is always in the right tail.

The Randomized Block F Test for Block Effect

- **The null and alternative hypotheses:**
    - $H_0 : \mu_{1.} = \mu_{2.} = \cdots = \mu_{r.}$ There is no block effect
    - $H_1 :$ Not all $\mu_{i.}$ are equal   There is some block effect
- **Test statistic:**
    - $F = \dfrac{MSBL}{MSE}$ with $(r-1)$ numerator degrees of freedom and $(r-1)(c-1)$ denominator degrees of freedom.
    - The rejection region is always in the right tail.

ANOVA Table for the Randomized Block Design

Source of Variation	Degrees of Freedom	Sum of Squares	Mean Squares	F Statistic
Among Treatment	$c-1$	SSA	MSA = SSA/(c − 1)	MSA/ MSE
Among Block	$r-1$	SSBL	MSBL = SSBL/(r − 1)	MSBL/ MSE
Error	$(r-1) \cdot (c-1)$	SSE	MSE = SSE/[(r − 1)•(c− 1)]	
Total	$rc-1$	SST		

The Tukey-Kramer Procedure for the Randomized Block Design

- Similar to the Tukey-Kramer procedure for the completely randomized design except the critical range $= Q_{U(c,(r-1)(c-1))} \sqrt{\dfrac{MSE}{r}}$, in which $Q_{U(c,(r-1)(c-1))}$ has c degrees of freedom in the numerator and $(r-1)(c-1)$ degrees of freedom in the denominator.

The Two-Factor Factorial Design

- There is one dependent variable and two treatment factors.
- There can be interaction between the two treatment factors.
- **Assumptions:**
    - Populations are normally distributed.
    - Populations have equal variances.
    - Samples are drawn independently and randomly.

Some Important Identities in the Two-Factor Factorial Design

- $SST = SSA + SSB + SSAB + SSE$

- $SST = \sum\limits_{i=1}^{r}\sum\limits_{j=1}^{c}\sum\limits_{k=1}^{n'}\left(X_{ijk} - \bar{\bar{X}}\right)^2$

- $SSA = cn'\sum\limits_{i=1}^{r}\left(\bar{X}_{i\cdot\cdot} - \bar{\bar{X}}\right)^2$

- $SSB = rn'\sum\limits_{j=1}^{c}\left(\bar{X}_{\cdot j\cdot} - \bar{\bar{X}}\right)^2$

- $SSAB = n'\sum\limits_{i=1}^{r}\sum\limits_{j=1}^{c}\left(\bar{X}_{ij\cdot} - \bar{X}_{i\cdot\cdot} - \bar{X}_{\cdot j\cdot} + \bar{\bar{X}}\right)^2$

- $SSE = \sum\limits_{i=1}^{r}\sum\limits_{j=1}^{c}\sum\limits_{k=1}^{n'}\left(X_{ijk} - \bar{X}_{ij\cdot}\right)^2$

- $MSA = \dfrac{SSA}{r-1}$

- $MSB = \dfrac{SSB}{c-1}$

- $MSAB = \dfrac{SSAB}{(r-1)(c-1)}$

- $MSE = \dfrac{SSE}{rc(n'-1)}$

where n: total number of observations $\left(n = rcn'\right)$

r: the number of level of factor A

c: the number of level of factor B

n' : the number of replication in each cell (combination of a particular level of factor A and a particular level of factor B)

X_{ijk} : the value of the kth observation for level i of factor A and level j of factor B

$$\bar{X}_{i\cdot\cdot} = \frac{\sum\limits_{j=1}^{c}\sum\limits_{k=1}^{n'}X_{ijk}}{cn'} \quad : \text{the mean of the } i^{th} \text{ level of factor } A$$

$$\bar{X}_{\cdot j\cdot} = \frac{\sum\limits_{i=1}^{r}\sum\limits_{k=1}^{n'}X_{ijk}}{rn'} \quad : \text{the mean of the } j^{th} \text{ level of factor } B$$

$$\bar{X}_{ij\cdot} = \sum\limits_{k=1}^{n'}\frac{X_{ijk}}{n'} : \text{mean of the cell } ij, \text{ the combination of the } i^{th} \text{ level of factor } A \text{ and } j^{th}$$

level of factor B

$$\overline{\overline{X}} = \frac{\displaystyle\sum_{j=1}^{c}\sum_{i=1}^{r}\sum_{k=1}^{n'} X_{ijk}}{rcn'} : \text{the overall or grand mean}$$

The Two-Factor Factorial Design F Test for Interaction

- **The null and alternative hypotheses:**
  - H_0 : The interaction of A and B is equal to zero
  - H_1 : The interaction of A and B is not equal to zero
- **Test statistic:**
  - $F = \dfrac{MSAB}{MSE}$ with $(r-1)(c-1)$ numerator degrees of freedom and $rc(n'-1)$ denominator degrees of freedom.
  - The rejection region is always in the right tail.
  - In the two-factor factorial design, the test for interaction should be performed prior to the tests for factor A effect and factor B effect.
  - Only when there is no evidence of interaction will the test and interpretation of the main effect be meaningful.

The Two-Factor Factorial Design F Test for Factor A Effect

- **The null and alternative hypotheses:**
  - $H_0 : \mu_{1..} = \mu_{2..} = \cdots = \mu_{r..}$ There is no factor A treatment effect
  - H_1 : Not all $\mu_{i..}$ are equal   There is some factor A treatment effect
- **Test statistic:**
  - $F = \dfrac{MSA}{MSE}$ with $(r-1)$ numerator degrees of freedom and $rc(n'-1)$ denominator degrees of freedom.
  - The rejection region is always in the right tail.
  - This main effect test should be performed only after the test for interaction has concluded that there is insufficient evidence of interaction between factor A and B.

The Two-Factor Factorial Design F Test for Factor B Effect

- **The null and alternative hypotheses:**
  - $H_0 : \mu_{.1.} = \mu_{.2.} = \cdots = \mu_{.c.}$ There is no factor B treatment effect
  - H_1 : Not all $\mu_{.j.}$ are equal   There is some factor B treatment effect
- **Test statistic:**
  - $F = \dfrac{MSB}{MSE}$ with $(c-1)$ numerator degrees of freedom and $rc(n'-1)$ denominator degrees of freedom.
  - The rejection region is always in the right tail.
  - This main effect test should be performed only after the test for interaction has concluded that there is insufficient evidence of interaction between factor A and B.

ANOVA Table for the Two-Factor Factorial Design

Source of Variation	Degrees of Freedom	Sum of Squares	Mean Squares	F Statistic
Factor A (Row)	$r - 1$	SSA	$MSA = SSA/(r - 1)$	MSA/MSE
Factor B (Column)	$c - 1$	SSB	$MSB = SSB/(c - 1)$	MSB/MSE
AB (Interaction)	$(r - 1)(c - 1)$	$SSAB$	$MSAB = SSAB/[(r - 1)(c - 1)]$	$MSAB/MSE$
Error	$r \cdot c \cdot (n' - 1)$	SSE	$MSE = SSE/[r \cdot c \cdot (n' - 1)]$	
Total	$r \cdot c \cdot n' - 1$	SST		

The Tukey-Kramer Procedure for the Two-Factor Factorial Design

- **For factor A:** Similar to the Tukey-Kramer procedure for the completely randomized design except the critical range $= Q_{U(r, rc(n'-1))} \sqrt{\dfrac{MSE}{rn'}}$, in which $Q_{U(r, rc(n'-1))}$ has $= r$ degrees of freedom in the numerator and $rc(n' - 1)$ degrees of freedom in the denominator.

- **For factor B:** Similar to the Tukey-Kramer procedure for the completely randomized design except the critical range $= Q_{U(c, rc(n'-1))} \sqrt{\dfrac{MSE}{rn'}}$, in which $Q_{U(c, rc(n'-1))}$ has $= c$ degrees of freedom in the numerator and $rc(n' - 1)$ degrees of freedom in the denominator.

- These multiple comparisons should be performed only after the test for interaction has concluded that there is insufficient evidence of interaction between factor A and B.

The Kruskal-Wallis Rank Test for Differences in c Medians

- It is used to analyze the completely randomized design.
- This is an extension of Wilcoxon rank sum test for difference in two medians.
- It is a distribution free test procedure without any distribution assumption on the population.
- **The null and alternative hypotheses:**
  - $H_0 : M_1 = M_2 = \cdots = M_c$
  - H_1 : Not all M_j are the same.
- **Assumptions:**
  - Samples are randomly and independently drawn.
  - The dependent variable is a continuous variable.
  - Data may be ranked both within and among samples.
  - Each sample group size is greater than five.
  - The populations have the same variation and shape.
  - The test is robust to the same variation and shape assumption.

- **The Kruskal-Wallis rank test procedure:**
  1. Obtain the ranks of the observations.
  2. Add the ranks for each of the c groups.
  3. Compute the H statistic: $H = \left[\dfrac{12}{n(n+1)} \displaystyle\sum_{j=1}^{c} \dfrac{T_j^2}{n_j} \right] - 3(n+1)$ where $n = n_1 + n_2 + \cdots + n_c$.
  4. The distribution of the H test statistic can be approximated by a χ^2 distribution with $(c-1)$ degrees of freedom if each sample group size is greater than 5
  5. The rejection region is in the right tail.

Friedman Rank Test for Differences in c Medians

- It is used to analyze a randomized block design.
- It is a distribution free test procedure without any distribution assumption on the population.
- It can be used when the data collected are only in rank form within each block.
- **The null and alternative hypotheses:**
  - $H_0 : M_{.1} = M_{.2} = \cdots = M_{.c}$
  - H_1 : Not all $M_{.j}$ are the same.

- **Assumptions:**
  - The r blocks are independent.
  - The underlying random variable of interest is continuous.
  - The observed data constitute at least an ordinal scale of measurement within each of the r blocks.
  - There is no interaction between the r blocks and the c treatment levels.
  - The c populations have the same variability.
  - The c populations have the same shape.
- **The Friedman rank test procedure:**
  1. In each of the r independent blocks, the c observations are replaced by their corresponding ranks such that rank 1 is given to the smallest observation in the block and rank c to the largest. If any values in a block are tied, they are assigned the average of the ranks that they would otherwise have been given.
  2. **Test statistic:** $F_R = \dfrac{12}{rc(c+1)} \displaystyle\sum_{j=1}^{c} R_{.j}^2 - 3r(c+1)$

     where $R_{.j}^2$ is the square of the rank total for group j ($j = 1, 2, \ldots, c$)
     > r is the number of independent blocks
     > c is the number of groups or treatment levels
  3. F_R can be approximated by the chi-square distribution with $(c-1)$ degrees of freedom when $r > 5$.
  4. The rejection region is in the right tail.

SOLUTIONS TO END OF SECTION AND CHAPTER REVIEW EVEN PROBLEMS

11.2   (a) $SSW = SST - SSA = 210 - 60 = 150$

        (b) $MSA = \dfrac{SSA}{c-1} = \dfrac{60}{5-1} = 15$

        (c) $MSW = \dfrac{SSW}{n-c} = \dfrac{150}{35-5} = 5$

        (d) $F = \dfrac{MSA}{MSW} = \dfrac{15}{5} = 3$

11.4   (a) $df\ A = c - 1 = 3 - 1 = 2$

        (b) $df\ W = n - c = 21 - 3 = 18$

        (c) $df\ T = n - 1 = 21 - 1 = 20$

11.6   (a)-(b)   Decision rule: If $F > 2.95$, reject H_0.

        (c)   Decision: Since $F_{calc} = 4.00$ is above the critical bound of $F = 2.95$, reject H_0. There is enough evidence to conclude that the four group means are not all the same.

        (d)   To perform the Tukey-Kramer procedure, we use $c = 4$ degrees of freedom in the numerator and $n - c = 32 - 4 = 28$ degrees of freedom in the denominator.

        (e)   Since Table E.7 does not contain a value for 4 and 28 degrees of freedom, we will use the next larger (and more conservative) value for 4 and 24 degrees of freedom as an upper bound. That value is 3.90.

        (f)   critical range $= Q_{U(c,\,n-c)} \cdot \sqrt{\dfrac{MSW}{2} \cdot \left(\dfrac{1}{n_j} + \dfrac{1}{n_{j'}} \right)} = 3.90 \cdot \sqrt{\dfrac{20}{2} \cdot \left(\dfrac{1}{8} + \dfrac{1}{8} \right)} = 6.166$

11.8   (a) $H_0 : \mu_1 = \mu_2 = \mu_3$ where 1 = Experts, 2 = Readers, 3 = Darts

            $H_1 :$ Not all μ_j are equal   where $j = 1, 2, 3$

            Decision Rule: If p-value < 0.05, reject H_0.

            SPSS output:

	Sum of Squares	df	Mean Square	F	Sig.
Between Groups	9195.435	2	4597.718	10.994	.004
Within Groups	3763.928	9	418.214		
Total	12959.363	11			

Since p-value $= 0.003835 > 0.05$, reject the null hypothesis. There is enough evidence to conclude that there is a significant difference in the average returns for the three categories.

11.8 (b)
cont.

To determine which of the means are significantly different from one another, we use

the Tukey-Kramer procedure to establish the critical range: $Q_{U(c,\,n-c)} = Q_{U(3,\,9)} = 3.95$

SPSS output

Multiple Comparisons

Dependent Variable: RETURNS

Tukey HSD

(I) FACTOR	(J) FACTOR	Mean Difference (I-J)	Std. Error	Sig.	95% Confidence Interval	
					Lower Bound	Upper Bound
1.00	2.00	48.9750	14.4605	.020	8.6008	89.3492
	3.00	-16.1250	14.4605	.529	-56.4992	24.2492
2.00	1.00	-48.9750	14.4605	.020	-89.3492	-8.6008
	3.00	-65.1000	14.4605	.004	-105.4742	-24.7258
3.00	1.00	16.1250	14.4605	.529	-24.2492	56.4992
	2.00	65.1000	14.4605	.004	24.7258	105.4742

* The mean difference is significant at the .05 level.

At 5% level of significance, the Tukey Kramer multiple comparison test shows that there is enough evidence to conclude that Experts and Readers, and Readers and Darts differ in average return.

(c) The data collected are the returns of the selected stocks by the 3 categories not the amount of drops compared to the previous returns of the stocks. Even if average returns are concerned, the experts have the sample average return of 6.475% while the readers have a sample average return of –42.5%, and the stocks chosen using the darts have a sample average return of 22.6%. However, these differences in sample averages do not lead to the conclusion of significant differences between the Expert and Darts in population averages according to the result of the Tukey-Kramer multiple comparison procedure in part (b).

(d) $H_0: \sigma_1^2 = \sigma_2^2 = \sigma_3^2$ H_1: At least one variance is different.

Minitab output for Levene's test for homogeneity of variance:

Test of Homogeneity of Variances

Levene's Test (any continuous distribution)

Test Statistic: 0.101
P-Value   : 0.905

Since the p-value = 0.905 > 0.05, do not reject H_0. There is not enough evidence of a significant difference in the variation in the return for the three categories.

11.10   (a) H_0: $\mu_A = \mu_B = \mu_C = \mu_D$ H_1: At least one mean is different.

ANOVA

Source of Variation	SS	df	MS	F	P-value	F crit
Between Groups	1986.475	3	662.1583	48.10838	1.12E-12	2.866265
Within Groups	495.5	36	13.76389			
Total	2481.975	39				

Since the p-value is essentially zero, we can reject H_0. There is sufficient evidence of a difference in the average strength of the four brands of trash bags.

(b)

Tukey Kramer Multiple Comparisons

Group	Sample Mean	Sample Size	Comparison	Absolute Difference	Std. Error of Difference	Critical Range	Results
1	35.4	10	Group 1 to Group 2	0.9	1.17319601	4.446	Means are not differe
2	36.3	10	Group 1 to Group 3	0.5	1.17319601	4.446	Means are not differe
3	34.9	10	Group 1 to Group 4	16.1	1.17319601	4.446	Means are different
4	19.3	10	Group 2 to Group 3	1.4	1.17319601	4.446	Means are not differe
			Group 2 to Group 4	17	1.17319601	4.446	Means are different
Other Data			Group 3 to Group 4	15.6	1.17319601	4.446	Means are different
Level of significance	0.05						
Numerator d.f.	4						
Denominator d.f.	36						
MSW	13.76389						
Q Statistic	3.79						

From the Tukey-Kramer procedure, there is a difference in average strength between Kroger and Tuffstuff, Glad and Tuffstuff, and Hefty and Tuffstuff.

(c) H_0: $\sigma_A^2 = \sigma_B^2 = \sigma_C^2 = \sigma_D^2$ H_1: At least one variance is different.

ANOVA output for Levene's test for homogeneity of variance:

ANOVA

Source of Variation	SS	df	MS	F	P-value	F crit
Between Groups	24.075	3	8.025	1.457619	0.242358	2.86626
Within Groups	198.2	36	5.505556			
Total	222.275	39				

Since the p-value = 0.2423 > 0.05, do not reject H_0. There is not sufficient evidence to conclude that the variances in strength among the four brands of trash bags are different.

(d)   From the results obtained in (a) and (b), Tuffstuff has the lowest average strength and should be avoided.

1.12 (a) $H_0: \mu_A = \mu_B = \mu_C = \mu_D = \mu_E$ H_1: At least one mean is different.

ANOVA

Source of Variation	SS	df	MS	F	P-value	F crit
Between Groups	377.8667	4	94.46667	12.56206	9.74E-06	2.758711
Within Groups	188	25	7.52			
Total	565.8667	29				

Since the p-value is essentially zero, reject H_0. There is evidence of a difference in the average rating of the five advertisements.

(b)

Tukey Kramer Multiple Comparisons							
Group	Sample Mean	Sample Size	Comparison	Absolute Difference	Std. Error of Difference	Critical Range	Results
1	18	6	Group 1 to Group 2	0.333333	1.11952371	4.668	Means are not different
2	17.66667	6	Group 1 to Group 3	6.666667	1.11952371	4.668	Means are different
3	11.33333	6	Group 1 to Group 4	9	1.11952371	4.668	Means are different
4	9	6	Group 1 to Group 5	2.666667	1.11952371	4.668	Means are not different
5	15.33333	6	Group 2 to Group 3	6.333333	1.11952371	4.668	Means are different
			Group 2 to Group 4	8.666667	1.11952371	4.668	Means are different
Other Data			Group 2 to Group 5	2.333333	1.11952371	4.668	Means are not different
Level of significance	0.05		Group 3 to Group 4	2.333333	1.11952371	4.668	Means are not different
Numerator d.f.	5		Group 3 to Group 5	4	1.11952371	4.668	Means are not different
Denominator d.f.	25		Group 4 to Group 5	6.333333	1.11952371	4.668	Means are different
MSW	7.52						
Q Statistic	4.17						

There is a difference in the average rating between advertisement A and C, between A and D, between B and C, between B and D and between D and E.

(c) $H_0: \sigma_A^2 = \sigma_B^2 = \sigma_C^2 = \sigma_D^2 = \sigma_E^2$ H_1: At least one variance is different.

ANOVA output for Levene's test for homogeneity of variance:

ANOVA

Source of Variation	SS	df	MS	F	P-value	F crit
Between Groups	14.13333	4	3.533333	1.927273	0.137107	2.758711
Within Groups	45.83333	25	1.833333			
Total	59.96667	29				

Since the p-value = 0.137 > 0.05, do not reject H_0. There is no evidence of a difference in the variation in rating among the five advertisements.

(d)   There is no significant difference between advertisement A and B, and they have the highest average rating among the five and should be used. There is no significant difference between advertisement C and D, and they are among the lowest in average rating and should be avoided.

11.14 (a)   To test at the 0.05 level of significance whether there is any evidence of a difference in the average distance traveled by the golf balls differing in design, we conduct an F test:

H_0: $\mu_1 = \mu_2 = \mu_3 = \mu_4$ H_1: At least one mean is different.

Decision rule: df: 3, 36. If $F > 2.866$, reject H_0.

ANOVA

Source of Variation	SS	df	MS	F	P-value	F crit
Between Groups	2990.99	3	996.9966	53.02982	2.73E-13	2.866265
Within Groups	676.8244	36	18.80068			
Total	3667.814	39				

Since $F_{calc} = 53.03$ is above the critical bound of $F = 2.866$, reject H_0. There is enough evidence to conclude that there is significant difference in the average distance traveled by the golf balls differing in design.

(b)   To determine which of the means are significantly different from one another, we use the Tukey-Kramer procedure to establish the critical range:

$Q_{U(c, n-c)} = Q_{U(4, 36)}$. We use $Q_{U(4, 40)} = 3.79$

$$\text{critical range} \quad = Q_{U(c,n-c)} \cdot \sqrt{\frac{MSW}{2} \cdot \left(\frac{1}{n_j} + \frac{1}{n_{j'}}\right)} = 3.79 \cdot \sqrt{\frac{18.8007}{2} \cdot \left(\frac{1}{10} + \frac{1}{10}\right)} =$$

5.1967

Tukey Kramer Multiple Comparisons					
Group	Sample Mean	Sample Size	Comparison	Absolute Difference	Results
1	206.614	10	Group 1 to Group 2	11.902	Means are different
2	218.516	10	Group 1 to Group 3	19.974	Means are different
3	226.588	10	Group 1 to Group 4	22.008	Means are different
4	228.622	10	Group 2 to Group 3	8.072	Means are different
			Group 2 to Group 4	10.106	Means are different
MSW	18.800677		Group 3 to Group 4	2.034	Means are not different

At 5% level of significance, there is enough evidence to conclude that average traveling distances between all pairs of designs are different with the only exception of the pair between design 3 and design 4.

(c)   The assumptions needed in (a) are (i) samples are randomly and independently drawn, (ii) populations are normally distributed, and (iii) populations have equal variances.

11.14 (d)
cont.

To test at the 0.05 level of significance whether the variation within the groups is similar for all groups, we conduct a Levene's test for homogeneity of variance:

H_0: $\sigma_1^2 = \sigma_2^2 = \sigma_3^2 = \sigma_4^2$ H_1: At least one variance is different.

ANOVA

Source of Variation	SS	df	MS	F	P-value	F crit
Between Groups	40.63675	3	13.54558	2.093228	0.118276	2.866265
Within Groups	232.9613	36	6.471147			
Total	273.598	39				

Since p-value = 0.1182 > 0.05, do not reject the null hypothesis. There is not enough evidence to conclude that there is any difference in the variation of the distance traveled by the golf balls differing in design.

(e)   In order to produce golf balls with the furthest traveling distance, either design 3 or 4 can be used.

11.16 (a) $SSE = SST - SSA - SSBL = 210 - 60 - 75 = 75$

(b) $MSA = \dfrac{SSA}{c-1} = \dfrac{60}{4} = 15$

(c) $MSBL = \dfrac{SSBL}{r-1} = \dfrac{75}{6} = 12.5$

(d) $MSE = \dfrac{SSE}{(r-1)\cdot(c-1)} = \dfrac{75}{6\cdot 4} = 3.125$

(e) $F = \dfrac{MSA}{MSE} = \dfrac{15}{3.125} = 4.80$

(f) $F = \dfrac{MSBL}{MSE} = \dfrac{12.5}{3.125} = 4.00$

11.18 (a)-(b) $Q_{U[c,\,(r-1)(c-1)]} = Q_{U(5,\,24)} = 4.17$

(c)   critical range $= Q_{U[c,\,(r-1)(c-1)]} \cdot \sqrt{\dfrac{MSE}{r}} = 4.17 \cdot \sqrt{\dfrac{3.125}{7}} = 2.786$

11.20 (a) $MSE = \dfrac{MSA}{F} = \dfrac{18}{6} = 3$

(b) $SSE = (MSE)(df\,E) = (3)(12) = 36$

(c) $SSBL = (F)(MSE)(df\,BL) = (4)(3)(6) = 72$

(d) $SST = SSA + SSBL + SSE = 36 + 72 + 36 = 144$

(e)   Since $F = 6 < F_{0.01,2,12} = 6.9266$, do not reject the null hypothesis of no treatment effect.

(f)   Since $F = 4.0 < F_{0.01,6,12} = 4.821$, do not reject the null hypothesis of no block effect.

11.22 (a)-(b) Decision rule: If $F > 3.07$, reject H_0.

(c)   Decision: Since $F_{calc} = 5.185$ is above the critical bound $F = 3.07$, reject H_0. There is enough evidence to conclude that the treatment means are not all equal.

(d)-(e) Decision rule: If $F > 2.49$, reject H_0.

(f)   Decision: Since $F_{calc} = 5.000$ is above the critical bound $F = 2.49$, reject H_0. There is enough evidence to conclude that the block means are not all equal.

11.24   (a) $H_0: \mu_A = \mu_B = \mu_C = \mu_D$ where A = Bazooka, B = Bubbletape, C =
Babblevum, D = Bubblicious
H_1: At least one mean differs.

ANOVA

Source of Variation	SS	df	MS	F	P-value	F crit
Rows (students)	9.28125	3	3.09375	1.072202	0.408518	3.862539
Columns (brands)	16.625	3	5.541667	1.920578	0.196803	3.862539
Error	25.96875	9	2.885417			
Total	51.875	15				

$F = 1.9206$. Since the p-value $= 0.1968 > 0.05$, do not reject H_0. There is no
evidence of a difference in the mean diameter of the bubbles produced by the
different brands.

(b)   It is inappropriate to perform the Tukey procedure.

(c) $H_0: \mu_A = \mu_B = \mu_C = \mu_D$ where A = Kyle, B = Sarah, C = Leigh, D = Isaac
H_1: At least one mean differs.
$F = 1.0722$. Since the p-value $= 0.4084 > 0.05$, do not reject H_0. There is no
evidence of difference in the mean diameter of the bubbles across the different
students. Hence, there is no significant block effect in this experiment.

(d)   From the conclusion in (c), there is not sufficient evidence to conclude that Kyle is
the best at blowing big bubbles.

11.26   To test at the 0.05 level of significance whether there is any difference in the average
thickness of the wafers for the five positions, we conduct an F test:
$H_0: \mu_1 = \mu_2 = \mu_3 = \mu_4 = \mu_5$ where 1 = position 1, 2 = position 2, 3 = position 18,
4 = position 19, 5 = position 28

H_1: At least one mean is different.
Decision rule: df: 4, 116. If $F > 3.4852$, reject H_0.

ANOVA

Source of Variation	SS	df	MS	F	P-value	F crit
Rows	601.5	29	20.74138	5.922219	1.93E-12	1.878497
Columns	1417.733	4	354.4333	101.2002	6.84E-37	3.485212
Error	406.2667	116	3.502299			
Total	2425.5	149				

Test statistic: $F = 101.2$

Decision: Since $F_{calc} = 101.2$ is above the critical bound of $F = 3.4852$, reject H_0. There is
enough evidence to conclude that the average thickness of the wafers are different across the
five positions.

To determine which of the means are significantly different from one another, we use the
Tukey-Kramer procedure to establish the critical range:
$Q_{U(c,(r-1)(c-1))} = Q_{U(5,\,116)} = 4.71$

critical range $= Q_{U(c,(r-1)(c-1))} \cdot \sqrt{\dfrac{MSE}{r}} = 4.71 \cdot \sqrt{\dfrac{3.5023}{30}} = 1.609$

11.26
cont. $|\overline{X}_1 - \overline{X}_2| = 2.2*$ $|\overline{X}_1 - \overline{X}_3| = 5.533*$ $|\overline{X}_1 - \overline{X}_4| = 8.567*$

$|\overline{X}_1 - \overline{X}_5| = 6.533*$ $|\overline{X}_2 - \overline{X}_3| = 3.333*$ $|\overline{X}_2 - \overline{X}_4| = 6.367*$

$|\overline{X}_2 - \overline{X}_5| = 4.333*$ $|\overline{X}_3 - \overline{X}_4| = 3.033*$ $|\overline{X}_3 - \overline{X}_5| = 1$

$|\overline{X}_4 - \overline{X}_5| = 2.033*$

At 1% level of significance, the F test concludes that there are significant differences in the average thickness of the wafers among the 5 positions. The Tukey-Kramer multiple comparison test reveals that the average thickness between all the pairs are significantly different with the only exception of the pair between position 18 and position 28.

11.28 (a) $df\ A = r - 1 = 3 - 1 = 2$
   (b) $df\ B = c - 1 = 3 - 1 = 2$
   (c) $df\ AB = (r - 1)(c - 1) = (3 - 1)(3 - 1) = 4$
   (d) $df\ E = rc(n' - 1) = 3 \times 3 \times (4 - 1) = 27$
   (e) $df\ T = n - 1 = 35$

11.30 (a) $F_{(2, 27)} = 3.35$ (b) $F_{(2, 27)} = 3.35$ (c) $F_{(4, 27)} = 2.73$
   (d)   Decision: Since $F_{calc} = 1.00$ is below the critical bound of $F = 2.73$, do not reject H_0. There is insufficient evidence to conclude there is an interaction effect.
   (e)   Decision: Since $F_{calc} = 6.00$ is above the critical bound of $F = 3.35$, reject H_0. There is evidence of a difference among factor A means.
   (f)   Decision: Since $F_{calc} = 5.50$ is above the critical bound of $F = 3.35$, reject H_0. There is evidence of a difference among factor B means.

11.32

Source	df	SS	MS	F
Factor A	2	$2 \times 80 = 160$	80	$80 \div 5 = 16.00$
Factor B	$8 \div 2 = 4$	220	$220 \div 4 = 55$	11.00
Interaction, AB	8	$8 \times 10 = 80$	10	$10 \div 5 = 2.00$
Error, E	30	$30 \times 5 = 150$	$55 \div 11 = 5$	
Total, T	44	$160+220+80+150 = 610$		

11.34 Two-way ANOVA output from Excel:

ANOVA

Source of Variation	SS	df	MS	F	P-value	F crit
Sample	52.5625	1	52.5625	23.57944	0.000394	4.747221
Columns	1.5625	1	1.5625	0.700935	0.418832	4.747221
Interaction	3.0625	1	3.0625	1.373832	0.2639	4.747221
Within	26.75	12	2.229167			
Total	83.9375	15				

   (a) H_0: There is no interaction between development time and developer strength.
   H_1: There is an interaction between development time and developer strength.
   Decision rule: If $F > 4.747$, reject H_0.   Test statistic: $F = 1.374$.

Decision: Since $F_{calc} = 1.374$ is below the critical bound of $F = 4.747$, do not reject H_0. There is insufficient evidence to conclude that there is any interaction between development time and developer strength.

11.34   (b) H_0: $\mu_1 = \mu_2$ H_1: The two means differ.
cont.
Decision rule: If $F > 4.747$, reject H_0.   Test statistic: $F = 23.58$.
Decision: Since $F_{calc} = 23.58$ is above the critical bound of $F = 4.747$, reject H_0. There is sufficient evidence to conclude that developer strength affects the density of the photographic plate film.

(c) H_0: $\mu_{10} = \mu_{14}$ H_1: The two means differ.
Decision rule: If $F > 4.747$, reject H_0.   Test statistic: $F = 0.701$.
Decision: Since $F_{calc} = 0.701$ is below the critical bound of $F = 4.747$, do not reject H_0. There is inadequate evidence to conclude that development time affects the density of the photographic plate film.

(d)

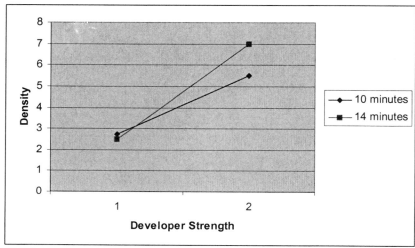

(e)   At 5% level of significance, developer strength has a positive effect on the density of the photographic plate film while the developer time does not have any impact on the density. There is no significant interaction between developer time and developer strength on the density.

11.36   Two-way ANOVA output from Excel:

Source of Variation	SS	df	MS	F	P-value	F crit
Sample	24274.85	1	24274.85	1986.507	7.07E-20	4.413863
Columns	356.0027	2	178.0014	14.56656	0.000173	3.554561
Interaction	506.3104	2	253.1552	20.7167	2.14E-05	3.554561
Within	219.9576	18	12.21986			
Total	25357.12	23				

(a) H_0: There is no interaction between brand and water temperature.
H_1: There is an interaction between brand and water temperature.
Since $F = 20.7167 > 3.554$ or the p-value $= 2.14E-05 < 0.05$, reject H_0. There is evidence of interaction between brand of pain-reliever and temperature of the water.

(b)   Since there is interaction between brand and the temperature of the water, it is inappropriate to analyze the main effect due to brand.

(c)   Since there is interaction between brand and the temperature of the water, it is inappropriate to analyze the main effect due to water temperature.

11.36   (d)
cont.

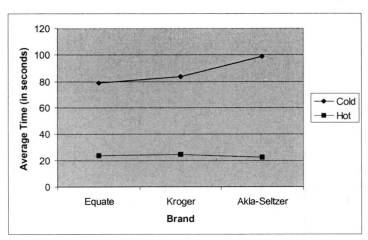

(e)   The difference in the average time a tablet took to dissolve in cold and hot water depends on the brand with Alka-Seltzer having the largest difference and equate with the smallest difference.

11.38   Excel output:

ANOVA

Source of Variation	SS	df	MS	F	P-value	F crit
Sample	0.632813	1	0.632813	0.018939	0.891528	4.195982
Columns	1519.383	1	1519.383	45.47136	2.54E-07	4.195982
Interaction	14.44531	1	14.44531	0.432312	0.516226	4.195982
Within	935.5938	28	33.41406			
Total	2470.055	31				

(a) H_0: There is no interaction between part positioning and tooth size.
H_1: There is an interaction between part positioning and tooth size.
Since $F = 0.4323 < 4.1960$ or the p-value $= 0.5162 > 0.05$, do not reject H_0. There is no evidence of interaction between part positioning and tooth size.

(b) $H_0 : \mu_{\text{Low Tooth Size}} = \mu_{\text{High Tooth Size}}$ H_1: means are different
Since $F = 0.0189 < 4.196$ or the p-value $= 0.8915 > 0.05$, do not reject H_0. There is no evidence of an effect that is due to tooth size.

(c) $H_0 : \mu_{\text{Low Positioning}} = \mu_{\text{High Positioning}}$ H_1: means are different
Since $F = 45.47 > 4.196$ or the p-value $= 2.54\text{E-}07 < 0.05$, reject H_0. There is evidence of an effect that is due to positioning.

11.38   (d)
cont.

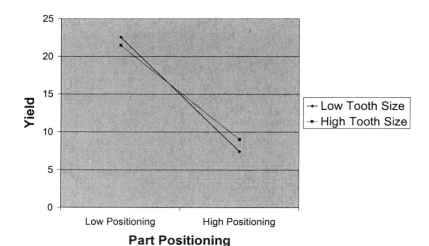

Part Positioning

(e)   There is no evidence of interaction between part positioning and tooth size. There is evidence of an effect due to the part partitioning but not the tooth size.

11.40   (a)   Decision rule: If $H > \chi_U^2 = 15.086$, reject H_0.

(b)   Decision: Since $H_{calc} = 13.77$ is below the critical bound of 15.086, do not reject H_0.

11.42   (a) $H_0: M_{Low} = M_{Normal} = M_{High} = M_{Very\ High}$
H_1: At least one of the medians differs.
Decision rule: If $H > \chi_U^2 = 7.815$, reject H_0.
Test statistic: $H = 11.91$
Decision: Since $H_{calc} = 11.91$ is above the critical bound of 7.815, reject H_0.

(b)   There is sufficient evidence to show there is a significant difference in the four pressure levels with respect to median battery life. The warranty policy should exploit the highest median battery life and explicitly specify that such median battery life level can only be warranted when the batteries are operated under normal pressure level.

Minitab Output

Kruskal-Wallis Test				
LEVEL	NOBS	MEDIAN	AVE. RANK	Z VALUE
Low	5	9.200	14.6	1.79
Norm	5	9.800	15.2	2.05
Hi	5	7.100	7.8	-1.18
V.Hi	5	5.900	4.4	-2.66
OVERALL	20		10.5	
H = 11.91 d.f. = 3 p = 0.008				

11.44   PHStat output:

Kruskal-Wallis Rank Test	
Data	
Level of Significance	**0.05**
Group 1	
Sum of Ranks	254
Sample Size	10
Group 2	
Sum of Ranks	270
Sample Size	10
Group 3	
Sum of Ranks	241
Sample Size	10
Group 4	
Sum of Ranks	55
Sample Size	10
Intermediate Calculations	
Sum of Squared Ranks/Sample Size	19852.2
Sum of Sample Sizes	40
Number of groups	4
H Test Statistic	22.26
Test Result	
Critical Value	**7.814725**
p-Value	**5.76E-05**
Reject the null hypothesis	

(a) H_0: $M_{Kroger} = M_{Glad} = M_{Hefty} = M_{Tuffstuff}$ H_1: At least one of the medians differs.
        Since the p-value is essentially zero, reject H_0. There is sufficient evidence of a
        difference in the median strength of the four brands of trash bags.

(b)   In (a), we conclude that there is evidence of a difference in the median strength of
        the four brands of trash bags while in problem 11.10, we conclude that there is
        evidence of a difference in the mean strength of the four brands.

11.46 $d.f. = 5$, $\alpha = 0.1$, $\chi_U^2 = 9.2363$

11.48   Minitab output:

Friedman Test: Rating versus Brand, Expert

```
Friedman test for Rating by Brand blocked by Expert

S =  20.03   DF = 3   P = 0.000
S =  20.72   DF = 3   P = 0.000 (adjusted for ties)

                    Est      Sum of
Brand        N    Median     Ranks
A            9    25.000      25.0
B            9    26.750      34.5
C            9    24.000      20.0
D            9    22.250      10.5

Grand median  =   24.500
```

(a) $H_0 : M_A = M_B = M_C = M_D$ H_1 : medians are different
        Since the p-value is essentially zero, reject H_0 at 0.05 level of significance. There is
        evidence of a difference in the median summated ratings of the four brands of
        Colombian coffee.

11.48   (b)   In (a), we conclude that there is evidence of a difference in the median summated
cont.   ratings of the four brands of Colombian coffee while in problem 11.23, we conclude
                         that there is evidence of a difference in the mean summated ratings of the four
                         brands of Colombian coffee.

11.50   Minitab output:
Friedman Test: Value versus Agent, House

```
Friedman test for Value by Agent blocked by House

S = 15.29   DF = 2   P = 0.000
S = 15.62   DF = 2   P = 0.000 (adjusted for ties)

                     Est      Sum of
Agent        N     Median     Ranks
1            12    180.56      17.5
2            12    180.78      19.5
3            12    182.84      35.0

Grand median  =    181.39
```

(a) $H_0 : M_1 = M_2 = M_3$ H_1 : medians are different
            Since the p-value is essentially zero, reject H_0 at 0.05 level of significance. There is
            evidence of a difference in the median appraised value for the three agents.

(b)   In (a), we conclude that there is evidence of a difference in the median appraised
            value for the three agents but in problem 11.25, we conclude that there is no
            evidence of a difference in the mean appraised value for the three agents.

11.52   Minitab output:
Friedman Test: Strength versus Days, Samples

```
Friedman test for Strength by Days blocked by Samples

S = 80.00   DF = 2   P = 0.000

                     Est      Sum of
Days         N     Median     Ranks
2            40    3.0863      40.0
7            40    3.5888      80.0
28           40    4.5838     120.0

Grand median  =    3.7529
```

(a) $H_0 : M_2 = M_7 = M_{28}$ H_1 : medians are different
            Since the p-value is essentially zero, reject H_0 at 0.05 level of significance. There is
            evidence of a difference in the median compressive strength after 2, 7 and 28 days.

(b)   In (a), we conclude that there is evidence of a difference in the median compressive
            strength after 2, 7 and 28 days and in problem 11.27, we conclude that there is
            evidence of a difference in the mean compressive strength after 2, 7 and 28 days.

11.54   In a completely randomized design, individual items in different samples are randomly and
            independently drawn. In a randomized block design, individual items in different samples
            are matched using common characteristics or repeated measurements are taken to reduce
            within group variation.

11.56   The major assumptions of ANOVA are randomness and independence, normality, and homogeneity of variance.

11.58   The Kruskal-Wallis test should be used if we cannot assume that the populations are normally distributed.

11.60   When the ANOVA has indicated that that at least one of the groups has a different population mean than the others. In such cases, the Tukey-Kramer procedure should be used to compare all pairs of means.

11.62   The completely randomized design is interested in measuring the existence of treatment effect of the treatment variable on the average level of the dependent variable while the Levene test is interested in testing whether the amount of variations of the dependent variable are the same across the different categories of the treatment variable.

11.64   Interaction measures the difference in the effect of one variable for the different levels of the second factor. If there is no interaction, any difference between levels of one factor will be the same at each level of the second factor.

11.66   (a) H_0: There is no interaction between detergent brand and length of washing cycle.
H_1: There is an interaction between detergent brand and length of washing cycle.
Decision rule: If $F > 2.54$, reject H_0.
Test statistic: $F = 1.49$
Decision: Since $F_{calc} = 1.49$ is below the critical bound of $F = 2.54$, do not reject H_0. There is not enough evidence to conclude that there is an interaction between detergent brand and length of washing cycle.

Minitab Output

Two-way Analysis of Variance

Analysis of Variance for Dirt, Lbs

Source	DF	SS	MS	F	p
Soap	3	0.000413	0.000138	0.7886	0.5178
Cycle	3	0.027338	0.009113	52.0743	0.0000
Interaction	9	0.002337	0.000260	1.4857	0.2346
Error	16	0.002800	0.000175		
Total	31	0.032888			

(b) H_0: $\mu_A = \mu_B = \mu_C = \mu_D$ H_1: At least one mean differs.
Decision rule: If $F > 3.24$, reject H_0.
Test statistic: $F = 0.79$
Decision: Since $F_{calc} = 0.79$ is below the critical bound of $F = 3.24$, do not reject H_0. There is insufficient evidence to conclude that there is any difference in the average amount of dirt removed from standard household laundry loads across the four detergent brands.

11.66   (c) H_0: $\mu_{18} = \mu_{20} = \mu_{22} = \mu_{24}$ H_1: At least one mean differs.
cont.   Decision rule: If $F > 3.24$, reject H_0.
                 Test statistic: $F = 52.07$
                 Decision: Since $F_{calc} = 52.07$ is above the critical bound of $F = 3.24$, reject H_0. There is adequate evidence to conclude the average amount of dirt removed from standard household laundry loads does differ across the four lengths of washing cycle (18, 20, 22, and 24 minutes).

    (d)

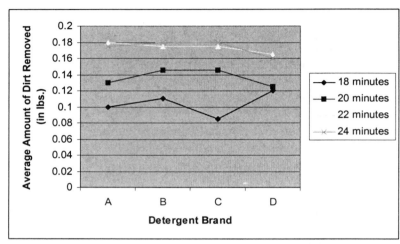

    (e)   The Tukey procedure is used for washing cycle times (F-test was significant) but not for detergent brands (F-test was not significant).
            For different lengths of washing cycle, $Q_{U[c, \ rc(n'-1)]} = Q_{U(4, \ 16)} = 4.05$

$$\text{critical range} = Q_{U[c, \ rc(n'-1)]} \sqrt{\frac{MSE}{rn'}} = 4.05 \sqrt{\frac{0.000175}{8}} = 0.0189$$

            Pairs of means that differ at the 0.05 level are marked with * below.
            $|\overline{X}_{18} - \overline{X}_{20}| = 0.0326*$ $|\overline{X}_{18} - \overline{X}_{22}| = 0.0700*$ $|\overline{X}_{18} - \overline{X}_{24}| = 0.0700*$
            $|\overline{X}_{20} - \overline{X}_{22}| = 0.0374*$ $|\overline{X}_{20} - \overline{X}_{24}| = 0.0374*$ $|\overline{X}_{22} - \overline{X}_{24}| = 0$

    (f)   Washing cycles for 22 and 24 minutes are not different with respect to dirt removal, but both of these cycles are superior to 18- or 20-minute cycles with respect to dirt removal.

11.66 (g)
cont.

Excel Output for the one-factor ANOVA:

ANOVA

Source of Variation	SS	df	MS	F	P-value	F crit
Between Groups	0.027338	3	0.009113	45.97297	6.04E-11	2.946685
Within Groups	0.00555	28	0.000198			
Total	0.032888	31				

H_0: $\mu_{18} = \mu_{20} = \mu_{22} = \mu_{24}$ H_1: At least one mean differs.
Decision rule: If $F > 2.95$, reject H_0.
Test statistic: $F = 45.97$
Decision: Since $F_{calc} = 45.97$ is above the critical bound of $F = 2.95$, reject H_0. There is adequate evidence to conclude the average amount of dirt removed from standard household laundry loads does differ across the four lengths of washing cycle (18, 20, 22, and 24 minutes).
The result is consistent with that in (c) where there is adequate evidence to conclude the average amount of dirt removed from standard household laundry loads does differ across the four lengths of washing cycle.

11.68 Part I
(a)

To test the homogeneity of variance, we perform a Levene's Test
H_0: $\sigma_1^2 = \sigma_2^2 = \sigma_3^2$ H_1: Not all σ_j^2 are the same
Excel output:

ANOVA

Source of Variation	SS	df	MS	F	P-value	F crit
Between Groups	0.07	2	0.035	0.07468	0.928383	3.682317
Within Groups	7.03	15	0.468667			
Total	7.1	17				

Since the p-value = 0.928 > 0.05, do not reject H_0. There is not enough evidence of a significant difference in the variances of the breaking strengths for the three air-jet pressures.

(b) H_0: $\mu_1 = \mu_2 = \mu_3$ H_1: At least one of the means differs.
Decision rule: If $F > 3.68$, reject H_0.
Test statistic: $F = 4.09$
Decision: Since $F_{calc} = 4.09$ is above the critical bound of $F = 3.68$, reject H_0. There is enough evidence to conclude that the average breaking strengths differ for the three air-jet pressures.
Minitab Output

One-Way Analysis of Variance

Analysis of Variance on Strength

Source	DF	SS	MS	F	p
Pressure	2	8.074	4.037	4.09	0.038
Error	15	14.815	0.988		
Total	17	22.889			

11.68   (c) $Q_{(c, n-c)} = Q_{U(3, 15)} = 3.67$

cont.   critical range $= Q_{U(c,\ n-c)} \sqrt{\dfrac{MSW}{2}\left(\dfrac{1}{n_j}+\dfrac{1}{n_{j'}}\right)} = 3.67\sqrt{\dfrac{0.988}{2}\left(\dfrac{1}{6}+\dfrac{1}{6}\right)} = 1.489$

The pair of means that differs at the 0.05 level is marked with * below.

$\left|\overline{X}_{30}-\overline{X}_{40}\right| = 1.30$ $\left|\overline{X}_{30}-\overline{X}_{50}\right| = 1.516*$ $\left|\overline{X}_{40}-\overline{X}_{50}\right| = 0.216$

Breaking strength scores under 30 psi are significantly higher than those under 50 psi.

(d)   Minitab output:

Kruskal-Wallis Test: BreakStr versus Pressure

```
Kruskal-Wallis Test on BreakStr

Pressure    N    Median    Ave Rank         Z
30          6    24.80        13.7       2.34
40          6    23.65         8.3      -0.66
50          6    23.00         6.5      -1.69
Overall    18                  9.5

H = 5.84   DF = 2   P = 0.054
H = 5.85   DF = 2   P = 0.054 (adjusted for ties)
```

$H_0 : M_{30\,psi} = M_{40\,psi} = M_{50\,psi}$ H_1 : medians are different

Since the p-value = 0.054 > 0.05, do not reject H_0. There is no evidence of a difference in median breaking strengths for the three air-jet pressures.

(e)   Other things being equal, use 30 psi.

Part II

(f) H_0: $\mu_1 = \mu_2 = \mu_3$ H_1: At least one of the means differs.

Decision rule: If $F > 4.10$, reject H_0.

Test statistic: $F = 3.7064$

Decision: Since $F_{calc} = 3.7064$ is below the critical bound of $F = 4.10$, do not reject H_0. There is not enough evidence to conclude that the average breaking strengths differ for the three air-jet pressures.

Minitab Output

Two-way Analysis of Variance

Analysis of Variance for Strength

Source	DF	SS	MS	F	p
Pressure	2	8.07	4.04	3.7064	0.0625
Yarn	5	3.90	0.78	0.7156	0.6261
Error	10	10.92	1.09		
Total	17	22.89			

(g)   The Tukey procedure should not be used since the null hypothesis in part (e) above was not rejected.

(h) H_0: $\mu_1 = \mu_2 = \mu_3 = \mu_4 = \mu_5 = \mu_6$ H_1: At least one of the means differs.

Decision rule: If $F > 3.33$, reject H_0.

Test statistic: $F = 0.7156$

Decision: Since $F_{calc} = 0.7156$ is below the critical bound of $F = 3.33$, do not reject H_0. There is not enough evidence to conclude that the average breaking strengths differ for the six yarn samples. There is no evidence of a block effect.

11.68 (i)

$$RE = \frac{(r-1)MSBL + r(c-1)MSE}{(rc-1)MSE} = \frac{5 \cdot (0.78) + 6 \cdot 2 \cdot (1.09)}{17 \cdot (1.09)} = 0.916$$

cont. (j)

Even though there is no evidence of blocking effect from the result in (h), we still perform a Friedman test on the difference in median to see what conclusion can be obtained.

Minitab output:

Friedman Test: BreakStr versus Pressure, YarnNum
```
Friedman test for BreakStr by Pressure blocked by YarnNum

S = 6.58   DF = 2   P = 0.037
S = 6.87   DF = 2   P = 0.032 (adjusted for ties)

                     Est      Sum of
Pressure     N     Median     Ranks
30           6     24.800     17.0
40           6     23.700     10.5
50           6     23.000      8.5

Grand median  =    23.833
```

$H_0 : M_{30\,psi} = M_{40\,psi} = M_{50\,psi}$ $H_1 :$ medians are different

Since the p-value $= 0.037 < 0.05$, do reject H_0. There is evidence of a difference in median breaking strengths for the three air-jet pressures.

(k)

If blocking is not effective, it should be avoided. In this study, there is no evidence of a blocking effect, so the completely randomized design model is superior to the randomized complete block design model. Notice that the relative efficiency measure indicates fewer observations would be needed in the one-way ANOVA design to obtain the same precision for comparison of treatment group means as would be needed for the randomized complete block design.

Part III

(l)

H_0: There is no interaction between side-to-side aspect and air-jet pressure.
H_1: There is an interaction between side-to-side aspect and air-jet pressure.
Decision rule: If $F > 3.89$, reject H_0.
Test statistic: $F = 1.9719$
Decision: Since $F_{calc} = 1.9719$ is below the critical bound of 3.89, do not reject H_0. There is insufficient evidence to conclude there is an interaction between side-to-side aspect and air-jet pressure.

Minitab Output:

Two-way Analysis of Variance

Analysis of Variance for Strength

Source	DF	SS	MS	F	p
Aspect	1	3.467	3.467	4.8694	0.0476
Pressure	2	8.074	4.037	5.6699	0.0185
Interaction	2	2.808	1.404	1.9719	0.1818
Error	12	8.540	0.712		
Total	17	22.889			

11.68 (m)
cont.
H_0: $\mu_1 = \mu_2$ H_1: $\mu_1 \neq \mu_2$
Decision rule: If $F > 4.75$, reject H_0.
Test statistic: $F = 4.8694$
Decision: Since $F_{calc} = 4.8694$ is above the critical bound of 4.75, reject H_0. There is sufficient evidence to conclude that average breaking strength does differ between the tw levels of side-to-side aspect.

(n)
H_0: $\mu_1 = \mu_2 = \mu_3$ H_1: At least one of the means differs.
Decision rule: If $F > 3.89$, reject H_0.
Test statistic: $F = 5.6699$
Decision: Since $F_{calc} = 5.6699$ is above the critical bound of 3.89, reject H_0. There is enough evidence to conclude that the average breaking strengths differ for the three air-jet pressures.

(o)

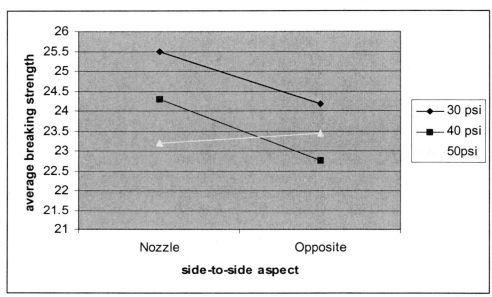

(p)
$Q_{U[c,\ rc(n'-1)]} = Q_{U(3,\ 12)} = 3.77$

critical range $= Q_{U[c,\ rc(n'-1)]} \cdot \sqrt{\dfrac{MSE}{rn'}} = 3.77 \cdot \sqrt{\dfrac{0.712}{2 \cdot 3}} = 1.30$

Pairs of means that differ at the 0.05 level are marked with * below.
$\left|\overline{X}_{30} - \overline{X}_{40}\right| = 1.30^*$ $\left|\overline{X}_{30} - \overline{X}_{50}\right| = 1.51^*$ $\left|\overline{X}_{40} - \overline{X}_{50}\right| = 0.21$

Average breaking strengths under 30 psi are higher than those under 40 psi or 50 psi.

(q) The average breaking strength is highest under 30 psi.

(r) The two-factor experiment gave a more complete, refined set of results than the one-fact experiment. Not only was the side-to-side aspect factor significant, the application of the Tukey procedure on the air-jet pressure factor determined that breaking strength scores are highest under 30 psi.

11.70 (a) H_0: $\mu_1 = ... = \mu_8$

Decision rule: If $F > 2.95$, reject H_0.

Note: Since the F-table does not include a value for 7 and 77 degrees of freedom, use 7 and 60 degrees of freedom.

Test statistic: $F = 7.6862$

Decision: Since $F_{calc} = 7.6862$ is above the critical bound of 2.95, reject H_0. There is sufficient evidence to show a difference in the average rating scores among the wines.

(b) One must assume that the samples of data were obtained randomly and independently, that they were drawn from normally distributed populations, that the population variances are approximately equal, and that there are no interacting effects between the treatments and blocks.

(c) $Q_{U[c,\,(r-1)(c-1)]} = Q_{U(8,\,77)} = 5.25$

$$\text{critical range} = Q_{U[c,(r-1)(c-1)]} \cdot \sqrt{\frac{MSE}{r}} = 5.25 \cdot \sqrt{\frac{8.1840}{12}} = 4.336$$

(c) Pair of means that differ at the 0.01 level are bolded and underlined below.

		Wines						
Wines	Means	2	3	4	5	6	7	8
1	10.42	4.25	0.75	1.09	4.00	2.00	1.41	0.67
2	14.67		3.50	**<u>5.34</u>**	0.25	**<u>6.25</u>**	2.84	**<u>4.92</u>**
3	11.17			1.84	3.25	2.75	0.66	1.42
4	9.33				**<u>5.09</u>**	0.91	2.50	0.42
5	14.42					**<u>6.00</u>**	2.59	**<u>4.67</u>**
6	8.42						3.41	1.33
7	11.83							2.08

11.70   (c)   Minitab output:
cont.

```
Analysis of Variance for Rating
Source   DF    SS      MS      F      p
Expert   11   521.50  47.41  5.7929  0.0000
Wine      7   440.33  62.90  7.6862  0.0000
Error    77   630.17   8.18
Total    95  1592.00

                  Individual 95% CI
 Expert   Mean  ----------+---------+---------+---------+-
    1     11.6                  (-----*-----)
    2      9.9             (-----*-----)
    3     10.8                 (-----*----)
    4     11.8                  (-----*----)
    5     11.5                  (-----*-----)
    6      5.7   (----*-----)
    7      8.7        (-----*-----)
    8     10.3.            (----*-----)
    9     13.0                    (-----*-----)
   10     13.3                    (-----*-----)
   11     14.1                     (----*-----)
   12     14.4                     (-----*-----)
                  ----------+---------+---------+---------+-
                          7.0      10.5     14.0     17.5
                  Individual 95% CI
 Wine    Mean  ---+---------+---------+---------+--------
    1    10.42      (------*-----)
    2    14.67                    (------*-----)
    3    11.17        (------*-----)
    4     9.33    (-----*------)
    5    14.42                   (------*-----)
    6     8.42  (------*-----)
    7    11.83          (-----*------)
    8     9.75     (------*------)
               ---+---------+---------+---------+--------
                 7.50     10.00    12.50    15.00
```

1.70   (d)   Country of origin: The two California wines had significantly lower ratings than a
ont.   particular French wine and a particular Italian wine.
       (e)   Type of wine: No evidence of a difference.
       (f)   Price of wine: No evidence of a difference.
       (g) $RE = 1.56$
       (h)   The RE indicates that 1.56 times as many observations in each treatment group will be
             needed in a one-way ANOVA design as compared to the randomized block design in order
             to obtain the same precision for comparison of treatment group means. Since the
             randomized block design appears to be more efficient, we will use the Friedman's test for
             the difference in median.
             Minitab output:

Friedman Test: Rating versus Wine, Expert

```
Friedman test for Rating by Wine blocked by Expert

S = 29.78   DF = 7   P = 0.000
S = 30.98   DF = 7   P = 0.000 (adjusted for ties)

                      Est      Sum of
Wine           N    Median     Ranks
1             12    10.266      47.5
2             12    14.516      78.5
3             12    11.266      54.5
4             12     9.016      38.0
5             12    14.203      78.0
6             12     8.141      34.5
7             12    11.641      62.0
8             12     9.578      39.0

Grand median   =    11.078
```

$H_0 : M_1 = \cdots = M_8$ H_1 : medians are different

Since the p-value is essentially zero, reject H_0. There is sufficient evidence of a difference
in the median rating scores between the wines at the 0.01 level of significance.

       (i)   In (a), we conclude that there is sufficient evidence of a difference in the mean rating
             scores between the wines while in (h), we conclude that there is sufficient evidence of a
             difference in the median rating scores.
       (j) $H_0: \mu_1 = \ldots = \mu_8$
             Decision rule: If $F > 2.95$, reject H_0.
             Note: Since the F-table does not include a value for 7 and 88 degrees of freedom,
             use 7 and 60 degrees of freedom.
             Test statistic: $F = 4.81$
             Decision: Since $F_{calc} = 4.81$ is above the critical bound of 2.95, reject H_0. There is
             sufficient evidence to show a difference in the average rating scores among the
             wines.

11.70   (j)
cont.

Minitab Output:

```
One-Way Analysis of Variance

Analysis of Variance on Rating
Source   DF     SS      MS      F      p
Wine      7    440.3   62.9   4.81   0.000
Error    88   1151.7   13.1
Total    95   1592.0
                        Individual 95% CIs For Mean
                        Based on Pooled StDev
Level   N    Mean    StDev  ---------+---------+---------+-------
  1    12   10.417   3.059      (------*------)
  2    12   14.667   2.995               (------*------)
  3    12   11.167   3.040      (------*------)
  4    12    9.333   2.774   (------*------)
  5    12   14.417   4.209               (------*------)
  6    12    8.417   4.502 (------*------)
  7    12   11.833   4.469          (-----*------)
  8    12    9.750   3.388   (-----*------)
                           ---------+---------+---------+-------
Pooled StDev =   3.618              9.0      12.0    15.0
```

(k)   The "within wines" term in (h) is *SSW*. It is comprised of the among blocks (*SSBL*) and "error" term (*SSE*) in (a).

(l)   In this study, the average rating scores among the eight wines are so significantly different that employing the wrong procedure did not affect the overall conclusion -- there is evidence of a difference among the wines. However, by not taking advantage of the actual blocking the experimental error was inflated in *SSW* and this could have led to an erroneous decision. Here the conclusions from the pairwise comparisons are much weaker. Using the Tukey-Kramer procedure, Wine #2 and Wine #5 are no longer significantly preferred over Wine #8. In addition, Wine #5 now differs from Wine #4 only by chance.

CHAPTER 12

OBJECTIVES

- To understand how to use and when to use the Z test for the differences between two proportions
- To understand how to use and when to use the Chi-Square test for contingency tables
- To understand how to use the Marascuilo procedure for determining the differences among more than two proportions
- To understand how to use the Chi-Square test to determine whether a set of data fits a specific probability distribution

OVERVIEW AND KEY CONCEPTS

Z Test for Differences in Two Proportions $(p_1 - p_2)$

- **Assumptions:**
    - Samples are independently drawn.
    - Populations follow the binomial distribution.
    - Both sample sizes are large enough: $n_1 p_1 \geq 5$, $n_1(1 - p_1) \geq 5$, $n_2 p_2 \geq 5$, $n_2(1 - p_2) \geq 5$

- **Test statistic:**
    - $Z = \dfrac{(p_{s_1} - p_{s_2}) - (p_1 - p_2)}{\sqrt{\bar{p}(1 - \bar{p})\left(\dfrac{1}{n_1} + \dfrac{1}{n_2}\right)}}$ where $\bar{p} = \dfrac{X_1 + X_2}{n_1 + n_2}$ is the pooled estimate of the population proportion.
    - The alternative hypothesis can be one-tail with a right-tail rejection region, one-tail with a left-tail rejection region or two-tail with both right-tail and left-tail rejection regions.

- **Confidence interval estimate:** Use the $100(1 - \alpha)\%$ confidence interval for the difference in two proportions.
    - $(p_{s_1} - p_{s_2}) \pm Z_{\alpha/2} \sqrt{\dfrac{p_{s_1}(1 - p_{s_1})}{n_1} + \dfrac{p_{s_2}(1 - p_{s_2})}{n_2}}$

χ^2 Test for Differences in Two Proportions

- **Assumptions:**
  - Large sample sizes: All expected frequencies ≥ 5.
- **Test statistic:**
  - $$\chi^2 = \sum_{\text{All Cells}} \frac{(f_0 - f_e)^2}{f_e} \text{ with 1 degree of freedom}$$

    where

    f_o : observed frequency in a cell

    f_e = [(row total)(column total)]/n : expected frequency in a cell

  - The rejection region is always in the right tail.

χ^2 Test for Differences among More Than Two Proportions

- **Assumptions:**
  - Large sample sizes: All expected frequencies ≥ 1.
- **Test statistic:**
  - $$\chi^2 = \sum_{\text{All Cells}} \frac{(f_0 - f_e)^2}{f_e} \text{ with } (c-1) \text{ degree of freedom}$$

    where

    f_o : observed frequency in a cell

    f_e = [(row total)(column total)]/n: expected frequency in a cell.

  - The rejection region is always in the right tail.

Marascuilo Procedure

- Enable one to make comparison between all pairs of groups.
- **The Marascuilo multiple comparison procedure:**

1. Compute the absolute differences $\left| p_{S_j} - p_{S_{j'}} \right|$ among all pairs of groups.

2. The critical range for a pair where $j \neq j'$ is $\sqrt{\chi_U^2} \sqrt{\dfrac{p_{S_j}\left(1 - p_{S_j}\right)}{n_j} + \dfrac{p_{S_{j'}}\left(1 - p_{S_{j'}}\right)}{n_{j'}}}$ where

   χ_U^2 is the upper-tail critical value from a χ^2 distribution with $(c-1)$ degrees of freedom.

3. A specific pair is considered significantly different if $\left| p_{S_j} - p_{S_{j'}} \right| >$ critical range.

χ^2 Test of Independence

- **Assumptions:**
    - One sample is drawn with two factors; each factor has two or more levels (categories) of responses.
    - Large sample sizes: All expected frequencies ≥ 1.
- **Test statistic:**
    - $\chi^2 = \sum_{\text{All Cells}} \dfrac{(f_0 - f_e)^2}{f_e}$ with $(r-1)(c-1)$ degree of freedom

    where

    f_o : observed frequency in a cell

    f_e = [(row total)(column total)]/n: expected frequency in a cell

    r: the number of rows in the contingency table.
    c: the number of columns in the contingency table.
    - The rejection region is always in the right tail.
    - The χ^2 test does not show the nature of any relationship nor causality.

χ^2 Goodness of Fit Test for Probability Distributions (Note: The chi-square goodness of fit test is covered in section 12.5 on the CD-ROM)

- **The χ^2 goodness of fit test procedure:**
    1. Determine the specific probability distribution to be fitted to the data.
    2. Hypothesize or estimate from the data the values of each parameter of the selected probability distribution.
    3. Determine the theoretical probability in each category using the selected probability distribution.
    4. Compute the χ^2 test statistic:

    $$\chi^2_{k-p-1} = \sum_{k} \dfrac{(f_0 - f_e)^2}{f_e}$$

    where f_0 = observed frequency

    f_e = theoretical or expected frequency = $nP(X)$

    k = number of categories or classes remaining after combining classes
    p = number of parameters estimated from the data
    n = sample size
    $P(X)$ = theoretical probability

    5. The χ^2_{k-p-1} test statistic can be approximated by a Chi-square distribution with $(k - p - 1)$ degrees of freedom.
    6. The rejection region is always in the right tail.

SOLUTIONS TO END OF SECTION
AND CHAPTER REVIEW EVEN PROBLEMS

12.2   (a) $p_{S_1} = \dfrac{X_1}{n_1} = \dfrac{45}{100} = 0.45$, $p_{S_2} = \dfrac{X_2}{n_2} = \dfrac{25}{50} = 0.50$,

and $\bar{p} = \dfrac{X_1 + X_2}{n_1 + n_2} = \dfrac{45 + 25}{100 + 50} = 0.467$

$H_0: p_1 = p_2$ $H_1: p_1 \neq p_2$

Decision rule: If $Z < -2.58$ or $Z > 2.58$, reject H_0.

Test statistic: $Z = \dfrac{(p_{S_1} - p_{S_2}) - (p_1 - p_2)}{\sqrt{\bar{p} \cdot (1 - \bar{p})\left(\dfrac{1}{n_1} + \dfrac{1}{n_2}\right)}} = \dfrac{0.45 - 0.50}{\sqrt{0.467 \cdot 0.533\left(\dfrac{1}{100} + \dfrac{1}{50}\right)}} = -0.58$

Decision: Since $Z_{calc} = -0.58$ is between the critical bound of $Z = \pm 2.58$, do not reject H_0. There is insufficient evidence to conclude that the population proportion of successes differs for group 1 and group 2.

(b) $(p_{S_1} - p_{S_2}) \pm Z\sqrt{\left(\dfrac{p_1(1 - p_1)}{n_1} + \dfrac{p_2(1 - p_2)}{n_2}\right)} = -0.05 \pm 2.5758\sqrt{\left(\dfrac{.45(.55)}{100} + \dfrac{.5(.5)}{50}\right)}$

$$-0.2727 < p_{S_1} - p_{S_2} < 0.1727$$

12.4   (a) $H_0: p_1 = p_2$ $H_1: p_1 \neq p_2$ where Populations: 1 = ages 2 to 7, 2 = ages 8 to 18

Decision rule: If $Z < -1.96$ or $Z > 1.96$, reject H_0.

Test statistic:

$Z = \dfrac{(p_{S_1} - p_{S_2}) - (p_1 - p_2)}{\sqrt{\bar{p} \cdot (1 - \bar{p})\left(\dfrac{1}{n_1} + \dfrac{1}{n_2}\right)}} = \dfrac{0.2596 - 0.5099}{\sqrt{0.4235 \cdot (1 - 0.4235)\left(\dfrac{1}{1090} + \dfrac{1}{2065}\right)}} = -13.53$

Decision: Since $Z_{calc} = -13.53$ is well below the lower critical bound of $Z = -1.96$, reject H_0. There is sufficient evidence to conclude that a significant difference exists in the proportion of children between the ages of 2 and 7, and between the age of 8 and 18 who use a computer each day.

(b) p-value is virtually 0. The probability of obtaining a difference in two sample proportions as large as -0.2503 or more is virtually 0 when the null hypothesis is true.

(c) $(p_{S_1} - p_{S_2}) \pm Z\sqrt{\left(\dfrac{p_1(1 - p_1)}{n_1} + \dfrac{p_2(1 - p_2)}{n_2}\right)}$ $-0.2841 < p_{S_1} - p_{S_2} < -0.2165$

12.6   (a) $H_0: p_1 \geq p_2$ $H_1: p_1 < p_2$
where Populations: 1 = large companies, 2 = small-to-midsized companies
Decision rule: If $Z < -1.645$, reject H_0.
Test statistic:

$$Z = \frac{(p_{S_1} - p_{S_2}) - (p_1 - p_2)}{\sqrt{\bar{p} \cdot (1 - \bar{p}) \left(\frac{1}{n_1} + \frac{1}{n_2} \right)}} = \frac{0.2116 - 0.2389}{\sqrt{0.2249 \cdot (1 - 0.2249) \left(\frac{1}{189} + \frac{1}{180} \right)}} = -0.6266$$

Decision: Since $Z_{calc} = -0.6266$ is above the critical bound of -1.645, do not reject H_0. There is insufficient evidence to conclude that large companies are less likely to offer their board members stock option.

(b)   Using Excel, the p-value is 0.2655. The probability of obtaining a difference in two sample proportions as small as -0.0272 or smaller is 0.2655 when the null hypothesis is true.

12.8   (a) $H_0: p_1 = p_2$ $H_1: p_1 \neq p_2$ where Populations: 1 = African American, 2 = Whites
Decision rule: If $Z < -1.96$ or $Z > 1.96$, reject H_0.
Test statistic:

$$Z = \frac{(p_{S_1} - p_{S_2}) - (p_1 - p_2)}{\sqrt{\bar{p} \cdot (1 - \bar{p}) \left(\frac{1}{n_1} + \frac{1}{n_2} \right)}} = \frac{0.74 - 0.84}{\sqrt{0.79 \cdot (1 - .79) \left(\frac{1}{500} + \frac{1}{500} \right)}} = -3.8819$$

Decision: Since $Z_{calc} = -3.8819$ is well below the lower critical bound of $Z = -1.96$, reject H_0. There is sufficient evidence to conclude that a significant difference exists in the proportion of African Americans and whites who invest in stocks.

(b) p-value is 0.0001. The probability of obtaining a test statistic as small as -3.8819 or smaller is 0.0001 when the null hypothesis is true.

(c)
$$\left(p_{S_1} - p_{S_2}\right) \pm Z \sqrt{\left(\frac{p_1(1 - p_1)}{n_1} + \frac{p_2(1 - p_2)}{n_2} \right)} = -0.1 \pm 1.96 \sqrt{\left(\frac{.74(.26)}{500} + \frac{.84(.16)}{500} \right)}$$

$$-0.1501 < p_{S_1} - p_{S_2} < -0.0499$$

12.10   (a)

Observed Freq Expected Freq	Observed Freq Expected Freq	Total Obs, Row 1
20 25	30 25	50
chi-sq contrib= 1.00	chi-sq contrib= 1.00	
Observed Freq Expected Freq	Observed Freq Expected Freq	Total Obs, Row 2
30 25	20 25	50
chi-sq contrib= 1.00	chi-sq contrib= 1.00	
Total Obs, Col 1	Total Obs, Col 2	GRAND TOTAL
50	50	100

(b)   Decision rule: If $\chi^2 > 3.841$, reject H_0.

Test statistic: $\chi^2 = \sum \frac{(f_0 - f_e)^2}{f_e} = 1.00 + 1.00 + 1.00 + 1.00 = 4.00$

Decision: Since $\chi^2_{calc} = 4.00$ is above the critical value of 3.841, reject H_0.

12.12 (a) $H_0: p_1 = p_2$ $H_1: p_1 \neq p_2$
Decision rule: $df = 1$. If $\chi^2 > 3.841$, reject H_0.
Test statistic: $\chi^2 = 183.07$
Decision: Since $\chi^2_{calc} = 183.07$ is above the upper critical bound of 3.841, reject H_0. There is enough evidence to conclude that there is significant difference between the two age groups in the proportion of children that use a computer each day.

(b) p value is virtually 0. The probability of obtaining a test statistic as large as 183.07 or larger when the null hypothesis is true is virtually 0.

(c)   The results of (a) – (c) are exactly the same as those of Problem 12.4. The χ^2_{cal} in (a) and the Z_{cal} in Problem 12.4(a) satisfy the relationship that

$\chi^2_{cal} = 183.07 = (Z_{cal})^2 = -13.5302^2$ and the p-value obtained in (b) is exactly the same as the p-value in Problem 12.4(b).

12.14 (a) $H_0: p_1 = p_2$ $H_1: p_1 \neq p_2$
Decision rule: $df = 1$. If $\chi^2 > 3.841$, reject H_0.
Test statistic: $\chi^2 = 15.0693$
Decision: Since $\chi^2_{calc} = 15.0693$ is above the upper critical bound of 3.841, reject H_0. There is enough evidence to conclude that there is a significant difference in the proportion of African American and whites who invest in stocks.

(b) p value is 0.0001. The probability of obtaining a test statistic as large as 15.0693 or larger when the null hypothesis is true is 0.0001.

(c)   The results of (a) and (b) are exactly the same as those of Problem 12.8. The χ^2_{cal} in (a) and the Z_{cal} in Problem 12.8(a) satisfy the relationship that $\chi^2_{cal} = 15.0693$

$= (Z_{cal})^2 = (-3.8819)^2$ and the p-value in Problem 12.8 (b) is exactly the same as the p-value obtained in (b).

12.16 (a) $H_0: p_1 = p_2$ $H_1: p_1 \neq p_2$
Decision rule: $df = 1$. If $\chi^2 > 3.841$, reject H_0.
Test statistic: $\chi^2 = 33.3333$
Decision: Since $\chi^2_{calc} = 33.3333$ is above the upper critical bound of 3.841, reject H_0. There is enough evidence to conclude that there is a significant difference between the proportion of males and females who place more importance on brand names today than a few years ago.

(b) p value is virtually 0. The probability of obtaining a test statistic as large as 33.3333 or larger when the null hypothesis is true is virtually 0.

12.18 (a)-(b) The expected frequencies in the first row are 20, 30, and 40.
The expected frequencies in the second row are 30, 45, and 60.
$\chi^2 = 12.500$. The critical value with 2 degrees of freedom and an $\alpha = .05$ level of significance is 5.991. The result is deemed significant.

(c) Pairs of proportions that differ at the 0.05 level are marked with * below:

Pairwise Comparisons	Critical Range	$p_{S_j} - p_{S_{j'}}$
A to B	0.19582	0.2*
A to C	0.1848	0.3*
B to C	0.1848	0.1

There are two (2) pairs of proportions that differ significantly.

12.20 (a) **PHStat output:**

Chi-Square Test					
Observed Frequencies					
	Institution				
Attitude Towards Institution	**American Online**	**Better Business Bureau**	**FBI**	**Microsoft**	**Total**
Warm	665	806	734	789	2994
Indifferent or Cool	527	386	435	401	1749
Total	1192	1192	1169	1190	4743
Expected Frequencies					
	Institution				
Attitude Towards Institution	American Online	Better Business Bureau	FBI	Microsoft	Total
Warm	752.4453	752.4453	737.9266	751.1828	2994
Indifferent or Cool	439.5547	439.5547	431.0734	438.8172	1749
Total	1192	1192	1169	1190	4743

Data	
Level of Significance	0.05
Number of Rows	2
Number of Columns	4
Degrees of Freedom	3

Results	
Critical Value	7.814725
Chi-Square Test Statistic	43.1152
p-Value	2.33E-09
Reject the null hypothesis	

12.20 $H_0: p_1 = p_2 = p_3 = p_4$ $H_1:$ Not all p_j are equal

cont.   Test statistic: $\chi^2 = \displaystyle\sum_{\text{All cells}} \frac{(f_o - f_e)^2}{f_e} = 43.1152$

Decision: Since the calculated test statistic 43.1152 is greater than the critical value of 7.8147, we reject H_0 and conclude that there is a difference in the proportion of peopl̶ who feel warm towards these institutions.

(b)   The p value is essentially zero. The probability of obtaining a data set which gives rise to a test statistic greater than 43.830 or more is essentially zero if there is no difference in the proportion of people who feel warm towards these institutions.

11.22 (a) $H_0: p_1 = p_2 = p_3$ $H_1:$ at least one proportion differs
where population 1 = under 35, 2 = 35-54, 3 = over 54
Decision rule: $df = (c-1) = (3-1) = 2$. If $\chi^2 > 5.9915$, reject H_0.
Test statistic: $\chi^2 = 16.5254$
Decision: Since $\chi^2_{\text{calc}} = 16.5254$ is above the upper critical bound of 5.9915, reject H_0. There is enough evidence to show that there is a significant relationship between age and major grocery shopping day.

(b) p-value = 0.0003. The probability of obtaining a sample that gives rise to a test statistic that is equal to or more than 16.5254 is 0.03% if the null hypothesis is true.

(c)

Pairwise Comparisons	Critical Range	$\lvert p_{S_j} - p_{S_{j'}} \rvert$
1 to 2	0.1073	0.04
2 to 3	0.0959	0.16*
1 to 3	0.0929	0.12*

There is a significance difference between the 35-54 and over 54 groups, and between the under 35 and over 54 groups.

(d)   The stores can use this information to target their marketing on the specific group of shoppers on Saturday and the days other than Saturday.

(e)   (a) $H_0: p_1 = p_2 = p_3$ $H_1:$ at least one proportion differs
where population 1 = under 35, 2 = 35-54, 3 = over 54
Decision rule: $df = (c-1) = (3-1) = 2$. If $\chi^2 > 5.9915$, reject H_0.
Test statistic: $\chi^2 = 4.1314$
Decision: Since $\chi^2_{\text{calc}} = 4.1314$ is below the upper critical bound of 5.9915, do not reject H_0. There is not enough evidence to show that there is a significant relationship between age and major grocery shopping day.

(b) p-value = 0.1267. The probability of obtaining a sample that gives rise to a test statistic that is equal to or more than 4.1314 is 12.67% if the null hypothesis is true.

(f)   The larger the sample size, the more power the χ^2 test has and, hence, there is a higher likelihood of rejecting a false null hypothesis.

12.24   (a)   Item #1: Use the guest's name:

$H_0 : p_1 = p_2 = p_3$ H_1 : Not all p_j are equal

where population 1 = Hong Kong, 2 = New York, 3 = Paris

Observed Frequencies:

Finding	City Hong Kong	New York	Paris	Total
Yes	26	39	28	93
No	74	61	72	207
Total	100	100	100	300

Expected Frequencies:

Finding	City Hong Kong	New York	Paris	Total
Yes	31	31	31	93
No	69	69	69	207
Total	100	100	100	300

Level of Significance	0.05
Number of Rows	2
Number of Columns	3
Degrees of Freedom	2
Critical Value	5.991476
Chi-Square Test Statistic	4.581581
p-Value	0.101186
Do not reject the null hypothesis	

Test statistic: $\chi^2 = \sum_{\text{All cells}} \dfrac{(f_o - f_e)^2}{f_e} = 4.582$

Decision: Since the measured test statistic of 4.582 is smaller than the critical value of 5.991, we do not reject the null hypothesis. There is not enough evidence to conclude that there is a difference in the proportion of hotels that use the guest's name among the three cities.

(b)   The p value is 0.101. The probability of obtaining a sample that gives rise to a test statistic more extreme than 4.582 is 0.101 if the null hypothesis is true.

(c)   Item #2: Minibar charges correctly posted at check-out:

$H_0 : p_1 = p_2 = p_3$ H_1 : Not all p_j are equal

Observed Frequencies:

Minibar Charges Posted	City Hong Kong	New York	Paris	Total
Yes	86	76	78	240
No	14	24	22	60
Total	100	100	100	300

Expected Frequencies:

Minibar Charges Posted	City Hong Kong	New York	Paris	Total
Yes	80	80	80	240
No	20	20	20	60
Total	100	100	100	300

Level of Significance	0.05
Number of Rows	2
Number of Columns	3
Degrees of Freedom	2
Critical Value	5.991476
Chi-Square Test Statistic	3.499998
p-Value	0.173774
Do not reject the null hypothesis	

12.24 (c)   Test statistic: $\chi^2 = \sum\limits_{\text{All cells}} \dfrac{(f_o - f_e)^2}{f_e} = 3.50$

cont.   Decision: Since the measured test statistic of 3.5 is smaller than the critical value of 5.991, we do not reject the null hypothesis. There is not sufficient evidence to conclude that there is a difference in the proportion of hotels that correctly post Minibar charges among the three cities.

(d)   The p value is 0.174. The probability of obtaining a sample that gives rise to a test statistic more extreme than 3.5 is 0.174 if the null hypothesis is true.

(e)   Item #3: Bathroom tub and shower spotlessly clean:

$H_0 : p_1 = p_2 = p_3$ $H_1 :$ Not all p_j are equal

Observed Frequencies:

Bathroom and Shower Clean	City			Total
	Hong Kong	New York	Paris	
Yes	81	76	79	236
No	19	24	21	64
Total	100	100	100	300

Expected Frequencies:

Bathroom and Shower Clean	City			Total
	Hong Kong	New York	Paris	
Yes	78.6666667	78.666667	78.66667	236
No	21.3333333	21.333333	21.33333	64
Total	100	100	100	300

Level of Significance	0.05
Number of Rows	2
Number of Columns	3
Degrees of Freedom	2
Critical Value	5.991476
Chi-Square Test Statistic	0.754766
p-Value	0.685653
Do not reject the null hypothesis	

(e)   Test statistic: $\chi^2 = \sum\limits_{\text{All cells}} \dfrac{(f_o - f_e)^2}{f_e} = 0.755$

Decision: Since the measured test statistic of 0.755 is smaller than the critical value of 5.991, we do not reject the null hypothesis and conclude that there is no significant relationship between item #3 and the city.

(f)   The p value is 0.686. The probability of obtaining a sample that gives rise to a test statistic more extreme than 0.755 is 0.686 if the null hypothesis is true.

(g)   Since the null hypotheses are not rejected for all the 3 items, it is not necessary to perform the Marascuilo procedure.

(h)   (a)   Item #1: Use the guest's name:

$H_0 : p_1 = p_2 = p_3$ $H_1 :$ Not all p_j are equal

Test statistic: $\chi^2 = \sum\limits_{\text{All cells}} \dfrac{(f_o - f_e)^2}{f_e} = 9.163$

Decision: Since the measured test statistic of 9.163 is greater than the critical value of 5.991, we reject the null hypothesis and conclude that there is a significant difference in the proportion of hotels that use the guest's name among the 3 cities.

(b)   The p value is 0.01. The probability of obtaining a sample that gives rise to a test statistic more extreme than 9.163 is 0.01 if the null hypothesis is true.

12.24 (h)
cont.

(c)   Item #2: Minibar charges correctly posted at check-out:

$$H_0: p_1 = p_2 = p_3 \qquad H_1: \text{Not all } p_j \text{ are equal}$$

Test statistic: $\chi^2 = \sum_{\text{All cells}} \dfrac{(f_o - f_e)^2}{f_e} = 7.0$

Decision: Since the measured test statistic of 7.0 is greater than the critical value of 5.991, we reject the null hypothesis and conclude that there is significant relationship between item #2 and the city.

(d)   The p value is 0.03. The probability of observing a sample that gives rise to a test statistic more extreme than 7.0 is 0.03 if the null hypothesis is true.

(e)   Item #3: Bathroom tub and shower spotlessly clean:

$$H_0: p_1 = p_2 = p_3 \qquad H_1: \text{Not all } p_j \text{ are equal}$$

Test statistic: $\chi^2 = \sum_{\text{All cells}} \dfrac{(f_o - f_e)^2}{f_e} = 1.51$

Decision: Since the measured test statistic of 1.51 is smaller than the critical value of 5.991, we do not reject the null hypothesis and conclude that there is no significant relationship between item #3 and the city.

(f)   The p value is 0.470. The probability of obtaining a sample that gives rise to a test statistic more extreme than 1.51 is 0.470 if the null hypothesis is true.

(g)   Marascuilo procedure for Item #1:

$$\sqrt{\chi_U^2} = 2.4478; \qquad \text{Critical range} = \sqrt{\chi_U^2}\sqrt{\dfrac{p_{S_j}(1-p_{S_j})}{n_j} + \dfrac{p_{S_{j'}}(1-p_{S_{j'}})}{n_{j'}}}$$

Group	Sample Proportion	Sample Size	Comparison	Absolute Difference	Std. Error of Difference	Critical Range	Results
1	0.26	200	Group 1 to Group 2	0.13	0.04638426	0.114	Means are different
2	0.39	200	Group 1 to Group 3	0.02	0.04438468	0.109	Means are not different
3	0.28	200	Group 2 to Group 3	0.11	0.0468775	0.115	Means are not different

There is a difference between Hong Kong and New York in the proportion of hotels that use the guest's name.

12.24 (h)   (g)
cont.

Marascuilo procedure for Item #2:

Group	Sample Proportion	Sample Size	Comparison	Absolute Difference	Std. Error of Difference	Critical Range	Results
1	0.86	200	Group 1 to Group 2	0.1	0.03891015	0.095	Means are differen
2	0.76	200	Group 1 to Group 3	0.08	0.03820995	0.094	Means are not differen
3	0.78	200	Group 2 to Group 3	0.02	0.04207137	0.103	Means are not differen

There is a difference between Hong Kong and New York in the proportion of hotels tha correctly post Minibar charges.

(i)   The larger is the sample size, the higher is the power of the test. When the sample size is doubled, the ability of the test to recognize a difference in the proportion of hotels that use the guest's name among the 3 cities and the proportion of hotels that correctly post Minibar charges among the 3 cities is increased. However, we still cannot conclude that there is a significant difference in the proportion of hotels with spotless bathroom tub and shower among the 3 cities at 0.05 level of significance.

12.26 (a) $\chi^2 = 21.026$ (d) $\chi^2 = 23.209$
       (b) $\chi^2 = 26.217$ (e) $\chi^2 = 23.209$
       (c) $\chi^2 = 30.578$

12.28 (a) H_0: There is no relationship between the commuting time of company employees and the level of stress-related problems observed on the job.
       H_1: There is a relationship between the commuting time of company employees and the level of stress-related problems observed on the job.
       Decision rule: If $\chi^2 > 13.277$, reject H_0.   Test statistic: $\chi^2 = 9.831$
       Decision: Since the $\chi^2_{calc} = 9.831$ is below the critical bound of 13.277, do not reject H_0. There is not enough evidence to conclude there is any relationship between the commuting time of company employees and the level of stress-related problems observed on the job.

       (b)   Decision rule: If $\chi^2 > 9.488$, reject H_0.   Test statistic: $\chi^2 = 9.831$
       Decision: Since the $\chi^2_{calc} = 9.831$ is above the critical bound of 9.488, reject H_0. There is enough evidence at the 0.05 level to conclude there is a relationship between the commuting time of company employees and the level of stress-related problems observed on the job.

12.30 H_0: There is no relationship between when the decision is made of what to have for dinner and the type of household.
H_1: There is a relationship between when the decision is made of what to have for dinner and the type of household.
Decision rule: $d.f. = 12$. If $\chi^2 > 21.026$, reject H_0.   Test statistic: $\chi^2 = 129.520$
Decision: Since the $\chi^2_{calc} = 129.520$ is greater than the critical bound of 21.026, reject H_0.
There is enough evidence to conclude there is a relationship between when the decision is made of what to have for dinner and the type of household.

12.32   The Z test for the difference between two proportions can be used when the alternative hypothesis is one-tailed or two-tailed.

12.34   Both the Z and Chi-square tests can be used when the alternative hypothesis is two-tailed, but only the Z test can be used when the alternative hypothesis is one-tailed.

12.36   The Chi-square test for independence can be used as long as all expected frequencies are at least one.

12.38   (a) H_0: There is no relationship between researching airline prices on the internet and booking airline tickets on the internet.
H_1: There is a relationship between researching airline prices on the internet and booking airline tickets on the internet.
Decision rule: $d.f. = 1$.   If $\chi^2 > 3.841$, reject H_0.
Test statistic: $\chi^2 = 48.178$
Decision: Since the $\chi^2_{calc} = 48.178$ is greater than the critical bound of 3.841, reject H_0. There is enough evidence to conclude that there is a relationship between researching airline prices on the internet and booking airline tickets on the internet.
(b) p-value is virtually 0. The probability of obtaining a sample that gives a test statistic equal to or greater than 48.178 is virtually 0 if the null hypothesis of no relationship between researching airline prices on the internet and booking airline tickets on the internet is true.

12.40   (a)   **Pay bills by mail:**
H_0: $p_1 = p_2$ H_1: $p_1 \neq p_2$ where Group: 1 = bank online, 2 = don't bank online
Decision rule: If $Z < -1.96$ or $Z > 1.96$ or $\chi^2 > 3.841$, reject H_0.
Test statistic: $Z = \dfrac{(p_{S_1} - p_{S_2}) - (p_1 - p_2)}{\sqrt{\bar{p}(1-\bar{p})\left(\dfrac{1}{n_1} + \dfrac{1}{n_2}\right)}} = -5.850$ or $\chi^2 = 34.223$

Decision: Since $Z_{calc} = -5.850$ is below the lower critical bound of -1.96 or $\chi^2_{calc} = 34.223$ is above the critical bound of 3.841, reject H_0. There is adequate evidence to conclude that there is a significant difference in the proportion that pay bills by mail between those who bank online and those who don't bank online.

12.40   (a)
cont.

Visit bank in person:

$H_0: p_1 = p_2$ $H_1: p_1 \neq p_2$ where Group: 1 = bank online, 2 = don't bank online
Decision rule: If $Z < -1.96$ or $Z > 1.96$ or $\chi^2 > 3.841$, reject H_0.

Test statistic: $Z = \dfrac{(p_{S_1} - p_{S_2}) - (p_1 - p_2)}{\sqrt{\bar{p}(1-\bar{p})\left(\dfrac{1}{n_1} + \dfrac{1}{n_2}\right)}} = -6.230$ or $\chi^2 = 38.813$

Decision: Since $Z_{calc} = -6.230$ is below the lower critical bound of -1.96 or $\chi^2_{calc} = 38.813$ is above the critical bound of 3.841, reject H_0. There is adequate evidence to conclude that there is a significant difference in the proportion that visit bank in person between those who bank online and those who don't bank online.

Use ATM:

$H_0: p_1 = p_2$ $H_1: p_1 \neq p_2$ where Group: 1 = bank online, 2 = don't bank online
Decision rule: If $Z < -1.96$ or $Z > 1.96$ or $\chi^2 > 3.841$, reject H_0.

Test statistic: $Z = \dfrac{(p_{S_1} - p_{S_2}) - (p_1 - p_2)}{\sqrt{\bar{p}(1-\bar{p})\left(\dfrac{1}{n_1} + \dfrac{1}{n_2}\right)}} = 7.391$ or $\chi^2 = 54.627$

Decision: Since $Z_{calc} = 7.391$ is above the upper critical bound of 1.96 or $\chi^2_{calc} = 54.627$ is above the critical bound of 3.841, reject H_0. There is adequate evidence to conclude that there is a significant difference in the proportion that use ATM between those who bank online and those who don't bank online.

Use direct deposit:

$H_0: p_1 = p_2$ $H_1: p_1 \neq p_2$ where Group: 1 = bank online, 2 = don't bank online
Decision rule: If $Z < -1.96$ or $Z > 1.96$ or $\chi^2 > 3.841$, reject H_0.

Test statistic: $Z = \dfrac{(p_{S_1} - p_{S_2}) - (p_1 - p_2)}{\sqrt{\bar{p}(1-\bar{p})\left(\dfrac{1}{n_1} + \dfrac{1}{n_2}\right)}} = 3.941$ or $\chi^2 = 15.532$

Decision: Since $Z_{calc} = 3.941$ is above the upper critical bound of 1.96 or $\chi^2_{calc} = 15.532$ is above the critical bound of 3.841, reject H_0. There is adequate evidence to conclude that there is a significant difference in the proportion that use direct deposit between those who bank online and those who don't bank online.

12.40 (a)
cont.

Call automated phone system:

$H_0: p_1 = p_2$ $H_1: p_1 \neq p_2$ where Group: 1 = bank online, 2 = don't bank online

Decision rule: If $Z < -1.96$ or $Z > 1.96$ or $\chi^2 > 3.841$, reject H_0.

Test statistic: $Z = \dfrac{(p_{s_1} - p_{s_2}) - (p_1 - p_2)}{\sqrt{\overline{p}(1-\overline{p})\left(\dfrac{1}{n_1} + \dfrac{1}{n_2}\right)}} = 1.277$ or $\chi^2 = 1.631$

Decision: Since $Z_{calc} = 1.277$ is in between the lower critical bound of -1.96 and the upper critical bound of 1.96 or $\chi^2_{calc} = 1.631$ is below the critical bound of 3.841, do not reject H_0. There is inadequate evidence to conclude that there is a significant difference in the proportion that call automated phone system between those who bank online and those who don't bank online.

Call customer service representative:

$H_0: p_1 = p_2$ $H_1: p_1 \neq p_2$ where Group: 1 = bank online, 2 = don't bank online

Decision rule: If $Z < -1.96$ or $Z > 1.96$ or $\chi^2 > 3.841$, reject H_0.

Test statistic: $Z = \dfrac{(p_{s_1} - p_{s_2}) - (p_1 - p_2)}{\sqrt{\overline{p}(1-\overline{p})\left(\dfrac{1}{n_1} + \dfrac{1}{n_2}\right)}} = -0.326$ or $\chi^2 = 0.107$

Decision: Since $Z_{calc} = -0.326$ is in between the lower critical bound of -1.96 and the upper critical bound of 1.96 or $\chi^2_{calc} = 0.1063$ is below the critical bound of 3.841, do not reject H_0. There is inadequate evidence to conclude that there is a significant difference in the proportion that call customer service representative between those who bank online and those who don't bank online.

(b) Based on the results obtained, we can conclude that there are significant differences in the proportions that pay bills by mail, visit bank in person, use ATM, and use direct deposit between those who bank online and those who don't bank online. However, there is no significant difference in the proportion that call automated phone system or call customer service representative at the 5% level of significance.

12.42 (a) H_0: There is no relationship between type of user and the seriousness of concern over the first statement.

H_1: There is a relationship between type of user and the seriousness of concern over the first statement.

Decision rule: If $\chi^2 > 3.841$, reject H_0.   Test statistic: $\chi^2 = 12.026$

Decision: Since the $\chi^2_{calc} = 12.026$ is above the critical bound of 3.841, reject H_0. There is enough evidence to conclude there is a relationship between type of user and the seriousness of concern over the first statement.

(b) The p-value = 0.000525. The probability of obtaining a sample that gives rise to a test statistic of 12.026 or larger is 0.000525 if there is in fact no relationship between type of user and the seriousness of concern over the first statement.

12.42   (c) H_0: There is no relationship between type of user and the seriousness of concern over
cont.   the second statement.

 H_1: There is a relationship between type of user and the seriousness of concern over
the first statement.

Decision rule: If $\chi^2 > 3.841$, reject H_0.   Test statistic: $\chi^2 = 7.297$

Decision: Since the $\chi^2_{calc} = 7.297$ is above the critical bound of 3.841, reject H_0. There
is enough evidence to conclude there is a relationship between type of user and the
seriousness of concern over the second statement.

(d)   The p-value = 0.00691. The probability of obtaining a sample that gives rise to a test
statistic of 7.297 or larger is 0.00691 if there is in fact no relationship between type of
user and the seriousness of concern over the second statement.

12.44   (a) H_0: There is no relationship between the attitudes of employees toward the use of
self-managed work teams and employee job classification.

 H_1: There is a relationship between the attitudes of employees toward the use of self-
managed work teams and employee job classification.

Decision rule: If $\chi^2 > 12.592$, reject H_0.

Test statistic: $\chi^2 = 11.895$

Decision: Since $\chi^2{}_{calc} = 11.895$ is below the critical bound 12.592, do not
reject H_0. There is not enough evidence to conclude that there is a relationship
between the attitudes of employees toward the use of self-managed work teams and
employee job classification.

(b) H_0: There is no relationship between the attitudes of employees toward
vacation time without pay and employee job classification.

 H_1: There is a relationship between the attitudes of employees toward vacation
time without pay and employee job classification.

Decision rule: If $\chi^2 > 12.592$, reject H_0.

Test statistic: $\chi^2 = 3.294$

Decision: Since $\chi^2{}_{calc} = 3.294$ is below the critical bound 12.592, do not
reject H_0. There is not enough evidence to conclude that there is a relationship
between the attitudes of employees toward vacation time without pay and
employee job classification.

12.46   (a) H_0: There is no relationship between the presence of environmental goals and the
type of manufacturing process

 H_1: There is a relationship between the presence of environmental goals and the type
of manufacturing process

Test statistic: $\chi^2 = \displaystyle\sum_{\text{All cells}} \frac{\left(f_o - f_e\right)^2}{f_e} = 11.635$

Decision rule: If $\chi^2 > 7.815$, reject H_0.

Decision: Since $\chi^2{}_{calc} = 11.635$ is above the critical bound 7.815, reject H_0. There is
enough evidence to conclude that there is a relationship between the presence of
environmental goals and the type of manufacturing process.

(b)   The p value is 0.00874. The probability of obtaining a data set which gives rise to a test
statistic of 11.635 or more is 0.00874 if there is no relationship between the presence of
environmental goals and the type of manufacturing process.

12.46 (c) $H_0: p_1 = p_2$ $H_1: p_1 \neq p_2$
cont.   where Populations: 1 = with cost-cutting goal, 2 = without cost cutting goal

Test statistic: $\chi^2 = \displaystyle\sum_{\text{All cells}} \frac{\left(f_o - f_e\right)^2}{f_e} = 10.94$

Decision rule: If $\chi^2 > 3.841$, reject H_0.

Decision: Since $\chi^2_{\text{calc}} = 10.94$ is above the critical bound 3.841, reject H_0. There is enough evidence to conclude that there is a difference in improved environmental performance for teams with a specified goal of cutting costs.

(d)   The p value is 0.000941. The probability of obtaining a data set which gives rise to a test statistic of 10.94 or more is 0.000941 if there is no difference in improved environmental performance for teams with a specified goal of cutting costs.

(e) $H_0: p_1 = p_2$ $H_1: p_1 \neq p_2$
        where Populations: 1 = with cost-cutting goal, 2 = without cost cutting goal

Test statistic: $\chi^2 = \displaystyle\sum_{\text{All cells}} \frac{\left(f_o - f_e\right)^2}{f_e} = 0.612$

Decision rule: If $\chi^2 > 3.841$, reject H_0.

Decision: Since $\chi^2_{\text{calc}} = 0.612$ is below the critical bound 3.841, do not reject H_0. There is not enough evidence to conclude that there is a difference in improved profitability for teams with a specified goal of cutting costs.

(f)   The p value is 0.4341. The probability of obtaining a data set which gives rise to a test statistic of 0.612 or more is 0.4341 if there is no difference in improved profitability for teams with a specified goal of cutting costs.

(g) $H_0: p_1 = p_2$ $H_1: p_1 \neq p_2$
        where Populations: 1 = with cost-cutting goal, 2 = without cost cutting goal

Test statistic: $\chi^2 = \displaystyle\sum_{\text{All cells}} \frac{\left(f_o - f_e\right)^2}{f_e} = 3.454$

Decision rule: If $\chi^2 > 3.841$, reject H_0.

Decision: Since $\chi^2_{\text{calc}} = 3.454$ is below the critical bound 3.841, do not reject H_0. There is not enough evidence to conclude that there is a difference in improved morale for teams with a specified goal of cutting costs.

(h)   The p value is 0.063. The probability of obtaining a data set which gives rise to a test statistic of 3.454 or more is 0.063 if there is no difference in improved morale for teams with a specified goal of cutting costs.

CHAPTER 13

OBJECTIVES

- To use regression analysis to predict the value of a dependent variable based on an independent variable
- To understand the meaning of the regression coefficient b_0 and b_1
- To be familiar with the assumptions of regression analysis, how to evaluate the assumptions, and what to do if the assumptions are violated
- To be able to make inferences about the slope and correlation coefficient
- To be able to estimate mean values and predict individual values

OVERVIEW AND KEY CONCEPTS

Purpose of Regression Analysis

- Regression analysis is used for predicting the values of a dependent (response) variable based on the value of at least one independent (explanatory) variable.

The Simple Linear Regression Model

- The relationship between the dependent variable (Y) and the explanatory variable (X) is described by a linear function.
- The change of the explanatory variable causes the explained (dependent) variable to change.
- The value of the explained variable depends on the explanatory variable.
- The population linear regression: $Y_i = \beta_0 + \beta_1 X_i + \varepsilon_i$ where β_0 is the intercept and β_1 is the slope of the population regression line $\mu_{Y|X} = \beta_0 + \beta_1 X_i$ and ε_i is called the error term.

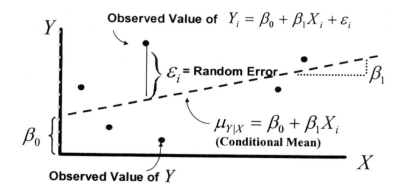

- The parameters β_0 and β_1 are unknown and need to be estimated.
- The least squares estimates for β_0 and β_1 are b_0 and b_1, respectively, obtained by minimizing the sum of squared residuals, $\sum_{i=1}^{n}\left(Y_i - \left(b_0 + b_1 X_i\right)\right)^2 = \sum_{i=1}^{n} e_i^2$.

- The sample linear regression: $Y_i = b_0 + b_1 X_i + e_i$ where b_0 is the intercept and b_1 is the slope of the simple linear regression equation $\hat{Y} = b_0 + b_1 X_i$ and e_i is called the residual.
- The simple linear regression equation (sample regression line) $\hat{Y} = b_0 + b_1 X_i$ can be used to predict the value of the dependent variable for a given value of the independent variable X.

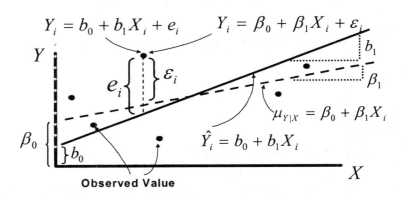

Interpretations of β_0, β_1, b_0 and b_1

- $\beta_0 = E(Y \mid X = 0) = \mu_{Y \mid X = 0}$ is the average value of Y when the value of X is zero.
- $b_0 = \hat{E}(Y \mid X = 0) = \hat{Y}(X = 0)$ is the **estimated** average value of Y when the value of X is zero.
- $\beta_1 = \dfrac{\text{change in } E(Y \mid X)}{\text{change in } X} = \dfrac{\text{change in } \mu_{Y \mid X}}{\text{change in } X}$ measures the change in the average value of Y as a result of a one-unit change in X.
- $b_1 = \dfrac{\text{change in } \hat{E}(Y \mid X)}{\text{change in } X} = \dfrac{\text{change in } \hat{Y}}{\text{change in } X}$ measures the **estimated** change in the average value of Y as a result of a one-unit change in X.

Some Important Identities in the Simple Linear Regression Model

- $Y_i = \beta_0 + \beta_1 X_i + \varepsilon_i = \mu_{Y \mid X} + \varepsilon_i$. The value of the dependent variable is decomposed into the value on the population regression line and the error term.
- $Y_i = b_0 + b_1 X_i + e_i = \hat{Y}_i + e_i$. The value of the dependent variable is decomposed into the value on the sample regression line (fitted regression line) and the residual term.
- $\mu_{Y \mid X} = \beta_0 + \beta_1 X_i = E(Y \mid X)$ is the population regression line, which measures the average value of the dependent variable Y for a particular value of the independent variable X. Hence, it is also sometimes called the conditional mean regression line.
- $\hat{Y}_i = b_0 + b_1 X_i$ is the sample regression line (simple linear regression equation), which measures the **estimated** average value of the dependent variable Y for a particular value of the independent variable X. It also provides prediction for the value of Y for a given value of X.
- $\varepsilon_i = Y_i - \mu_{Y \mid X} = Y_i - (\beta_0 + \beta_1 X_i)$ is the error.
- $e_i = Y_i - \hat{Y}_i = Y_i - (b_0 + b_1 X_i)$ is the residual.

- $SST = \sum_{i=1}^{n}(Y_i - \bar{Y})^2$ is the total sum of squares.

- $SSR = \sum_{i=1}^{n}(\hat{Y}_i - \bar{Y})^2$ is the regression (explained) sum of squares.

- $SSE = \sum_{i=1}^{n}(Y_i - \hat{Y}_i)^2 = \sum_{i=1}^{n} e_i^2$ is the error (residual) sum of squares.

- $MSR = \dfrac{SSR}{k} = \dfrac{SSR}{1}$ where k is the number of the independent variable, which is 1 in the simple linear regression model.

- $MSE = \dfrac{SSE}{n-k-1} = \dfrac{SSE}{n-2}$

- The coefficient of determination
  - $r^2 = \dfrac{SSR}{SST} = \dfrac{\text{Regression Sum of Squares}}{\text{Total Sum of Squares}}$
  - The coefficient of determination measures the proportion of variation in Y that is explained by the independent variable X in the regression model.

- Standard error of estimate
  - $S_{YX} = \sqrt{\dfrac{SSE}{n-2}} = \sqrt{\dfrac{\sum_{i=1}^{n}(Y - \hat{Y}_i)^2}{n-2}}$
  - The standard error of estimate is the standard deviation of the variation of observations around the sample regression line $\hat{Y}_i = b_0 + b_1 X_i$.

ANOVA					
	df	SS	MS	F	Significance F
Regression	k	SSR	MSR=SSR/k	MSR/MSE	p-value of the F Test
Residuals	n-k-1	SSE	MSE=SSE/(n-k-1)		
Total	n-1	SST			

The ANOVA Table for the Simple Linear Regression Model as Presented in Excel

Assumptions Needed for the Simple Linear Regression Model

- Normality of error: The errors around the population regression line are normally distributed at each X value. This also implies that the dependent variable is normally distributed at each value of the independent variable.
- Homoscedasticity: The variance (amount of variation) of the errors around the population regression line is the same at each X value.
- Independence of errors: The errors around the population regression line are independent for each value of X.

Residual Analysis

- Residual analysis is used to evaluate whether the regression model that has been fitted to the data is an appropriate model.
- **Residual analysis for linearity:**

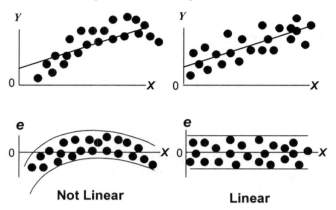

- **Residual analysis for homoscedasticity:**

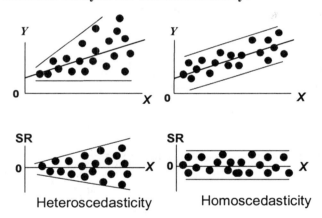

- **Residual analysis for independence:**

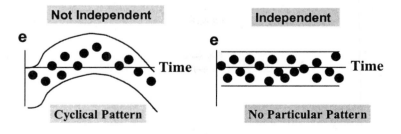

Residual Is Plotted Against Time to Detect Any Autocorrelation

- **Residual analysis for independence using Durbin-Watson statistic:**
  1. H_0: No autocorrelation (error terms are independent)

     H_1: There is autocorrelation (error terms are not independent)

  2. Compute the Durbin-Watson statistic $D = \dfrac{\sum\limits_{i=2}^{n}(e_i - e_{i-1})^2}{\sum\limits_{i=1}^{n} e_i^2}$

  3. Obtain the critical values d_L and d_U from a table.
  4. Compare the Durbin-Watson statistic with the critical values.

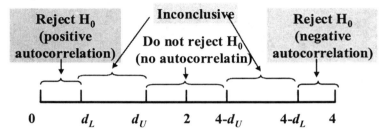

  5. Make a statistical decision.
  6. Draw a conclusion.

t Test for the Slope Parameter β_1

- $$H_0 : \beta_1 = 0 \quad (Y \text{ does not depend on } X)$$

  $H_1 : \beta_1 \neq 0 \quad (Y \text{ depends linearly on } X)$

- **Test statistic:**
  - $t = \dfrac{b_1 - \beta_1}{S_{b_1}}$ with $(n-2)$ degrees of freedom, where $S_{b_1} = \dfrac{S_{YX}}{\sqrt{\sum\limits_{i=1}^{n}(X_i - \bar{X})^2}}$

  - The *t* test can also be a one-tail test for a one-tail alternative.
- **Confidence interval estimate:** Use the $100(1-\alpha)\%$ confidence interval for the slope parameter β_1.
  - $b_1 \pm t_{\alpha/2, n-2} S_{b_1}$

F Test for the Slope Parameter β_1

- $H_0 : \beta_1 = 0$ (Y does not depend on X)

  $H_1 : \beta_1 \neq 0$ (Y depends linearly on X)

- **Test statistic:**

  - $F = \dfrac{\dfrac{SSR}{1}}{\dfrac{SSE}{(n-2)}}$ with 1 numerator degrees of freedom and $(n-2)$ denominator

  degrees of freedom.
  - The F test always has a right-tail rejection region and can only be used for the two-tail alternative.

The Relationship between the t Test and F Test for the Slope Parameter β_1

- For $H_0 : \beta_1 = 0$ vs $H_1 : \beta_1 \neq 0$, $t^2 = F$ and the p-value of the t test is identical to the p-value of the F test.

Correlation Analysis

- Correlation analysis is concerned with the strength of any linear relationship between 2 quantitative variables.
- There is no causal effect implied in a correlation analysis.
- The population correlation coefficient ρ is used to measure the strength of the linear relationship between the variables while the sample correlation coefficient r provides an estimate of the strength.
- **Features of ρ and r:**
  - They are unit free.
  - Their values range between -1 and 1.
  - The close is the value to -1, the stronger is the negative linear relationship.
  - The close is the value to $+1$, the stronger is the positive linear relationship.
  - The close is the value to 0, the weaker is any linear relationship.

t Test for a Linear Relationship

- **Hypotheses:**
  - $H_0 : \rho = 0$ (There is no linear relationship)
  - $H_1 : \rho \neq 0$ (There is some linear relationship)
- **Test statistic:**
  - $t = \dfrac{r - \rho}{\sqrt{\dfrac{1 - r^2}{n-2}}}$ with $(n-2)$ degrees of freedom, where

  $r = \sqrt{r^2} = \dfrac{\sum\limits_{i=1}^{n}(X_i - \bar{X})(Y_i - \bar{Y})}{\sqrt{\sum\limits_{i=1}^{n}(X_i - \bar{X})^2 \sum\limits_{i=1}^{n}(Y_i - \bar{Y})^2}}$.

  - The t test can be a one-tail test for a one-tail alternative.

Confidence Interval Estimate for the Mean of Y $\left(\mu_{Y|X}\right)$

- The point estimate for $\mu_{Y|X=X_i}$ is $\hat{Y}_i$
- The confidence interval estimate for $\mu_{Y|X}$ is

$$\hat{Y}_i \pm t_{\alpha/2,n-2} S_{YX} \sqrt{\frac{1}{n} + \frac{(X_i - \bar{X})^2}{\sum_{i=1}^{n}(X_i - \bar{X})^2}}$$

Prediction Interval for an Individual Response Y

- The point prediction for an individual response Y_i at a particular X_i, denoted as $Y_{x=X_i}$ is $\hat{Y}_i = b_0 + b_1 X_i$
- The prediction interval for an individual response Y_i is

$$\hat{Y}_i \pm t_{\alpha/2,n-2} S_{YX} \sqrt{1 + \frac{1}{n} + \frac{(X_i - \bar{X})^2}{\sum_{i=1}^{n}(X_i - \bar{X})^2}}$$

Common Pitfalls in Regression Analysis

- Lacking an awareness of the assumptions underlying least-squares regression
- Not knowing how to evaluate the assumptions
- Not knowing what the alternatives to least-squares regression are if a particular assumption is violated
- Using a regression model without knowledge of the subject matter
- Extrapolating outside the relevant range
- Concluding that a significant relationship identified in an observational study is due to a cause-and-effect relationship

Strategy for Avoiding the Pitfalls in Regression

- Always start with a scatter plot to observe the possible relationship between X and Y
- Check the assumptions of the regression after the regression model has been fit, before moving on to using the results of the model
- Plot the residuals versus the independent variable to determine whether the model fit to the data is appropriate and check visually for violations of the homoscedasticity assumption
- Use a histogram, stem-and-leaf display, box-and-whisker plot, or normal probability plot of the residuals to graphically evaluate whether the normality assumption has been seriously violated
- If the evaluations indicate violations in the assumptions, use alternative methods to least-squares regression or alternative least-squares models (quadratic or multiple regression) depending on what the evaluation has indicated
- If the evaluations do not indicate violations in the assumptions, then the inferential aspects of the regression analysis can be undertaken, tests for the significance of the regression coefficients can be done, and confidence and prediction intervals can be developed
- Avoid making predictions and forecasts outside the relevant range of the independent variable

- Always note that the relationships identified in observational studies may or may not be due to a cause-and-effect relationship, and remember that while causation implies correlation, correlation does not imply causation

SOLUTIONS TO END OF SECTION AND CHAPTER REVIEW EVEN PROBLEMS

13.2   (a)   When $X = 0$, the estimated expected value of Y is 16.
        (b)   For increase in the value X by 1 unit, we can expect a decrease in an estimated 0.5 units in the value of Y.
        (c) $\hat{Y} = 16 - 0.5X = 16 - 0.5(6) = 13$

13.4   (a)

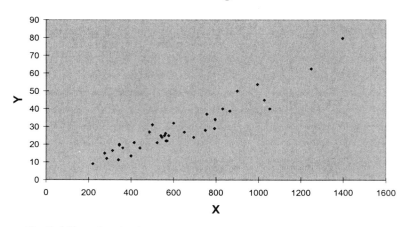

Scatter Diagram

        (b)   Partial Excel output:

	Coefficients	Standard Error	t Stat	P-value
Intercept	-2.3697	2.0733	-1.1430	0.2610
Feet	0.0501	0.0030	16.5223	0.0000

        (c)   The estimated average amount of labor will increase by 0.05 hour for each additional cubic foot moved.
        (d) $\hat{Y} = -2.3697 + 0.0501(500) = 22.6705$
        (e)   Other factors that might affect labor hours are size of the movers, how accessible is the building to the moving truck, etc.

13.6   (a)

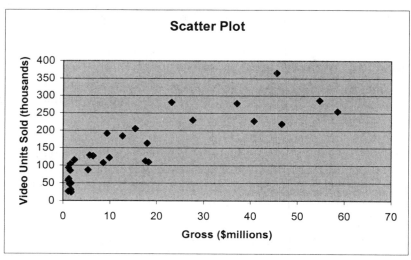

(b),(c) $\hat{Y} = 76.54 + 4.3331X$

(d)   For each increase of 1 million dollars in box office gross, expected home video units sold are estimated to increase by 4.3331 thousand, or 4333.1 units.

(e) $\hat{Y} = 76.54 + 4.3331X = 76.54 + 4.3331(20) = 163.202$ or 163,202 units.

(f)   Some other factors that might be useful in predicting video unit sales are (i) the number of days the movie was screened, (ii) the rating of the movie by critics, (iii) the amount of advertisement spent on the video release, etc.

13.8   (a)

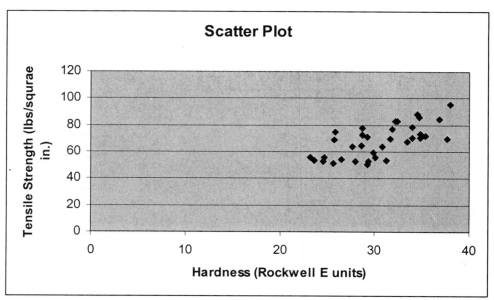

(b) $\hat{Y} = 6.0483 + 2.0191X$

(c)   For each increase of one additional Rockwell E unit in hardness, the estimated average tensile strength will increase by 2.0191 thousand pounds per square inch.

(d) $\hat{Y} = 6.0483 + 2.0191(70) = 147.382$ thousand pounds per square inch.

13.10 $SST = 40$ and $r^2 = 0.90$. So, 90% of the variation in the dependent variable can be explained by the variation in the independent variable.

13.12 $r^2 = 0.75$. So, 75% of the variation in the dependent variable can be explained by the variation in the independent variable.

13.14 (a) $r^2 = 0.684$. So, 68.4% of the variation in the dependent variable can be explained by the variation in the independent variable.

(b) $s_{YX} = 0.308$

(c) Based on (a) and (b), the model should be very useful for predicting sales.

13.16 (a) $r^2 = 0.9731$. So, 97.31% of the variation in the dependent variable can be explained by the variation in the independent variable.

(b) $s_{YX} = 0.7258$

(c) Based on (a) and (b), the model should be very useful for predicting the number of order.

13.18 (a) $r^2 = 0.723$. So, 72.3% of the variation in the dependent variable can be explained by the variation in the independent variable.

(b) $s_{YX} = 194.6$

(c) Based on (a) and (b), the model should be very useful for predicting monthly rent.

13.20 A residual analysis of the data indicates no apparent pattern. The assumptions of regression appear to be met.

13.22 (a)-(b) Based on a residual analysis, the model appears to be adequate.

13.24 (a)

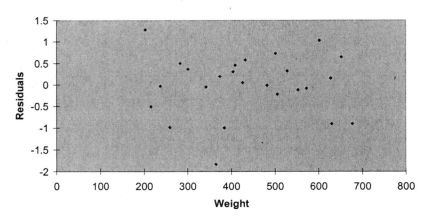

13.24   (a)
cont.

Normal Probability Plot

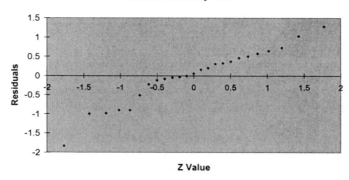

The residual plot does not reveal any obvious pattern. So a linear fit appears to be adequate.

(b)   The residual plot does not reveal any possible violation of the homoscedasticity assumption. This is not a time series data, so we do not need to evaluate the independence assumption. The normal probability plot shows that the distribution has a thicker left tail than a normal distribution but there is no sign of severe skewness.

13.26   (a)-(b)

Size Residual Plot

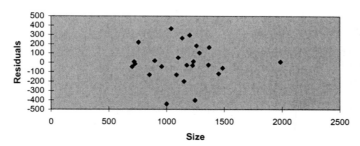

Normal Probability Plot

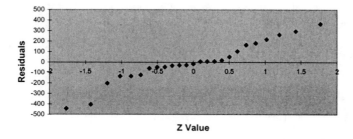

Based on a residual analysis of the residuals versus size, the model appears to be adequate. From the normal probability plot, it appears that the normality assumption is violated.

13.28 (a)   An increasing linear relationship exists. The critical values of the Durbin Watson statistic are $d_L = 1.08$ and $d_U = 1.36$

(b) $D = 0.109$

(c)   Since $D = 0.109 < d_L = 1.08$, there is enough evidence to conclude that there is strong positive autocorrelation among the residuals.

13.30 (a)   No, since the data have been collected for a single period for a set of stores.

(b)   If a single store was studied over a period of time and the amount of shelf space varied over time, computation of the Durbin-Watson statistic would be necessary.

13.32 (a)

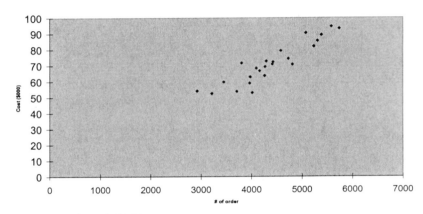

Scatter Diagram

(b) $b_0 = 0.458$, $b_1 = 0.0161$

(c)   For each increase of one order, the expected distribution cost is estimated to increase by 0.0161 thousand dollars, or $16.10.

(d) $\hat{Y} = 0.458 + 0.0161X = 0.458 + 0.0161(4500) = 72.908$ or $72,908

(e) $r^2 = 0.844$. So, 84.4% of the variation in distribution cost can be explained by the variation in the number of orders.

(f) $s_{YX} = 5.218$

(g)

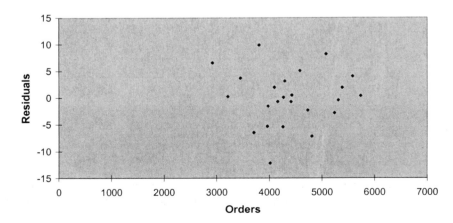

Orders Residual Plot

13.32   (h)
cont.

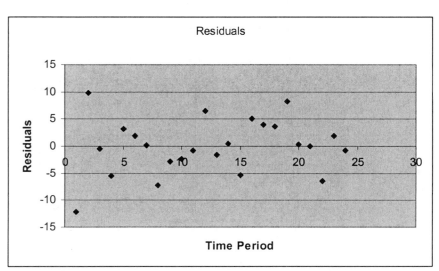

(i) $D = 2.08 > 1.45$. There is no evidence of positive autocorrelation among the residuals.
(j)   Based on a residual analysis, the model appears to be adequate.

13.34   (a)

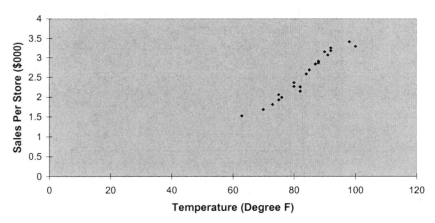

(b) $b_0 = -2.535$, $b_1 = 0.060728$
(c)   For each increase of one degree Fahrenheit in the high temperature, expected sales are estimated to increase by 0.060728 thousand dollars, or $60.73.
(d) $\hat{Y} = -2.535 + 0.060728X = -2.535 + 0.060728(83) = 2.5054$ or $2505.40
(e) $s_{YX} = 0.1461$
(f) $r^2 = 0.94$. So, 94% of the variation in sales per store can be explained by the variation in the daily high temperature.

13.34   (g)
cont.

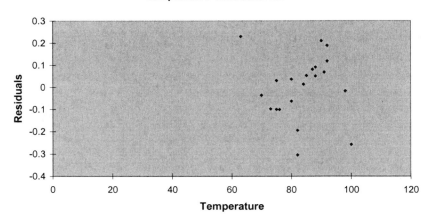

(h)

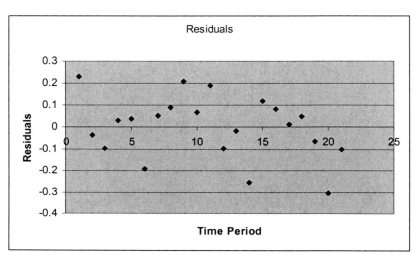

(i) $D = 1.64 > 1.42$. There is no evidence of positive autocorrelation among the residuals.
(j)   The plot of the residuals versus time period shows some clustering of positive and
       negative residuals for intervals in the domain, suggesting a nonlinear model might be
       better. Otherwise, the model appears to be adequate.
(k) $b_0 = -2.6281$, $b_1 = 0.061713$
       For each increase of one degree Fahrenheit in the high temperature, expected sales
       are estimated to increase by 0.061713 thousand dollars, or $61.71.

       $\hat{Y} = -2.6281 + 0.061713X = -2.6281 + 0.061713(83) = 2.4941$ or $2494.10

       $r^2 = 0.929$. 92.9% of the variation in sales per store can be explained by the variation
       in the daily high temperature.

       $s_{YX} = 0.1623$

       $D = 1.24$. The test of the Durbin-Watson statistic is inconclusive as to whether there
       is positive autocorrelation among the residuals.
       The plot of the residuals versus time period shows some clustering of positive and
       negative residuals for intervals in the domain, suggesting a nonlinear model might be
       better. Otherwise, the model appears to be adequate.
       The results are similar to those in (a)-(j).

13.36 (a) $MSR = SSR / p = 60/1 = 60$

$MSE = SSE / (n - p - 1) = 40/18 = 2.222$

$F = MSR / MSE = 60/2.222 = 27$

(b) $F_{1,18} = 4.41$

(c) Reject H_0. There is evidence that the fitted linear regression model is useful.

(d) $r^2 = \dfrac{SSR}{SST} = \dfrac{60}{100} = 0.6$ $\qquad\qquad r = -\sqrt{0.60} = -0.7746$

(e) $H_0 : \rho = 0$ $\qquad\qquad$ There is no correlation between X and Y.

$H_1 : \rho \neq 0$ $\qquad\qquad$ There is correlation between X and Y.

$d.f. = 18.$ $\qquad$ Decision rule: Reject H_0 if $|t_{cal}| > 2.1009$.

Test statistic: $t = \dfrac{r - \rho}{\sqrt{\dfrac{1 - r^2}{n - 2}}} = \dfrac{-0.7746}{\sqrt{\dfrac{1 - 0.6}{18}}} = -5.196$.

Since $t_{cal} = -5.196$ is below the lower critical bound of -2.1009, reject H_0. There is enough evidence to conclude that there is a significant correlation between X and Y.

13.38 (a) $t = 16.5223 > t_{34} = 2.0322$ with 18 degrees of freedom for $\alpha = 0.05$. Reject H_0. There is evidence that the fitted linear regression model is useful.

(b) $0.0439 \leq \beta_1 \leq 0.0562$

13.40 (a) $t = 8.65 > t_{28} = 2.0484$ with 28 degrees of freedom for $\alpha = 0.05$. Reject H_0. There is evidence that the fitted linear regression model is useful.

(b) $3.3073 \leq \beta_1 \leq 5.3589$

13.42 (a) p-value $= 7.26497\text{E-}06 < 0.05$. Reject H_0. There is evidence that the fitted linear regression model is useful.

(b) $1.2463 \leq \beta_1 \leq 2.7918$

13.44 (a) $(\% \text{ daily change in ULPIX}) = b_0 + 2.00(\% \text{ daily change in S\&P 500 Index})$

(b) If the S&P gains 30% in a year, the ULPIX is expected to gain an estimated 60%.

(c) If the S&P loses 35% in a year, the ULPIX is expected to lose an estimated 70%.

(d) Since the leverage funds have higher volatility and, hence, higher risk than the market, risk averse investors should stay away from these funds. Risk takers, on the other hand, will benefit from the higher potential gain from these funds.

13.46 (a) $r = -0.4014$.

(b) $t = -1.8071$, p-value $= 0.0885 > 0.05$. Do not reject H_0. At 0.05 level of significance, there is no significant linear relationship between the turnover rate of pre-boarding screeners and the security violations detected.

(c) There is not sufficient evidence to conclude that there is a linear relationship between the turnover rate of pre-boarding screeners and the security violations detected.

13.48 (a) $r = 0.4838$
       (b) $t = 2.5926$, p-value $= 0.0166 < 0.05$. Reject H_0. At 0.05 level of significance, there is significant linear relationship between the cold-cranking amps and the price.
       (c)   The higher the price of a battery is, the higher is its cold-cranking amps.
       (d)   Yes, the expectation that batteries with higher cranking amps to have a higher price is borne out by the data.

13.50 (a)   When $X = 4$, $\hat{Y} = 5 + 3X = 5 + 3(4) = 17$
$$h = \frac{1}{n} + \frac{(X_i - \bar{X})^2}{\sum_{i=1}^{n}(X_i - \bar{X})^2} = \frac{1}{20} + \frac{(4-2)^2}{20} = 0.25$$
95% confidence interval: $\hat{Y} \pm t_{18}s_{YX}\sqrt{h} = 17 \pm 2.1009 \cdot 1 \cdot \sqrt{0.25}$
$15.95 \le \mu_{YX} \le 18.05$
       (b)   95% prediction interval: $\hat{Y} \pm t_{18}s_{YX}\sqrt{1+h} = 17 \pm 2.1009 \cdot 1 \cdot \sqrt{1.25}$
$14.651 \le Y_I \le 19.349$
       (c)   The intervals in this problem are wider because the value of X is farther from $\bar{X}$.

13.52 (a) $20.7990 \le \mu_{Y|X} \le 24.5419$
       (b) $12.2755 \le Y_I \le 33.0654$
       (c)   Part (b) provides an estimate for an individual response and Part (a) provides an estimate for an average predicted value.

13.54 (a) $100.96 \le \mu_{Y|X} \le 138.77$
       (b) $20.1 \le Y_I \le 219.72$
       (c)   Part (b) provides an estimate for an individual response and Part (a) provides an estimate for an average predicted value.

13.56 (a) $116.7082 \le \mu_{Y|X} \le 178.0564$
       (b) $111.5942 \le Y_I \le 183.1704$
       (c)   Part (b) provides an estimate for an individual response and Part (a) provides an estimate for an average predicted value.

13.58 The coefficient of determination measures the proportion of variation in Y that is explained by the independent variable X in the regression model.

13.60 The explained variation or regression sum of squares (SSR) will be equal to zero only when there is no relationship between the Y and X variables, and the coefficient of determination equals 0.

13.62   The assumptions of regression are normality of error, homoscedasticity, and independence of errors. The normality of error assumption can be evaluated by obtaining a histogram, box-and-whisker plot, and/or normal probability plot of the residuals. The homoscedasticity assumption can be evaluated by plotting the residuals on the vertical axis and the X variable on the horizontal axis. The independence of errors assumption can be evaluated by plotting the residuals on the vertical axis and the time order variable on the horizontal axis. This assumption can also be evaluated by computing the Durbin-Watson statistic.

13.64   If the data in a regression analysis has been collected over time, then the assumption of independence of errors needs to be evaluated using the Durbin-Watson statistic.

13.66   (a)

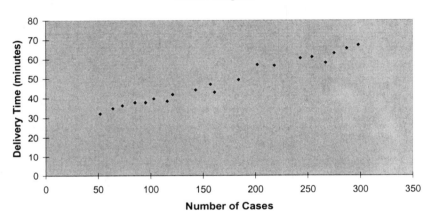

Scatter Diagram

(b) $b_0 = 24.84$, $b_1 = 0.14$

(c) $\hat{Y} = 24.84 + 0.14X$, where X is the number of cases and $\hat{Y}$ is the estimated delivery time.

(d)   For each additional case, the estimated delivery time increases by 0.14 minutes.

(e) $\hat{Y} = 24.84 + 0.14X = 24.84 + 0.14(150) = 45.84$

(f)   No, 500 cases is outside the relevant range of the data used to fit the regression equation.

(g) $r^2 = 0.972$. So, 97.2% of the variation in delivery time can be explained by the variation in the number of cases.

(h)   Since b_1 is positive, $r = +\sqrt{r^2} = +\sqrt{0.972} = +0.986$

(i) $s_{YX} = 1.987$

(j)   Based on a visual inspection of the graphs of the distribution of residuals and the residuals versus the number of cases, there is no pattern. The model appears to be adequate.

(k) $t = 24.88 > t_{18} = 2.1009$ with 18 degrees of freedom for $\alpha = 0.05$. Reject H_0.
       There is evidence that the fitted linear regression model is useful.

(l) $44.88 \leq \mu_{YX} \leq 46.80$

(m) $41.56 \leq Y_I \leq 50.12$

(n) $0.1282 \leq \beta_1 \leq 0.1518$

13.68   (a)

Scatter Diagram

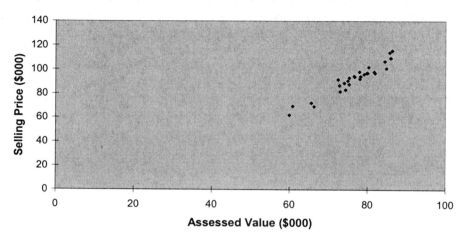

$b_0 = -44.172$, $b_1 = 1.78171$

(b)   For each additional dollar in assessed value, the estimated selling price increases by $1.78.

(c) $\hat{Y} = -44.172 + 1.78171X = -44.172 + 1.78171(70) = 80.458$ or $80,458

(d) $S_{YX} = 3.475$

(e) $r^2 = 0.926$. 92.6% of the variation in selling price can be explained by the variation in the assessed value.

(f)   Since b_1 is positive, $r = +\sqrt{r^2} = +\sqrt{0.926} = +0.962$

(g)   Based on a visual inspection of the graphs of the distribution of residuals and the residuals versus the assessed value, there is no pattern. The model appears to be adequate.

(h) $t = 18.66 > t_{28} = 2.0484$ with 28 degrees of freedom for $\alpha = 0.05$. Reject H_0. There is evidence that the fitted linear regression model is useful.

(i) $78.707 \le \mu_{YX} \le 82.388$

(j) $73.195 \le Y_I \le 87.900$

(k) $1.5862 \le \beta_1 \le 1.9772$

13.70   (a)

Scatter Diagram

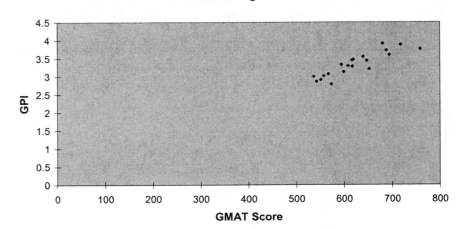

$b_0 = 0.30$, $b_1 = 0.00487$

(b)   For each additional point on the GMAT score, the estimated GPI increases by 0.00487.

(c) $\hat{Y} = 0.30 + 0.00487X = 0.30 + 0.00487(600) = 3.2225$

(d) $s_{YX} = 0.1559$

(e) $r^2 = 0.7978$. 79.78% of the variation in the GPI can be explained by the variation in the GMAT score.

(f)   Since b_1 is positive, $r = +\sqrt{r^2} = +\sqrt{0.7978} = +0.893$

(g)   Based on a visual inspection of the graphs of the distribution of residuals and the residuals versus the GMAT score, there is no pattern. The model appears to be adequate.

(h) $t = 8.428 > t_{18} = 2.1009$ with 18 degrees of freedom for $\alpha = 0.05$. Reject H_0.
There is evidence that the fitted linear regression model is useful.

(i) $3.144 \leq \mu_{YX} \leq 3.301$

(j) $2.886 \leq Y_I \leq 3.559$

(k) $0.00366 \leq \beta_1 \leq 0.00608$

(l) $b_0 = 0.258$, $b_1 = 0.00494$
For each additional point on the GMAT score, the estimated GPI increases by 0.00494.

$\hat{Y} = 0.258 + 0.00494X = 0.258 + 0.00494(600) = 3.221$

$s_{YX} = 0.147$

$r^2 = 0.820$. 82.0% of the variation in the GPI can be explained by the variation in the GMAT score.

13.70   (1)   Since b_1 is positive, $r = +\sqrt{r^2} = +\sqrt{0.82} = +0.906$

cont.   Based on a visual inspection of the graphs of the distribution of residuals and the residuals versus the GMAT score, there is no pattern. The model appears to be adequate.

$t = 9.06 > t_{18} = 2.1009$ with 18 degrees of freedom for $\alpha = 0.05$. Reject H_0. There is evidence that the fitted linear regression model is useful.

$3.147 \le \mu_{YX} \le 3.295$

$2.903 \le Y_I \le 3.539$

$0.00380 \le \beta_1 \le 0.00609$

13.72   (a)

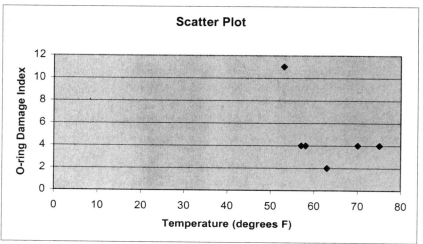

There is not any clear relationship between atmospheric temperature and O-ring damage from the scatter plot.

(b),(f)

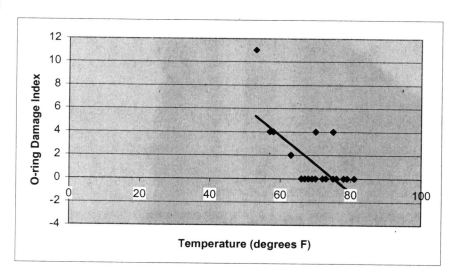

13.72   (c)   In (b), there are 16 observations with an O-ring damage index of 0 for a variety of
cont.   temperature. If one concentrates on these observations with no O-ring damage, there
                is obviously no relationship between O-ring damage index and temperature. If all
                observations are used, the observations with no O-ring damage will bias the
                estimated relationship. If the intention is to investigate the relationship between the
                degrees of O-ring damage to atmospheric temperature, it makes sense to focus only
                on the flight in which there was O-ring damage.

        (d)   Prediction should not be made for an atmospheric temperature of 31 ^{0}F because it is
                outside the range of the temperature variable in the data. Such prediction will
                involve extrapolation, which assumes that any relationship between two variables
                will continue to hold outside the domain of the temperature variable.

        (e) $\hat{Y} = 18.036 - 0.240X$

        (g)   A nonlinear model is more appropriate for these data.

        (h)

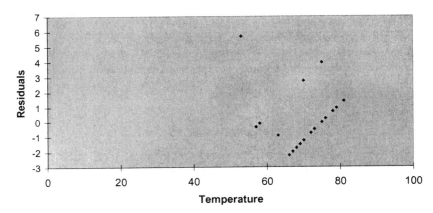

Temperature Residual Plot

                The string of negative residuals and positive residuals that lie on a straight line
                with a positive slope in the lower-right corner of the plot is a strong indication
                that a nonlinear model should be used if all 23 observations are to be used in
                the fit.

13.74   (a)

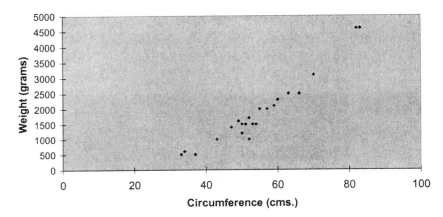

Scatter Diagram

13.74 (b) $\hat{Y} = -2629.222 + 82.4717X$

cont. (c)   For each increase in one additional cm in circumference, the estimated average weight of a pumpkin will increase by 82.4717 grams.

       (d) $\hat{Y} = -2629.222 + 82.4717(60) = 2319.080$ grams.

       (e)   There appears to be a positive relationship between weight and circumference of a pumpkin. It is a good idea for the farmer to sell pumpkin by circumference instead of weight for circumference is a good predictor of weight and it is much easier to measure the circumference of a pumpkin than its weight.

       (f) $r^2 = 0.9373$. 93.73% of the variation in pumpkin weight can be explained by the variation in circumference.

       (g) $S_{YX} = 277.7495$.

       (h)

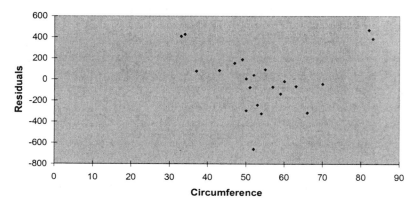

Circumference Residual Plot

There appears to be a nonlinear relationship between circumference and weight.

       (i) p-value is virtually 0. Reject H_0. There is sufficient evidence to conclude that there is a linear relationship between the circumference and the weight of a pumpkin.

       (j) $72.7875 < \beta_1 < 92.1559$

       (k) $2186.9589 < \mu_{Y|X} < 2451.2020$

       (l) $1726.5508 < Y_I < 2911.6101$

13.76 (a)

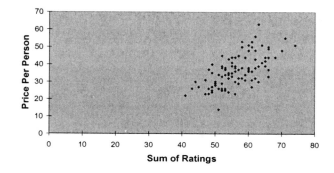

Scatter Diagram

13.76   (b) $\hat{Y} = -13.6561 + 0.8932X$

cont.   (c)   Since no restaurant will receive a summated rating of 0, it is not meaningful to interpret b_0. For each additional unit of increase in summated rating, the estimated average price per person will increase by \$0.8932.

         (d) $\hat{Y} = -13.6561 + 0.8932(50) = \$31.01$

         (e) $S_{YX} = 7.0167$

         (f) $r^2 = 0.4246$. 42.46% of the variation in price per person can be explained by the variation in summated rating.

         (g) $r = \sqrt{r^2} = \sqrt{0.4246} = 0.6516$.

         (h)

Summated rating Residual Plot

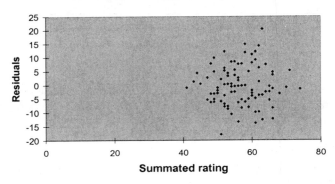

Based on a visual inspection of the residual plot of summated rating, there may be a violation of the homoscedasticity assumption.

         (i) p-value is virtually 0. Reject H_0. There is very strong evidence to conclude that there is a linear relationship between price per persona and summated rating.

         (j) $\$29.07 < \mu_{Y|X} < \$32.94$

         (k) $\$16.95 < Y_I < \$45.06$

         (l) $0.6848 < \beta_1 < 1.1017$

         (m)   The linear regression model appears to have provided an adequate fit and shown a significant linear relationship between price per person and summated rating. Since 42.46% of the variation in price per person can be explained by the variation in summated rating, price per person is moderately useful in predicting the price.

13.78   (a)

Scatter Diagram

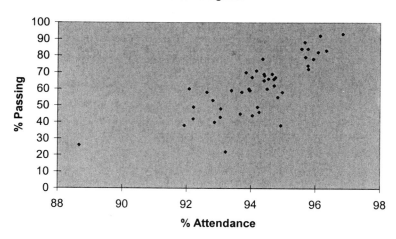

There is a very obvious positive relationship between % of students passing the proficiency test and the daily average of the percentage of students attending class.

(b) $b_0 = -771.5868$ $b_1 = 8.8447$

$\hat{Y} = -771.5869 + 8.8447X$

(c) $b_1 = 8.8447$ implies that as daily average percentage of students attending class increases by 1%, the estimated average percentage of students passing the ninth-grade proficiency test will increase by 8.8447%.

(d) $S_{YX} = 10.5787$

(e) $r^2 = 0.6024$. 60.24% of the total variation in % passing the proficiency test can be explained by % attendance.

(f) $r = \sqrt{r^2} = 0.7762$. There is a rather strong positive linear relationship between % of students passing the proficiency test and daily average of the % of students attending class.

13.78   (g)
cont.

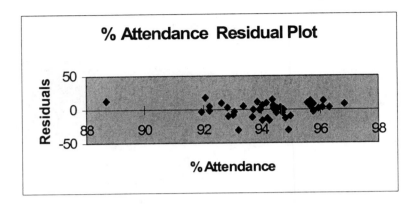

The residuals are evenly distributed across difference range of % attendance. There is no obvious violation of the homoscedasticity assumption.

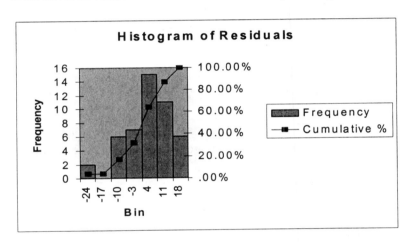

The distribution of the residuals is left skewed. However, with the exception of 2 extremely negative residuals, the histogram is not too badly skewed.

(h) $H_0 : \rho = 0$ $H_1 : \rho \neq 0$

Test statistic: $t = \dfrac{r}{\sqrt{\dfrac{1-r^2}{n-2}}} = 8.2578$

Decision rule: Reject H_0 when $|t| > 2.0141$.

Decision: Since $t = 8.2578$ is above the upper critical bound 2.0141, reject H_0.

There is enough evidence to conclude that there is a linear relationship between % passing and % attendance.

(i) $b_1 \pm t_{n-2} S_{b_1} = 8.8447 \pm 2.0141(1.0711)$ $6.6874 < \beta_1 < 11.0020$

13.78   (j)   (a)
cont.

Scatter Diagram

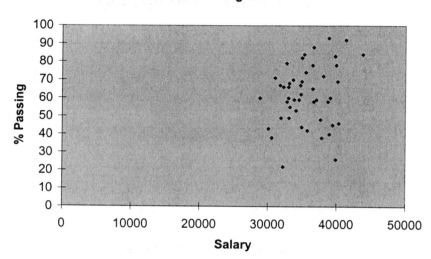

There seems to be a slightly positive relationship between % of students passing the proficiency test and average teacher salary.

(b) $\hat{Y} = 23.065 + 0.0011X$

(c) $b_1 = 0.0011$ implies that as average teacher salary increase by \$1, the estimated average percentage of students passing the ninth-grade proficiency test will increase by 0.0011%.

(d) $S_{YX} = 16.3755$

(e) $r^2 = 0.0474$. Only 4.74% of the total variation in % passing the proficiency test can be explained by average teacher salary.

(f) $r = \sqrt{r^2} = 0.2177$. There seems to be a rather weak positive linear relationship between % of students passing the proficiency test and average teacher salary.

13.78   (j)   (g)
cont.

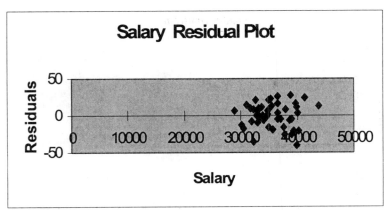

The residuals are evenly distributed across difference range of % attendance. There is no obvious violation of the homoscedasticity assumption.

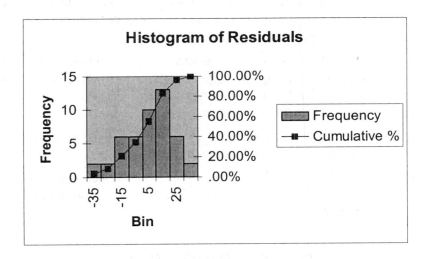

The distribution of the residuals is slightly left skewed but not too far from a normal distribution.

(h) $H_0 : \rho = 0$ $H_1 : \rho \neq 0$

Test statistic: $t = \dfrac{r}{\sqrt{\dfrac{1-r^2}{n-2}}} = 1.496$

Decision rule: Reject H_0 when $|t| > 2.0141$.

Decision: Since $t = 1.496$ is below the upper critical bound 2.0141, do not reject H_0. There is not enough evidence to conclude that there is a linear relationship between % passing and average teacher salary

(i) $b_1 \pm t_{n-2} S_{b_1} = 0.0011 \pm 2.0141(0.00073)$ $-0.000375 < \beta_1 < 0.002542$

13.78   (k)   (a)
cont.

Scatter Diagram

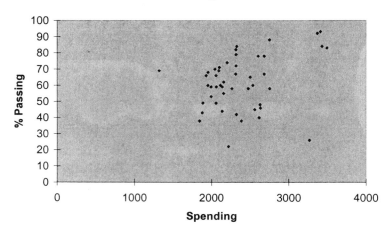

There seems to be a slightly positive relationship between % of students passing the proficiency test and spending per pupil.

(b) $\hat{Y} = 35.7843 + 0.0109X$

(c) $b_1 = 0.0109$ implies that as spending per pupil increase by \$1, the estimated average percentage of students passing the ninth-grade proficiency test will increase by 0.019%.

(d) $S_{YX} = 15.9984$

(e) $r^2 = 0.0907$. Only 9.07% of the total variation in % passing the proficiency test can be explained by spending per pupil.

(f) $r = \sqrt{r^2} = 0.3012$. There seems to be a rather weak positive linear relationship between % of students passing the proficiency test and spending per pupil.

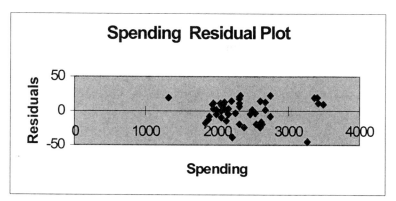

The residuals are evenly distributed across difference range of % attendance. There is no obvious violation of the homoscedasticity assumption.

13.78 (k)   (g)
cont.

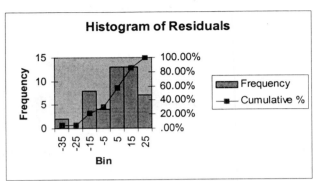

The distribution of the residuals is slightly left skewed. Excluding the largest negative residual, the histogram is quite symmetric.

(h) $H_0 : \rho = 0$ $H_1 : \rho \neq 0$

Test statistic: $t = \dfrac{r}{\sqrt{\dfrac{1-r^2}{n-2}}} = 2.1192$

Decision rule: Reject H_0 when $|t| > 2.0141$.

Decision: Since $t = 2.1192$ is above the upper critical bound 2.0141, reject H_0. There is enough evidence to conclude that there is a linear relationship between % passing and spending.

(i) $b_1 \pm t_{n-2} S_{b_1} = 0.0109 \pm 2.0141(0.0052)$ $0.00054 < \beta_1 < 0.02129$

(l)   The model with % attendance is the best model to use for predicting % passing since it has the highest R-square of 60.24%.

13.80 (a)

Excel output:

	GM	Ford	IAL	HCR
GM	1			
Ford	-0.00638	1		
IAL	-0.00049	-0.46514	1	
HCR	0.391803	-0.25165	0.778198	1

(b)   There is almost no correlation between the stock prices of GM and Ford with an $r = -0.00638$, an also almost no correlation between the prices of IAL and GM with an $r = -0.00049$, a moderately negative correlation of $r = -0.46514$ between the prices of Ford and IAL, a weak positive correlation of $r = 0.391803$ between the prices of GM and HCR, a weak negative correlation of $r = -0.25165$ between the prices of Ford and HCR, and a rather strong positive correlation of $r = 0.77920$ between IAL and HCR.

(c)   It is not a good idea to have all the stocks in an individual's portfolio be strongly positively correlated for that will increase the variance, a measure of risk, of the portfolio. Some negatively correlated stock prices in a portfolio can reduce the combined variance (portfolio risk).

CHAPTER 14

OBJECTIVES
- To understand multiple regression model as an extension of the simple linear regression model
- To know how to measure the coefficient of partial determination
- To be able to use dummy variable and interaction terms in regression models
- To understand the logistic regression model for predicting a categorical response variable

OVERVIEW AND KEY CONCEPTS
The Multiple Regression Model
- The multiple regression model describes the relationship between one dependent variable and 2 or more independent variables in a linear function.

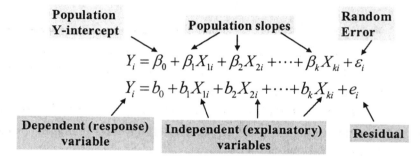

$$Y_i = \beta_0 + \beta_1 X_{1i} + \beta_2 X_{2i} + \cdots + \beta_k X_{ki} + \varepsilon_i$$

$$Y_i = b_0 + b_1 X_{1i} + b_2 X_{2i} + \cdots + b_k X_{ki} + e_i$$

The Simple Linear Regression and Multiple Regression Compared
- Coefficients in a simple regression pick up the impact of that variable plus the impacts of other variables that are correlated with it and the dependent variable.
- Coefficients in a multiple regression net out the impacts of other variables in the equation. Hence, they are called *net regression coefficients*.

Interpretation of the Estimated Coefficients
- **The Y intercept (b_0):** The estimated average value of Y_i when all $X_i = 0$.
- **Slope (b_i):** Estimated that the average value of Y changes by b_i for each one-unit increase in X_i holding constant the effect of all other independent variables.

Predicting the Dependent Variable Y
- Use the estimated sample regression equation (multiple linear regression equation):
$$\hat{Y}_i = b_0 + b_1 X_{1i} + \cdots + b_k X_{ki}$$

The Venn Diagram and Explanatory Power of the Multiple Regression Model

Variations in X_1 not used in explaining variation in Y

Variations in Y not explained by X_1 (SSE)

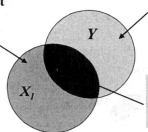

Variations in Y explained by X_1 or variations in X_1 used in explaining variation in Y (SSR)

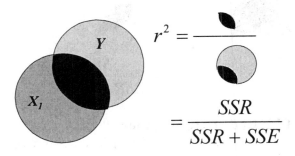

$$r^2 = \frac{\text{◖}}{\text{◕}}$$

$$= \frac{SSR}{SSR + SSE}$$

Variation *NOT* explained by X_1 nor X_2 (SSE)

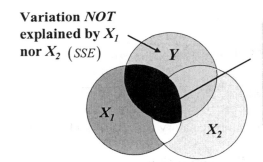

Overlapping variation in both X_1 and X_2 are used in explaining the _variation_ in Y but _NOT_ in the _estimation_ of β_1 nor β_2

Coefficient of Multiple Determination

- Coefficient of multiple determination measures the proportion of total variation in Y explained by all X variables taken together.
- $r^2_{Y \bullet 12 \cdots k} = \dfrac{SSR}{SST} = \dfrac{\text{Explained Variation}}{\text{Total Variation}}$
- It never decreases when an additional X variable is added to the model, which is a disadvantage when comparing among models.

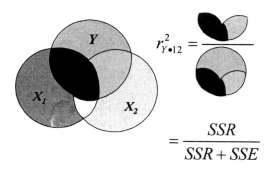

$$r^2_{Y \bullet 12} = \frac{}{}$$

$$= \frac{SSR}{SSR + SSE}$$

Adjusted Coefficient of Multiple Determination

- It measures the proportion of variation in Y explained by all X variables adjusted for the number of X variables used.
- $r^2_{adj} = 1 - \left[\left(1 - r^2_{Y \bullet 12 \cdots k} \right) \dfrac{n-1}{n-k-1} \right]$
- It penalizes excessive use of independent variables.
- It is smaller than $r^2_{Y \bullet 12 \cdots k}$.
- It is useful in comparing among models.
- It can have a negative value.
- Its value can decrease when an additional explanatory variable is added to the existing model.

Interpretation of Coefficient of Multiple Determination

- $r^2_{Y \bullet 12 \cdots k}$ measures the proportion of total variation in Y that can be explained by all X variables.
- r^2_{adj} measures the proportion of total variation in Y that can be explained by all X variables after adjusting for the number of independent variables and sample size.

F Test for the Significance of the Entire Multiple Regression Model

- **The hypotheses:**
  - $H_0: \beta_1 = \beta_2 = \cdots = \beta_k = 0$ (There is no linear relationship)
  - $H_1:$ At least one $\beta_i \neq 0$ (At least one independent variable affects Y)
- **Test statistic:**
  - $F = \dfrac{MSR}{MSE} = \dfrac{SSR(\text{all})/k}{SSE(\text{all})/(n-k-1)}$ with k numerator degrees of freedom and $(n-k-1)$ denominator degrees of freedom.
  - The rejection region is always in the right tail.

t Test for the Significance of Individual Variables
- **The hypotheses:**
  - $H_0: \beta_i = 0$ (X_i does not affect Y)
  - $H_1: \beta_i \neq 0$ (X_i affects Y)
- **Test statistic:**
  - $t = \dfrac{b_j - \beta_j}{S_{b_j}}$ with $(n - k - 1)$ degrees of freedom.
  - The *t* test can also be a one-tail test for a one-tail alternative.
- Confidence interval estimate for β_j: Use the $100(1 - \alpha)\%$ confidence interval for β_j.
  - $b_j \pm t_{\alpha/2, n-k-1} S_{b_j}$

Contribution of a Single Independent Variable X_j
- The contribution of an independent variable X_j to the regression model is measured by

$SSR\left(X_j \mid \text{all variables except } X_j\right)$
$= SSR\left(\text{all variables including } X_j\right) - SSR\left(\text{all variables except } X_j\right)$

The Partial *F* Test for Determining the Contribution of an Independent Variable
- **The hypotheses:**
  - H_0: Variable X_j does not significantly improve the model after all the other X have been included
  - H_1: Variable X_j significantly improve the model once all the other X have been included
- **Test statistic:**
  - $F = \dfrac{SSR\left(X_j \mid \text{all variables except } X_j\right)}{MSE(\text{all})}$ with 1 and $(n - k - 1)$ degrees of freedom.
  - The rejection region is always in the right tail.
  - This partial *F* test statistic $F_{1, n-k-1}$ always equals to the squared of the *t* test statistic for the significance of X_j, i.e., $\left(t_{n-k-1}\right)^2 = F_{1, n-k-1}$.

Coefficient of Partial Determination

- It measures the proportion of variation in the dependent variable that is explained by X_j while controlling for (holding constant) the other independent variables.

- $r^2_{Yj \bullet \text{all variables except } X_j} = \dfrac{SSR\left(X_j \mid \text{all variables except } X_j\right)}{SST - SSR\left(\text{all variables including } X_j\right) + SSR\left(X_j \mid \text{all variables excep}\right.}$

Two independent variables model

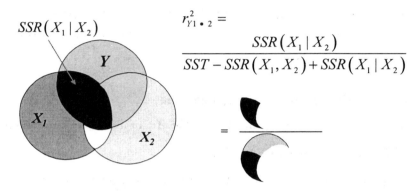

$$r^2_{Y1 \bullet 2} = \frac{SSR\left(X_1 \mid X_2\right)}{SST - SSR\left(X_1, X_2\right) + SSR\left(X_1 \mid X_2\right)}$$

Dummy-Variable Model and Interactions

- Dummy variables are used to represent categorical explanatory variables with two or more levels.
- A dummy variable is always coded as 0 and 1.
- The number of dummy variables needed is equal to the number of levels minus 1.
- **Interpretation of the estimated slope coefficient of a dummy variable:** The slope coefficient of a dummy variable measures the estimated average incremental effect of the presence of the characteristic captured by the dummy variable holding constant the effect of all other independent variables.
- In the dummy-variable model, it is assumed that the slope of the dependent variable Y with an independent variable X is the same for each of the two levels of the dummy variable.
- To test whether the slope of the dependent variable Y with an independent variable X is the same for each of the two levels of the dummy variable, we can introduce the interaction term and test for the significance of this interaction term.

  E.g., Let X_1 and X_2 be two numerical independent variables, and X_3 be a dummy variable.

  To test whether the slopes of Y with X_1 and/or X_2 are the same for each of the two levels of X_3, the regression model is $Y_i = \beta_0 + \beta_1 X_{1i} + \beta_2 X_{2i} + \beta_3 X_{3i} + \beta_4 X_{1i} X_{3i} + \beta_5 X_{2i} X_{3i} + \varepsilon_i$

  - **The hypotheses:**

    $H_0 : \beta_4 = \beta_5 = 0$ (no interaction of X_1 with X_3 or X_2 with X_3)

    $H_1 : \beta_4$ and/or $\beta_5 \neq 0$ (X_1 and/or X_2 interacts with X_3)

  - **Partial F test statistic:** $F = \dfrac{\left(SSR(X_1, X_2, X_3, X_4, X_5) - SSR(X_1, X_2, X_3)\right)/2}{MSE(X_1, X_2, X_3, X_4, X_5)}$

    with 2 and $(n-6)$ degrees of freedom.

- To test only whether the slope of Y with X_1 is the same for each of the two level of X_3, we can perform a t test on $H_0 : \beta_4 = 0$ vs. $H_1 : \beta_4 \neq 0$. Likewise, to test only whether the slope of Y with just X_2 along is the same for each of the two level of X_3, one can perform a t test on $H_0 : \beta_5 = 0$ vs. $H_1 : \beta_5 \neq 0$.

- If all the independent variables are numerical variables, the above analysis can be extended to test for whether the independent variables interact with each other.

  E.g., Let X_1, X_2 and X_3 be three numerical independent variables. To evaluate possible interaction between the independent variables, the regression model to use is

  $$Y_i = \beta_0 + \beta_1 X_{1i} + \beta_2 X_{2i} + \beta_3 X_{3i} + \beta_4 X_{1i} X_{2i} + \beta_5 X_{1i} X_{3i} + \beta_6 X_{2i} X_{3i} + \varepsilon_i$$

  - To test whether the three interaction terms significantly improve the regression model:

    - **The hypotheses**:

      $H_0 : \beta_4 = \beta_5 = \beta_6 = 0$ (There are no interaction among X_1, X_2 and X_3)

      $H_1 : \beta_4 \neq 0$ and/or $\beta_5 \neq 0$ and/or $\beta_6 \neq 0$ (X_1 interact with X_2, and/or X_1 interacts with X_3, and/or X_2 interacts with X_3)

    - **Partial F test statistic**:

      $$F = \frac{\left(SSR(X_1,X_2,X_3,X_4,X_5,X_6) - SSR(X_1,X_2,X_3)\right)/3}{MSE(X_1,X_2,X_3,X_4,X_5,X_6)}$$ with 3 and

      $(n-7)$ degrees of freedom.

  - To test the contribution of each interaction separately to determine which interaction terms should be included in the model, we can perform separate t test.

Logistic Regression

- **Odd ratio:** Odds ratio $= \dfrac{\text{probability of success}}{1 - \text{probability of success}}$

- **Logistic regression model:** $\ln(\text{odds ratio}) = \beta_0 + \beta_1 X_{1i} + \beta_2 X_{2i} + \cdots + \beta_k X_{ki} + \varepsilon_i$

- **Logistic regression equation:** $\ln(\text{estimated odds ratio}) = b_0 + b_1 X_{1i} + b_2 X_{2i} + \cdots + b_k X_{ki}$

- **Estimated odds ratio:** $e^{\ln(\text{estimated odds ratio})}$

- **Estimated probability of success:** $\dfrac{\text{estimated odds ratio}}{1 + \text{estimated odds ratio}}$

- **Interpretation of the estimated slope coefficient b_j:** b_j measures the estimated change in the natural logarithm of the odds ratio as a result of a one unit change in X_j holding constant the effects of all the other independent variables.

Testing whether the Logistic Regression is a Good-Fitting Model
- **The hypotheses:**
  - H_0 : The model is a good-fitting model
  - H_1 : The model is not a good-fitting model
- **Test statistic:**
  - The ***deviance statistic*** has a χ^2 distribution with $(n - k - 1)$ degrees of freedom.
  - The rejection region is always in the right tail.

Testing whether an Independent Variable Makes a Significant Contribution to a Logistic Model
- **The hypotheses:**
  - $H_0 : \beta_j = 0$ (X_j does not make a significant contribution to the logistic model)
  - $H_1 : \beta_j \neq 0$ (X_j makes a significant contribution to the logistic model)
- **Test statistic:**
  - The ***Wald statistic*** is normally distributed.
  - This is a two-tail test with left and right-tail rejection regions.

SOLUTIONS TO END OF SECTION AND CHAPTER REVIEW EVEN PROBLEMS

14.2   (a)   Holding constant the effect of X_2, for each additional unit of X_1 the response variable Y is expected to decrease on average by 2 units. Holding constant the effect of X_1, for each additional unit of X_2 the response variable Y is expected to increase on average by 7 units.

         (b)   The Y-intercept 50 estimates the value of Y if X_1 and X_2 are both 0.

         (c)   40% of the variation in Y can be explained or accounted for by the variation in X_1 and the variation in X_2.

14.4   (a) $\hat{Y} = -2.72825 + 0.047114X_1 + 0.011947X_2$

         (b)   For a given number of orders, each increase of $1000 in sales is expected to result in an estimated average increase in distribution cost by $47.114. For a given amount of sales, each increase of one order is expected to result in the estimated average increase in distribution cost by $11.95.

         (c)   The interpretation of b_0 has no practical meaning here because it would have been the estimated average distribution cost when there were no sales and zero number of orders.

         (d) $\hat{Y}_i = -2.72825 + 0.047114(400) + 0.011947(4500) = 69.878$ or $69,878

         (e) $\$66,419.93 < \mu_{Y|X} < \$73,337.01$

         (f) $\$59,380.61 < Y_I < \$80,376.33$

         (g) $r_{Y.12}^2 = SSR / SST = 3368.087 / 3845.13 = 0.8759$. So, 87.59% of the variation in distribution cost can be explained by variation in sales and variation in number of orders.

         (h) $r_{adj}^2 = 1 - \left[(1 - r_{Y.12}^2)\dfrac{n-1}{n-p-1} \right] = 1 - \left[(1 - 0.8759)\dfrac{24-1}{24-2-1} \right] = 0.8641$

14.6   (a) $\overset{sales}{}\;\; \hat{Y} = 156.4 + 13.081\overset{radio}{X_1} + 16.795\overset{newspaper}{X_2}$

         (b)   For a given amount of newspaper advertising, each increase by $1000 in radio advertising is expected to result in an average increase in sales by $13,081. For a given amount of radio advertising, each increase by $1000 in newspaper advertising is expected to result in the average increase in sales by $16,795.

         (c)   When there is no money spent on radio advertising, and newspaper advertising, the estimated average sales is $156,430.44.

         (d) $\hat{Y}_i = 156.4 + 13.081(20) + 16.795(20) = 753.95$ or $753,950

         (e) $\$623,038.31 < \mu_{Y|X} < \$884,860.93$ (f) $\$396,522.63 < Y_I < \$1,111,376.60$

         (g) $r_{Y.12}^2 = SSR / SST = 2028033 / 2507793 = 0.8087$. So, 80.87% of the variation in sales can be explained by variation in radio advertising and variation in newspaper advertising.

         (h) $r_{adj}^2 = 1 - \left[(1 - r_{Y.12}^2)\dfrac{n-1}{n-p-1} \right] = 1 - \left[(1 - 0.8087)\dfrac{22-1}{22-2-1} \right] = 0.7886$

14.8   (a)   68% of the total variability in team performance can be explained by team skills after adjusting for the number of predictors and sample size. 78% of the total variability in team performance can be explained by clarity in expectation after adjusting for the number of predictors and sample size. 97% of the total variability in team performance can be explained by both team skills and clarity in expectations after adjusting for the number of predictors and sample size.

        (b)   Model 3 is the best predictor of team performance since it has the highest adjusted r^2.

14.10   There appears to be a quadratic relationship in the plot of the residuals against the predicted values of MPG, the horsepower and the weight. Thus, variable transformations or quadratic terms for the explanatory variables should be considered for inclusion in the model.

14.12   (a)

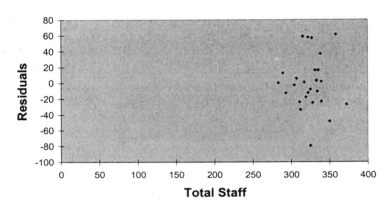

Total Staff Residual Plot

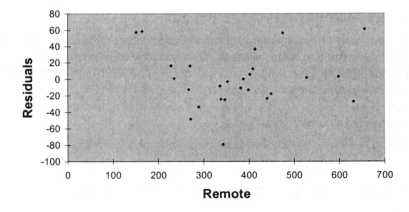

Remote Residual Plot

        Based upon a residual analysis, the model appears adequate.

        (b)   There is no evidence of a pattern over time.

        (c)   D = 1.79

        (d)   D = 1.79 > 1.55. There is no evidence of positive autocorrelation in the residuals.

14.14 (a) $MSR = SSR / p = 30/2 = 15$

$MSE = SSE /(n - p - 1) = 120/10 = 12$

(b) $F = MSR / MSE = 15/12 = 1.25$

(c) $F = 1.25 < F_{U(2,13-2-1)} = 4.103$. Do not reject H_0. There is not sufficient evidence of a significant linear relationship.

14.16 (a) $MSR = SSR / p = 3368.087/2 = 1684$

$MSE = SSE /(n - p - 1) = 477.043/21 = 22.7$

$F = MSR / MSE = 1684/22.7 = 74.13$

$F = 74.13 > F_{U(2,24-2-1)} = 3.467$. Reject H_0. There is evidence of a significant linear relationship.

(b) The p value or probability of obtaining an F test statistic based on 2 and 21 degrees when H_0 is true is less than 0.001.

14.18 (a) $MSR = SSR / p = 2028033/2 = 1014016$

$MSE = SSE /(n - p - 1) = 479759.9/19 = 25251$

$F = MSR / MSE = 1014016/25251 = 40.16$

$F = 40.16 > F_{U(2,22-2-1)} = 3.522$. Reject H_0. There is evidence of a significant linear relationship.

(b) The p value or probability of obtaining an F test statistic based on 2 and 19 degrees when H_0 is true is less than 0.001.

14.20 (a) Variable X_1 has a larger slope in terms of the t statistic of 2.5 than variable X_2, which has a smaller slope in terms of the t statistic of 1.25.

(b) 95% confidence interval on $\beta_1 : b_1 \pm t_{n-p-1}s_{b_1}$, $5 \pm 2.0739 \cdot 2$

$0.85225 \le \beta_1 \le 9.14775$

(c) For X_1: $t = b_1 / s_{b_1} = 5/2 = 2.50 > t_{22} = 2.0739$ with 22 degrees of freedom for $\alpha = 0.05$. Reject H_0. There is evidence that the variable X_1 contributes to a model already containing X_2.

For X_2: $t = b_2 / s_{b_2} = 10/8 = 1.25 < t_{22} = 2.0739$ with 22 degrees of freedom for $\alpha = 0.05$. Do not reject H_0. There is not sufficient evidence that the variable X_2 contributes to a model already containing X_1.

Only variable X_1 should be included in the model.

14.22 (a) 95% confidence interval on $\beta_1 : b_1 \pm t_{n-p-1}s_{b_1}$, $0.79116 \pm 2.1788 \cdot 0.06295$

$0.65400 \le \beta_1 \le 0.92832$

(b) For X_1: $t = b_1 / s_{b_1} = 0.79116/0.06295 = 12.57 > t_{12} = 2.1788$ with 12 degrees of freedom for $\alpha = 0.05$. Reject H_0. There is evidence that the variable X_1 contributes to a model already containing X_2.

For X_2: $t = b_2 / s_{b_2} = 0.60484/0.07174 = 8.43 > t_{12} = 2.1788$ with 12 degrees of freedom for $\alpha = 0.05$. Reject H_0. There is evidence that the variable X_2 contributes to a model already containing X_1.

Both variables X_1 and X_2 should be included in the model.

14.24   (a)   95% confidence interval on $\beta_1 : b_1 \pm t_{n-p-1} s_{b_1}, -0.11753 \pm 2.0117 \cdot 0.0326$

$-0.18311 \le \beta_1 \le -0.05195$

(b)   For X_1: $t = b_1 / s_{b_1} = -0.11753 / 0.0326 = -3.605 < -t_{47} = -2.0117$ with 47 degrees of freedom for $\alpha = 0.05$. Reject H_0. There is evidence that the variable X_1 contributes to a model already containing X_2.

For X_2: $t = b_2 / s_{b_2} = -0.00687 / 0.0014 = -4.91 < -t_{47} = -2.0117$ with 47 degrees of freedom for $\alpha = 0.05$. Reject H_0. There is evidence that the variable X_2 contributes to a model already containing X_1.

Both variables X_1 and X_2 should be included in the model.

14.26   (a)   95% confidence interval on $\beta_1 : b_1 \pm t_{n-p-1} s_{b_1}, 1.7649 \pm 2.0687 \cdot 0.379$

$0.9809 \le \beta_1 \le 2.5489$

(b)   For X_1: $t = b_1 / s_{b_1} = 1.7649 / 0.379 = 4.66 > t_{23} = 2.0687$ with 23 degrees of freedom for $\alpha = 0.05$. Reject H_0. There is evidence that the variable X_1 contributes to a model already containing X_2.

For X_2: $t = b_2 / s_{b_2} = -0.1390 / 0.0588 = -2.36 < -t_{23} = -2.0687$ with 23 degrees of freedom for $\alpha = 0.05$. Reject H_0. There is evidence that the variable X_2 contributes to a model already containing X_1.

Both variables X_1 and X_2 should be included in the model.

14.28   (a)   For X_1: $SSR(X_1 | X_2) = SSR(X_1 \ and \ X_2) - SSR(X_2) = 30 - 15 = 15$

$$F = \frac{SSR(X_1 | X_2)}{MSE} = \frac{15}{120/10} = 1.25 < F_{U(1,10)} = 4.965 \text{ with 1 and 10 degrees of}$$

freedom and $\alpha = 0.05$. Do not reject H_0. There is not sufficient evidence that the variable X_1 contributes to a model already containing X_2.

For X_2: $SSR(X_2 | X_1) = SSR(X_1 \ and \ X_2) - SSR(X_1) = 30 - 20 = 10$

$$F = \frac{SSR(X_2 | X_1)}{MSE} = \frac{10}{120/10} = 0.833 < F_{U(1,10)} = 4.965 \text{ with 1 and 10 degrees of}$$

freedom and $\alpha = 0.05$. Do not reject H_0. There is not sufficient evidence that the variable X_2 contributes to a model already containing X_1.

Neither independent variable X_1 nor X_2 makes a significant contribution to the model in the presence of the other variable. Also the overall regression equation involving both independent variables is not significant:

$$F = \frac{MSR}{MSE} = \frac{30/2}{120/10} = 1.25 < F_{U(2,10)} = 4.103$$

Neither variable should be included in the model and other variables should be investigated.

14.28   (b)
cont.

$$r_{Y1.2}^2 = \frac{SSR(X_1 | X_2)}{SST - SSR(X_1 \; and \; X_2) + SSR(X_1 | X_2)} = \frac{15}{150 - 30 + 15}$$

= 0.1111. Holding constant the effect of variable X_2, 11.11% of the variation in Y can be explained by the variation in variable X_1.

$$r_{Y2.1}^2 = \frac{SSR(X_2 | X_1)}{SST - SSR(X_1 \; and \; X_2) + SSR(X_2 | X_1)} = \frac{10}{150 - 30 + 10}$$

= 0.0769. Holding constant the effect of variable X_1, 7.69% of the variation in Y can be explained by the variation in variable X_2.

14.30   (a)   For X_1:

$$SSR(X_1 | X_2) = SSR(X_1 \; and \; X_2) - SSR(X_2) = 2451.974 - 2225.864 = 226.11$$

$$F = \frac{SSR(X_1 | X_2)}{MSE} = \frac{226.11}{819.8681/47} = 12.96 > F_{U(1,47)} = 4.047 \text{ with 1 and 47}$$

degrees of freedom and $\alpha = 0.05$. Reject H_0. There is evidence that the variable X_1 contributes to a model already containing X_2.

For X_2:

$$SSR(X_2 | X_1) = SSR(X_1 \; and \; X_2) - SSR(X_1) = 2451.974 - 2032.546 = 419.428$$

$$F = \frac{SSR(X_2 | X_1)}{MSE} = \frac{419.428}{819.8681/47} = 24.04 > F_{U(1,47)} = 4.047 \text{ with 1 and 47}$$

degrees of freedom and $\alpha = 0.05$. Reject H_0. There is evidence that the variable X_2 contributes to a model already containing X_1.

Since each independent variable X_1 and X_2 makes a significant contribution to the model in the presence of the other variable, both variables should be included in the model.

(b)

$$r_{Y1.2}^2 = \frac{SSR(X_1 | X_2)}{SST - SSR(X_1 \; and \; X_2) + SSR(X_1 | X_2)} = \frac{226.11}{3271.842 - 2451.974 + 226.11}$$

= 0.2162. Holding constant the effect of weight, 21.62% of the variation in Y can be explained by the variation in horsepower.

$$r_{Y2.1}^2 = \frac{SSR(X_2 | X_1)}{SST - SSR(X_1 \; and \; X_2) + SSR(X_2 | X_1)} = \frac{419.428}{3271.842 - 2451.974 + 419.428}$$

= 0.3384. Holding constant the effect of horsepower, 33.84% of the variation in Y can be explained by the variation in weight.

14.32 (a) For X_1:
$$SSR(X_1|X_2) = SSR(X_1 \text{ and } X_2) - SSR(X_2) = 27662.54 - 513.2846 = 27149.255$$

$$F = \frac{SSR(X_1|X_2)}{MSE} = \frac{27149.255}{28802.07/23} = 21.68 > F_{U(1,23)} = 4.279 \text{ with 1 and 23}$$

degrees of freedom and $\alpha = 0.05$. Reject H_0. There is evidence that the variable X_1 contributes to a model already containing X_2.

For X_2:
$$SSR(X_2|X_1) = SSR(X_1 \text{ and } X_2) - SSR(X_1) = 27662.54 - 20667.4 = 6995.14$$

$$F = \frac{SSR(X_2|X_1)}{MSE} = \frac{6995.14}{28802.07/23} = 5.586 > F_{U(1,23)} = 4.279 \text{ with 1 and 23}$$

degrees of freedom and $\alpha = 0.05$. Reject H_0. There is evidence that the variable X_2 contributes to a model already containing X_1.

Since each independent variable X_1 and X_2 makes a significant contribution to the model in the presence of the other variable, both variables should be included in the model.

(b) $$r_{Y1.2}^2 = \frac{SSR(X_1|X_2)}{SST - SSR(X_1 \text{ and } X_2) + SSR(X_1|X_2)}$$

$$= \frac{27149.255}{56464.62 - 27662.54 + 27149.255} = 0.4852.$$ Holding constant the effect of remote hours, 48.52% of the variation in Y can be explained by the variation in total staff present.

$$r_{Y2.1}^2 = \frac{SSR(X_2|X_1)}{SST - SSR(X_1 \text{ and } X_2) + SSR(X_2|X_1)}$$

$$= \frac{6995.14}{56464.62 - 27662.54 + 6995.14} = 0.1954.$$ Holding constant the effect of total staff present, 19.54% of the variation in Y can be explained by the variation in remote hours.

14.34 (a) First develop a multiple regression model using X_1 as the variable for the SAT score and X_2 a dummy variable with $X_2 = 1$ if a student had a grade of B or better in the introductory statistics course. If the dummy variable coefficient is significantly different than zero, you need to develop a model with the interaction term $X_1 X_2$ to make sure that the coefficient of X_1 is not significantly different if $X_2 = 0$ or $X_2 = 1$.

(b) If a student received a grade of B or better in the introductory statistics course, the student would be expected to have a grade point average in accountancy that is 0.30 higher than a student who had the same SAT score, but did not get a grade of B or better in the introductory statistics course.

14.36 (a) $\hat{Y} = 43.737 + 9.219X_1 + 12.697X_2$, where X_1 = number of rooms and X_2 = neighborhood (east = 0).

     (b)   Holding constant the effect of neighborhood, for each additional room, the selling price is expected to increase on average by 9.219 thousands of dollars, or $9219. For a given number of rooms, a west neighborhood is expected to increase selling price over an east neighborhood by 12.697 thousands of dollars, or $12,697.

     (c) $\hat{Y} = 43.737 + 9.219(9) + 12.697(0) = 126.71$ or $126,710

            $109.5600 < Y_{X=X_i} < 143.8551$ $121.4714 < \mu_{Y|X=X_i} < 131.9437$

     (d)   Based on a residual analysis, the model appears adequate.

     (e) $F = 55.39 > F_{2,17} = 3.5915$. Reject H_0. There is evidence of a relationship between selling price and the two dependent variables.

     (f)   For X_1: $t = 8.95 > t_{17} = 2.1098$. Reject H_0. Number of rooms makes a significant contribution and should be included in the model.
            For X_2: $t = 3.59 > t_{17} = 2.1098$. Reject H_0. Neighborhood makes a significant contribution and should be included in the model.
            Based on these results, the regression model with the two independent variables should be used.

     (g) $7.0466 \le \beta_1 \le 11.3913$, $5.2377 \le \beta_2 \le 20.1557$

     (h) $r^2_{Y.12} = 0.867$. 86.7% of the variation in selling price can be explained by variation in number of rooms and variation in neighborhood.

     (i) $r^2_{adj} = 0.851$

     (j) $r^2_{Y1.2} = 0.825$. Holding constant the effect of neighborhood, 82.5% of the variation in selling price can be explained by variation in number of rooms. $r^2_{Y2.1} = 0.431$.
            Holding constant the effect of number of rooms, 43.1% of the variation in selling price can be explained by variation in neighborhood.

     (k)   The slope of selling price with number of rooms is the same regardless of whether the house is located in an east or west neighborhood.

     (l) $\hat{Y} = 53.95 + 8.032X_1 - 5.90X_2 + 2.089X_1X_2$.
            For $X_1 X_2$: the p-value is 0.330. Do not reject H_0. There is no evidence that the interaction term makes a contribution to the model.

     (m)   The two-variable model in (a) should be used.

14.38 (a) $\hat{Y} = 8.0100 + 0.0052X_1 - 2.1052X_2$, where X_1 = depth (in feet) and X_2 = type of drilling (wet = 0, dry = 1).

     (b)   Holding constant the effect of type of drilling, for each foot increase in depth of the hole, the additional drilling time is estimated to increase on average by 0.0052 minutes. For a given depth, a dry drilling is estimated to reduce average additional drilling time over wet drilling by 2.1052 minutes.

     (c)   Dry drilling: $\hat{Y} = 8.0101 + 0.0052(100) - 2.1052 = 6.4276$ minutes.
            $6.2096 < \mu_{Y|X} < 6.6457$, $4.92304 < Y_I < 7.9322$

14.38   (d)
cont.

Depth Residual Plot

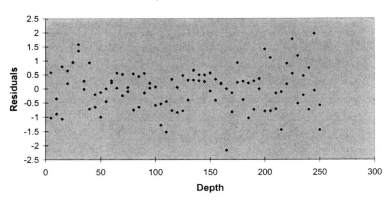

Based on a residual analysis, the model appears adequate.

(e) $F = 111.109$ with 2 and 97 degrees of freedom, $F_{2,97} = 3.09$ using Excel. p-value is virtually 0. Reject H_0 at 5% level of significance. There is evidence of a relationship between additional drilling time and the two dependent variables.

(f)   For X_1: $t = 5.0289 > t_{97} = 1.9847$. Reject H_0. Depth of the hole makes a significant contribution and should be included in the model.

For X_2: $t = -14.0331 < t_{97} = -1.9847$. Reject H_0. Type of drilling makes a significant contribution and should be included in the model.

Based on these results, the regression model with the two independent variables should be used.

(g) $0.0032 \leq \beta_1 \leq 0.0073$, $-2.4029 \leq \beta_2 \leq -1.8075$

(h) $r_{Y.12}^2 = 0.6961$. 69.61% of the variation in additional drilling time can be explained by the depth of the hole and variation in type of drilling.

(i) $r_{adj}^2 = 0.6899$

(j) $r_{Y1.2}^2 = 0.2068$. Holding constant the effect of type of drilling, 20.68% of the variation in additional drilling time can be explained by variation in depth of the hole.

$r_{Y2.1}^2 = 0.6700$. Holding constant the effect of the depth of the hole, 67% of the variation in additional drilling time can be explained by variation in type of drilling.

(k)   The slope of additional drilling time with depth of the hole is the same regardless of whether it is dry drilling hole or wet drilling hole.

(l) $\hat{Y} = 7.9120 + 0.0060X_1 - 1.9091X_2 - 0.0015X_1X_2$.

For X_1X_2: the p-value is $0.4624 > 0.05$. Do not reject H_0. There is not evidence that the interaction term makes a contribution to the model.

(m)   The two-variable model in (a) should be used.

14.40   (a) $\hat{Y} = 31.5594 + 0.0296X_1 + 0.0041X_2 + 1.7159 \cdot 10^{-5} X_1X_2$.

where X_1 = sales, X_2 = orders, $X_3 = X_1 X_2$

For X_1X_2: the p-value is $0.3249 > 0.05$. Do not reject H_0. There is not enough evidence that the interaction term makes a contribution to the model.

(b)   Since there is not enough evidence of any interaction effect between sales and orders, the model in problem 14.4 should be used.

14.42 (a) $\hat{Y} = -1293.3105 + 43.6600X_1 + 56.9335X_2 - 0.8430X_1X_2$.

where X_1 = radio advertisement, X_2 = newspaper advertisement, $X_3 = X_1 X_2$
For X_1X_2: the p-value is $0.0018 < 0.05$. Reject H_0. There is enough evidence that the interaction term makes a contribution to the model.

(b)   Since there is enough evidence of an interaction effect between radio and newspaper advertisement, the model in this problem should be used.

14.44 (a) $\hat{Y} = -63.9813 + 1.1258X_1 - 22.2887X_2 + 8.0880X_3$

where X_1 = proficiency exam, X_2 = traditional method dummy, X_3 = CD-ROM-based dummy

(b)   Holding constant the effect of training method, for each point increase in proficiency exam score, the end-of-training exam score is estimated to increase on average by 1.1258 points. For a given proficiency exam score, the end-of-training exam score of a trainee who has been trained by the traditional method will have an estimated average score that is 22.2887 points below a trainee that has been trained using the web-based method. For a given proficiency exam score, the end-of-training exam score of a trainee who has been trained by the CD-ROM-based method will have an estimated average score that is 8.0880 points above a trainee that has been trained using the web-based method

(c) $\hat{Y} = -63.9813 + 1.1258(100) = 48.5969$

(d)

Proficiency   Residual Plot

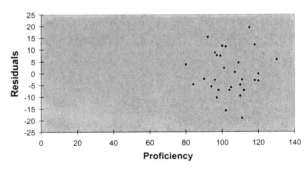

Residuals vs Predicted Y

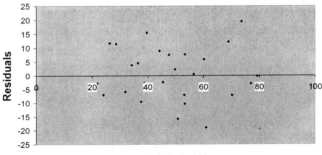

There appears to be quadratic effect from the residual plots.

14.44   (d)
cont.

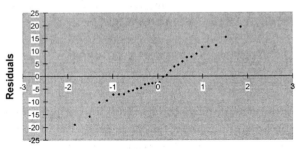

There is no severe departure from the normality assumption from the normal probability plot.

(e) $F = 31.77$ with 3 and 26 degrees of freedom. The p-value is virtually 0. Reject H_0 at 5% level of significance. There is evidence of a relationship between end-of-training exam score and the dependent variables.

(f)   For X_1: $t = 7.0868$ and the p-value is virtually 0. Reject H_0. Proficiency exam score makes a significant contribution and should be included in the model.
For X_2: $t = -5.1649$ and the p-value is virtually 0. Reject H_0. The traditional method dummy makes a significant contribution and should be included in the model.
For X_3: $t = 1.8765$ and the p-value = 0.07186. Do not reject H_0. There is not sufficient evidence to conclude that there is a difference in the traditional method and the web-based method on the average end-of-training exam scores.
Base on the above result, the regression model should use the proficiency exam score and the traditional dummy variable.

(g) $0.7992 \le \beta_1 \le 1.4523$, $-31.1591 \le \beta_2 \le -13.4182$, $-0.7719 \le \beta_2 \le 16.9480$

(h) $r_{Y.12}^2 = 0.7857$. 78.57% of the variation in the end-of-training exam score can be explained by the proficiency exam score and whether the trainee is trained by the traditional or web-based method.

(i) $r_{adj}^2 = 0.7610$

(j) $r_{Y1.23}^2 = 0.6589$. Holding constant the effect of training method, 65.89% of the variation in end-of-training exam score can be explained by variation in the proficiency exam score. $r_{Y2.13}^2 = 0.5064$. Holding constant the effect of proficiency exam score, 50.64% of the variation in end-of-training exam score can be explained by the difference between traditional and web-based methods. $r_{Y3.12}^2 = 0.1193$.
Holding constant the effect of proficiency exam score, 11.93% of the variation in end-of-training exam score can be explained by the difference between CD-ROM-based and web-based methods.

(k)   The slope of proficiency score with end-of-training exam score is the same regardless of the proficiency exam score.

14.44 (l) Let $X_4 = X_1 X_2$, $X_5 = X_1 X_3$.
cont.
$H_0 : \beta_4 = \beta_5 = 0$ There is no interaction among X_1, X_2 and X_3.

H_1 : At least one of β_4 and β_5 is not zero.
There is interaction among at least a pair of X_1, X_2 and X_3.

$$F = \frac{SSR(X_4, X_5 \mid X_1, X_2, X_3)}{MSE(X_1, X_2, X_3, X_4, X_5)} = \frac{\left[SSR(X_1, X_2, X_3, X_4, X_5) - SSR(X_1, X_2, X_3) \right]/2}{MSE(X_1, X_2, X_3, X_4, X_5)} =$$

0.8122. The p-value $= 0.46 > 0.05$. Do not reject H_0. The interaction terms do not make a significant contribution to the model.

(m) The regression model should use the proficiency exam score and the traditional dummy variable.

14.46 Estimated Probability of Success = Odds Ratio / (1 + Odds Ratio) = 2.5/(1 + 2.5) = 0.7143

14.48 (a) Holding constant the effects of X_2, for each additional unit of X_1 the natural logarithm of the odds ratio is estimated to increase on average by 0.5. Holding constant the effects of X_1, for each additional unit of X_2 the natural logarithm of the odds ratio is estimated to increase on average by 0.2.

(b) ln(estimated odds ratio) $= 0.1 + 0.5\, X_1 + 0.2\, X_2 = 0.1 + 0.5(2) + 0.2(1.5) = 1.4$

Estimated odds ratio $= e^{1.4} = 4.055$. The odds of "success" to failure are 4.055 to 1.

(c) Estimated Probability of Success = Odds Ratio / (1 + Odds Ratio)
$$= 4.055/(1 + 4.055) = 0.8022$$

14.50 (a) Let $X_1 =$ grade point average and $X_2 =$ GMAT score
ln(estimated odds) $= -121.95 + 8.053\, X_1 + 0.15729\, X_2$

(b) Holding constant the effects of GMAT score, for each increase of one point in GPA, ln(odds) increases by an estimate of 8.053. Holding constant the effects of GPA, for each increase of one point in GMAT score, ln(odds) increases by an estimate of 0.15729.

(c) ln(estimated odds ratio) $= -121.95 + 8.053\,(3.25) + 0.15729\,(600) = -1.40375$

Estimated odds ratio $= e^{-1.04375} = 0.246$
Estimated Probability of Success = Odds Ratio / (1 + Odds Ratio)
$$= 0.246/(1 + 0.246) = 0.197$$

(d) The deviance statistic is 8.122, which is less than the critical value of 40.113 and which has a p-value of virtually 1.000. Do not reject H_0. There is not sufficient evidence that this does not have a good fitting model.

(e) For GPA variable: $Z = 1.60 < 1.96$. Do not reject H_0. There is not sufficient evidence that undergraduate grade point average makes a significant contribution to the model. For GMAT: $Z = 2.07 > 1.96$. Reject H_0. There is sufficient evidence that GMAT score makes a significant contribution to the model.

(f) ln(estimated odds) $= -2.765 + 1.02\, X_1$
Deviance statistic $= 29.172$, p-value $= 0.257$
Z-value for β_1: 0.83, p-value $= 0.406$

(g) ln(estimated odds) $= -60.15 + 0.09904\, X_2$
Deviance statistic $= 9.545$, p-value $= 0.998$
Z-value for β_2: 2.3, p-value $= 0.021$

(h) Based on the p-values corresponding to the Z-values for the variable coefficients in the logistic regression equation and corresponding to the deviance statistics, the model in part (a) is a better fit than the model in part (f). However, the model in part (g) appears to be about as good a fit as the model in part (a).

14.52   (a)   Let X_1 = price of the pizza.
                ln(estimated odds) = 1.243 -0.25034 X_1
                For X_1: Z = -2.68 < -1.96. Reject H_0. There is sufficient evidence that price of the pizza makes a significant contribution to the model.
        (b)   Let X_1 = price of the pizza, X_2 = gender.
                ln(estimated odds) = 1.220 -0.25019 X_1 + 0.0377 X_2
                For X_1: Z = -2.68 < -1.96. Reject H_0. There is sufficient evidence that price of the pizza makes a significant contribution to the model.
                For X_2: Z = 0.10 < 1.96. Do not reject H_0. There is not sufficient evidence to conclude that gender makes a significant contribution to the model.
        (c)   Model (a): Deviance statistic = 0.258. p-value = 0.998 > 0.05. Do not reject H_0.
                There is insufficient evidence to conclude that model (a) is not a good fit.
                Model (b): Deviance statistic = 7.804. p-value = 0.731 > 0.05. Do not reject H_0.
                There is insufficient evidence to conclude that model (a) is not a good fit. However, the Z test in (b) suggests that there is not sufficient evidence to conclude that gender makes a significant contribution to the model. Using the parsimony principle, the model in (a) is preferred to the model in (b).
        (d)   ln(estimated odds ratio) = 1.243 -0.25034 X_1 = 1.243 -0.25034 (8.99) = -1.0076
                Estimated odds ratio = $e^{-1.0076}$ = 0.3651
                Estimated Probability of Success = estimated odds ratio / (1 + estimated odds ratio)
                = 0.3651/(1 + 0.3651) = 0.2675
        (e)   ln(estimated odds ratio) = 1.243 -0.25034 X_1 = 1.243 -0.25034 (11.49) = -1.6334
                Estimated odds ratio = $e^{-1.6334}$ = 0.1953
                Estimated Probability of Success
                = estimated odds ratio / (1 + estimated odds ratio)
                = 0.1953/(1 + 0.1953) = 0.1634
        (f)   ln(estimated odds ratio) = 1.243 -0.25034 X_1 = 1.243 -0.25034 (13.99) = -2.2593
                Estimated odds ratio = $e^{-2.2593}$ = 0.1044
                Estimated Probability of Success
                = estimated odds ratio / (1 + estimated odds ratio)
                = 0.1044/(1 + 0.1044) = 0.0946

14.54   In the case of the simple linear regression model, the slope b_1 represents the change in the estimated mean of Y per unit change in X and does not take into account any other variables other than the single independent variable included in the model. In the multiple linear regression model, the slope b_1 represents the change in the estimated mean of Y per unit change in X_1, taking into account the effect of all the other independent variables. It is referred to as a net regression coefficient.

14.56   The coefficient of partial determination measures the proportion of variation in Y explained by a particular X variable holding constant the effect of the other independent variables in the model. The coefficient of multiple determination measures the proportion of variation in Y explained by all the X variables included in the model.

14.58   Dummy variables are used to represent categorical independent variables in a regression model. One category is coded as 0 and the other category of the variable is coded as 1.

14.60   Dummy variables will be included to represent a categorical independent variable.

14.62   (a) $\hat{Y} = -44.988 + 1.7506X_1 + 0.368X_2$, where X_1 = assessed value (in thousands of dollars) and X_2 = time period (in months).

(b)   Holding constant the effects of time period, for each additional thousand dollars in assessed value the selling price of the house is expected to increase on the average by 1.7506 thousands of dollars, or $1,750.60. Holding constant the effects of assessed value, for each additional month the selling price of the house is expected to increase on the average by 0.368 thousands of dollars, or $368.

(c) $\hat{Y} = -44.988 + 1.7506(70) + 0.368(12) = 81.969$ or $81,969

(d)   All four residual plots indicate that the fitted model appears to be adequate.

(e) $F = 223.46 > F_{U(2,27)} = 3.35$ with 2 and 27 degrees of freedom. Reject H_0. At least one of the independent variables is linearly related to the dependent variable.

(f)   The p value is less than 0.001. This means that the probability of obtaining an F test statistic of 223.46 or greater if there were not relationship between the dependent variable and independent variables is less than 0.001.

(g) $r^2_{Y.12} = 0.943$. So, 94.3% of the variation in selling price can be explained by the variation in assessed value and the variation in time period.

(h) $r^2_{adj} = 0.939$

(i)   For X_1: $t = 20.41 > t_{27} = 2.0518$ with 27 degrees of freedom. Reject H_0. There is evidence that X_1 significantly contributes to a model already containing X_2. For X_2: $t = 2.873 > t_{27} = 2.0518$ with 27 degrees of freedom. Reject H_0. There is evidence that X_2 significantly contributes to a model already containing X_1. Therefore, each independent variable makes a significant contribution in the presence of the other variable, and both variables should be included in the model.

(j)   For X_1, the p value is less than 0.001. This means the probability of obtaining a t-test statistic which differs from zero by 20.41 or more (positively or negatively) when the null hypothesis that $\beta_1 = 0$ is true is less than 0.001. For X_2, the p value is 0.008. This means the probability of obtaining a t-test statistic which differs from zero by 2.873 or more (positively or negatively) when the null hypothesis that $\beta_2 = 0$ is true is 0.008.

(k) $1.575 \le \beta_1 \le 1.927$. This is a net regression coefficient. That is, taking into account the time period, this coefficient measures the expected average increase in selling price for each additional thousand dollars in assessed value. In Problem 10.66(l) the coefficient did not take into account (and hold constant) the effects of the time period.

(l) $r^2_{Y1.2} = 0.9392$. For a given time period, 93.92% of the variation in selling price can be explained by variation in assessed value. $r^2_{Y2.1} = 0.2342$. For a given assessed value, 23.42% of the variation in selling price can be explained by variation in time period.

14.64   (a) $\hat{Y} = 63.7751 + 10.7252X_1 - 0.2843X_2$, where X_1 = size (in thousands of square feet) and X_2 = age (in years).

(b)   Holding constant the effects of age, for each additional thousand square feet the assessed value of the house is expected to increase on the average by 10.7252 thousands of dollars, or \$10,725.20. Holding constant the effects of size, for each year of age the assessed value of the house is expected to decrease on the average by 0.2843 thousands of dollars, or \$284.30.

(c) $\hat{Y} = 63.7751 + 10.7252(1.75) - 0.2843(10) = 79.702$ or \$79,702

(d)   The residual plot against age indicates a potential pattern that may require the addition of nonlinear terms. One value appears to be an outlier in all four plots.

(e) $F = 28.58 > F_{U(2,12)} = 3.89$ with 2 and 12 degrees of freedom. Reject H_0. At least one of the independent variables is linearly related to the dependent variable.

(f)   The p value is less than 0.001. This means that the probability of obtaining an F test statistic of 28.58 or greater if there were not relationship between the dependent variable and independent variables is less than 0.001.

(g) $r^2_{Y.12} = 0.8265$. 82.65% of the variation in assessed value can be explained by the variation in size and the variation in age.

(h) $r^2_{adj} = 0.7976$

(i)   For X_1: $t = 3.558 > t_{12} = 2.1788$ with 12 degrees of freedom. Reject H_0. There is evidence that X_1 significantly contributes to a model already containing X_2. For X_2: $t = -3.400 < -t_{12} = -2.1788$ with 12 degrees of freedom. Reject H_0. There is evidence that X_2 significantly contributes to a model already containing X_1. Therefore, each independent variable makes a significant contribution in the presence of the other variable, and both variables should be included in the model.

(j)   For X_1, the p value is 0.004. This means the probability of obtaining a t-test statistic which differs from zero by 3.558 or more (positively or negatively) when the null hypothesis that $\beta_1 = 0$ is true is 0.004. For X_2, the p value is 0.005. This means the probability of obtaining a t-test statistic which differs from zero by 3.4 or more (positively or negatively) when the null hypothesis that $\beta_2 = 0$ is true is 0.005.

(k) $4.158 \leq \beta_1 \leq 17.293$. This is a net regression coefficient. That is, taking into account the age of the house, this coefficient measures the expected average increase in assessed value for each additional thousand square feet of size. In Problem 10.67(l) the coefficient did not take into account (and hold constant) the effects of age.

(l) $r^2_{Y1.2} = 0.5134$. For a given age of the house, 51.34% of the variation in assessed value can be explained by variation in size. $r^2_{Y2.1} = 0.4907$. For a given amount of size in square feet, 49.07% of the variation in assessed value can be explained by variation in age.

(m)   No. The age of the house does have a significant bearing on its assessed value.

14.66   (a) $\hat{Y} = 40.8765 - 0.0121$ length $- 0.0050$ weight

         (b) $b_1 = -0.0121$: Holding weight fixed, the estimated average mileage of a car will decrease by 0.0121 miles per gallon as the length of the car increases by one inch. $b_2 = -.0050$: Holding length fixed, the estimate average mileage of a car will decrease by .0050 miles per gallon as the weight of the car increases by one pound.

         (c)   23.6603 miles per gallon.

         (d)

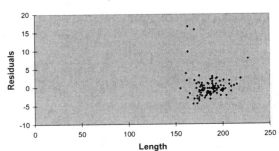

Length Residual Plot

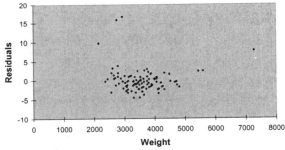

Weight Residual Plot

According to the residual plot of length, the homoscedasticity assumption seems to have been violated. From the residual plot of weight, there seems to be a quadratic relationship between mileage and weight.

         (e)   Yes, there is a significant relationship between gasoline mileage and the two explanatory variables at the 0.05 level of significance because the p-value of the F test is essentially zero.

         (f)   The p-value is essentially zero. It is almost impossible to have observed data which will give rise to an F test statistic more extreme than 92.9287 if there is really no significant relationship between gasoline mileage and the two explanatory variables.

         (g)   61.17% of the total variation in gasoline mileage can be explained by length and weight of a car.

         (h) $r^2_{adj} = 0.6051$

14.66   (i)   PHStat output:
cont.

	Coefficients	Standard Error	t Stat	P-value
Intercept	40.87650495	4.059910501	10.06832661	1.3805E-17
Length	-0.012071414	0.02632727	-0.458513689	0.647426793
Weight	-0.004954095	0.000483677	-10.24256569	5.32269E-18

At 0.05 level of significance, only weight makes a significant contribution to the regression model. The model should include only weight as the explanatory variable.

(j)   The p-value for length is 0.6474. The probability of observing a data set which yields a t-test statistic for length more extreme than -0.4585 is 64.74%. The p-value for weight is essentially zero. The probability of observing a data set which yields a t test statistic for weight more extreme than -10.2426 is essentially zero.

(k) $[-0.0059, -0.0040]$

(l) $r^2_{Y1 \bullet 2} = 0.0018$, $r^2_{Y2 \bullet 1} = 0.4706$. Holding weight constant, 0.18% of the variation in mileage can be explained by length. Holding length constant, 47.06% of the variation in mileage can be explained by weight.

14.68   (a) $\hat{Y} = 170.8022 - 3.0654X_1 - 19.9941X_2$, where X_1 = league dummy (0 = American, 1 = National) and X_2 = ERA.

(b)   Holding constant the effect of ERA, the estimated average number of wins for a team in the American league is 3.0654 above that of the National league. Holding constant the effect of league, for each unit increase in ERA, the estimated average number of wins is estimated to decrease by 19.9941.

(c) $\hat{Y} = 170.8022 - 3.0654(0) - 19.9941(4.5) = 80.83 \cong 81$ wins.

(d)   Based on a residual analysis, the model appears adequate.

(e) $F = 20.257$ with 2 and 27 degrees of freedom. p-value = 4.23207E-06 < 0.05. Reject H_0. There is evidence of a relationship between number of wins and the two dependent variables.

(f)   For X_1: $t = -0.9755$. p-value = 0.3380 > 0.05. Do not reject H_0. Which league the team is in does not make a significant contribution and should not be included in the model.
For X_2: $t = -6.3616$. p-value = 8.20671E-07 < 0.05. Reject H_0. ERA makes a significant contribution and should be included in the model.
The model should include ERA but not the league dummy.

(g) $-9.5130 \le \beta_1 \le 3.3823$, $\qquad\qquad$ $-26.4429 \le \beta_2 \le -13.5453$

(h) $r^2_{Y.12} = 0.6001$. 60.01% of the variation in number of wins can be explained by variation in type of league and variation in ERA.

(i) $r^2_{adj} = 0.5705$

(j) $r^2_{Y1.2} = 0.0340$. Holding constant the effect of ERA, 3.4% of the variation in number of wins can be explained by variation in the type of league.
$r^2_{Y2.1} = 0.5998$. Holding constant the effect of league, 59.98% of the variation in number of wins can be explained by variation in ERA.

(k)   The slope of number of wins with ERA is the same regardless of whether the team is in the American or National league.

14.68   (l) $\hat{Y} = 174.9646 - 13.0547X_1 - 20.9238X_2 + 2.2671X_1X_2$.

cont.   For X_1X_2: the p-value is 0.7299. Do not reject H_0. There is not evidence that the interaction term makes a contribution to the model.

         (m)   The model with only ERA should be used.

CHAPTER 15

OBJECTIVES

- To be able to use quadratic terms in a regression model
- To be able to use transformed variables in a regression model
- To examine the effect of each observation on the regression model
- To be able to measure the correlation among the independent variables
- To build a regression model using either the stepwise or best-subsets approach
- To understand the pitfalls involved in developing a multiple regression model

OVERVIEW AND KEY CONCEPTS

The Quadratic Regression Model

- In a quadratic regression model, the relationship between the dependent variable and one or more independent variable is a quadratic polynomial function.
- The quadratic regression model is useful when the residual plot reveals nonlinear relationship.
- The quadratic regression model:
  - $Y_i = \beta_0 + \beta_1 X_{1i} + \beta_2 X_{1i}^2 + \varepsilon_i$
  - The quadratic relationship can be between Y and more than one X variable as well.
- **Testing for the overall significance of the quadratic regression model:**
  - The test for the overall significance of the quadratic regression model is exactly the same as testing for the overall significance of any multiple regression model.
  - **Test statistic:** $F = \dfrac{MSR}{MSE}$.
- **Testing for quadratic effect:**
  - **The hypotheses:** $H_0 : \beta_2 = 0$ (no quadratic effect) vs. $H_1 : \beta_2 \neq 0$ (the quadratic term is needed)
  - **Test statistic:** $t = \dfrac{b_2 - \beta_2}{S_{b_2}}$.
  - This is a two-tail test with a left tail and a right-tail rejection region.

Using Transformation in Regression Models
- The following three transformation models are often used to overcome violations of the homoscedasticity assumption, as well as to transform a model that is not linear in form into one that is linear.
- **Square-root transformation:**
  - $Y_i = \beta_0 + \beta_1 \sqrt{X_{1i}} + \varepsilon_i$
  - The dependent variable is Y_i and the independent variable is $\sqrt{X_{1i}}$.
- **Transformed multiplicative model:**
  - $\log Y_i = \log \beta_0 + \beta_1 \log X_{1i} + \cdots + \beta_k \log X_{ki} + \log \varepsilon_i$
  - The dependent variable is $\log Y_i$ and the independent variables are $\log X_{1i}$, $\log X_{2i}$, etc.
- **Transformed exponential model:**
  - $\ln Y_i = \beta_0 + \beta_1 X_{1i} + \cdots + \beta_k X_{ki} + \ln \varepsilon_i$
  - The dependent variable is $\ln Y_i$ and the independent variables are X_{1i}, X_{2i}, etc.

Influential Analysis
- Influential analysis is performed to determined observations that have influential effect on the fitted model.
- Potentially influential points become candidate for removal from the model
- Criteria used are
  - **The hat matrix elements h_i:** If $h_i > 2(k+1)/n$, X_i is an influential point.
  - **The Studentized deleted residuals t_i^*:** X_i is influential if $\left| t_i^* \right| > t_{0.05,n-k-2}$ where $t_{0.05,n-k-2}$ is the critical value of a two-tail test at a 10% level of significance.
  - **Cooks' distance statistic D_i:** X_i is considered influential if $D_i > F_{k+1,n-k-1}$ where $F_{k+1,n-k-1}$ is the critical value of an F distribution with $k+1$ and $n-k-1$ degrees of freedom at a 0.50 level of significance.
- All three criteria are complementary. Only when all 3 criteria provide consistent result should an observation be removed.

Collinearity
- Some of the explanatory variables are highly correlated with each other.
- The collinear variables do not provide new information and it becomes difficult to separate the effect of such variables on the dependent variable.
- The values of the regression coefficient for the correlated variables may fluctuate drastically depending on which independent variables are included in the model.

Large *Overlap* reflects collinearity between X_1 and X_2

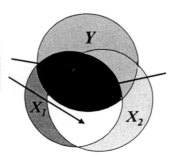

Large *Overlap* in variation of X_1 and X_2 is used in explaining the variation in Y but *NOT* in estimating β_1 and β_2

- Variance inflationary factor (VIF) is used to measure collinearity.

  - $VIF_j = \dfrac{1}{\left(1 - R_j^2\right)}$ where R_j^2 is the coefficient determination of regressing X_j on all the other explanatory variables.

  - If $VIF_j > 5$, X_j is considered highly correlated with the other explanatory variables.

Model Building

- The goal is to develop a good model with the fewest explanatory variables that is easier to interpret and has lower probability of collinearity.
- **Stepwise regression procedure:** Provides limited evaluation of alternative models.
- **Best-subsets approach:** Uses the Mallow's C_p and selects the models with small C_p near $k+1$.
- **Model building flowchart:**

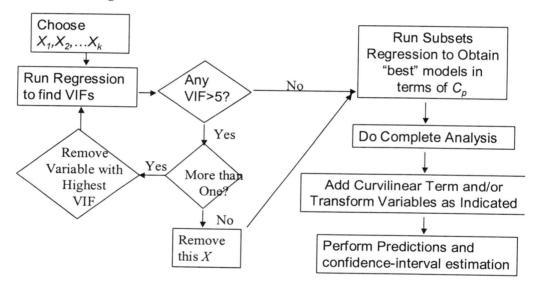

SOLUTIONS TO END OF SECTION
AND CHAPTER REVIEW EVEN PROBLEMS

15.2   (a)

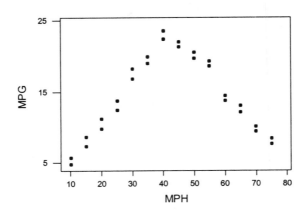

(b) $\hat{Y} = -7.556 + 1.2717X - 0.0145X^2$

(c) $\hat{Y} = -7.556 + 1.2717(55) - 0.0145(55^2) = 18.52$

(d)   Based on residual analysis, there are patterns in the residuals vs. highway speed, vs. the quadratic variable (speed squared), and vs. the fitted values.

(e) $F = 141.46 > F_{2,25} = 3.39$. Reject H_0. The overall model is significant. The p-value < 0.001.

(f) $t = -16.63 < -t_{25} = -2.0595$. Reject H_0. The quadratic effect is significant. The p-value < 0.001.

(g) $r^2_{Y.12} = 0.919$. 91.9% of the variation in miles per gallon can be explained by the quadratic relationship between miles per gallon and highway speed.

(h) $r^2_{adj} = 0.912$

15.4   (a)

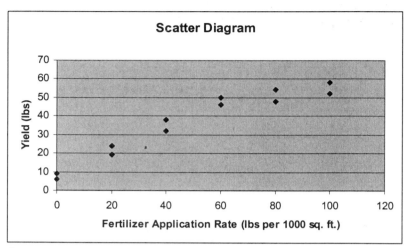

(b) $\hat{Y} = 6.643 + 0.895X - 0.0041X^2$

(c) $\hat{Y} = 6.643 + 0.895(70) - 0.0041(70^2) = 49.17$

(d)

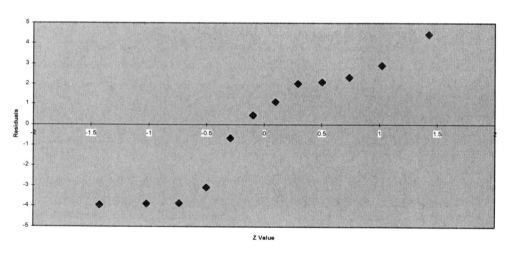

A residual analysis indicates no strong patterns. However, the distribution of residuals appears to deviate from a normal distribution according to the normal probability plot.

(e) $F = 157.32 > F_{2,9} = 4.26$. Reject H_0. The overall model is significant.

(f)   The p-value < 0.001 indicates that the probability of having an F-test statistic of at least 157.32 when $\beta_1 = 0$ and $\beta_2 = 0$ is less than 0.001.

(g) $t = -4.27 < -t_9 = -2.2622$. Reject H_0. The quadratic effect is significant.

(h)   The p-value $= 0.002$ indicates that the probability of having a t-test statistic with an absolute value of at least 4.27 when $\beta_2 = 0$ is equal to 0.013.

(i) $r^2_{Y.12} = 0.972$. So, 97.2% of the variation in yield can be explained by the quadratic relationship between yield and fertilizer application rate.

(j) $r^2_{adj} = 0.966$

15.6 (a) $\ln \hat{Y} = 3.07 + 0.9\ln(8.5) + 1.41\ln(5.2) = 7.32067$

$\hat{Y} = e^{7.32067} = 1511.22$

(b) Holding constant the effects of X_2, for each additional unit of the natural logarithm of X_1 the natural logarithm of Y is expected to increase on average by 0.9. Holding constant the effects of X_1, for each additional unit of the natural logarithm of X_2 the natural logarithm of Y is expected to increase on average by 1.41.

15.8 (a) $\hat{Y} = 9.04 + 0.852\sqrt{X_1}$

(b) $\hat{Y} = 9.04 + 0.852\sqrt{55} = 15.36$ miles per gallon

(c) The residual analysis indicates a clear quadratic pattern. The model does not adequately fit the data.

(d) $t = 1.35 < t_{26} = 2.0555$. Do not reject H_0. The model does not provide a significant relationship.

(e) $r^2 = 0.066$. Only 6.6% of the variation in miles per gallon can be explained by variation in the square root of highway speed.

(f) $r^2_{adj} = 0.030$

(g) The quadratic regression model in Problem 15.2 is far superior to the inadequate model here. The square root of highway speed did virtually nothing to enhance the fit.

15.10 (a) $\ln \hat{Y} = 2.475 + 0.018546X_1$

(b) $\ln \hat{Y} = 2.475 + 0.018546(55) = 3.495$ $\hat{Y} = e^{3.495} = 32.95$ pounds.

(c) The residual analysis indicates a clear quadratic pattern. The model does not adequately fit the data.

(d) $t = 6.11 > t_{10} = 2.2281$. Reject H_0. The model provides a significant relationship.

(e) $r^2 = 0.789$. So, 78.9% of the variation in the natural logarithm of yield can be explained by variation in the amount of fertilizer applied.

(f) $r^2_{adj} = 0.768$

(g) The quadratic regression model in Problem 15.4 is superior to the model here.

15.12 Observations 14 ($h_i = 0.3568$) and 19 ($h_i = 0.2828$) are influential as they have $h_i > 2(2+1)/24 = 0.25$.

Observations 1, 2, and 14 had an effect on the model: $\left|t_1^*\right| = 2.5783$, $\left|t_2^*\right| = 1.8465$, and

$\left|t_{14}^*\right| = 1.8429$. All of these values exceed $t_{24-2-2,.05} = 1.7247$.

The largest value for Cook's D_i is 0.5637, which is less than $F_{.50,2+1,24-2-1} = 0.8149$. Thus, there is insufficient evidence to delete any observations in the model.

15.14   Observations 1 ($h_i = 0.2924$), 2 ($h_i = 0.2924$), 13 ($h_i = 0.3564$) and 14 ($h_i = 0.3564$) are influential as they have $h_i > 2(2+1)/22 = 0.2727$.

Observations 2, 4, 7, and 13 had an effect on the model: $\left|t_2^*\right| = 2.44$, $\left|t_4^*\right| = 1.98$, $\left|t_7^*\right| = 1.87$, and $\left|t_{13}^*\right| = 1.96$. All of these values exceed $t_{22-2-2,.05} = 1.7341$.

The largest value for Cook's D_i is 0.652 for Observation 2, which is less than $F_{.50,2+1,22-2-1} = 0.8177$. However, since this value and the D_i value for Observation 13 were substantially above the D_i values for the other observations and were also found to have had an effect on the model and to be influential, a model was studied with Observations 2 and 13 deleted. In this model, $b_0 = -24.7$, $b_1 = 14.932$ and $b_2 = 19.107$, with $r_{Y.12}^2 = 0.88$.

15.16 $$VIF = \frac{1}{1-0.2} = 1.25$$

15.18 $$R_1^2 = 0.64, \; VIF_1 = \frac{1}{1-0.64} = 2.778$$

$$R_2^2 = 0.64, \; VIF_2 = \frac{1}{1-0.64} = 2.778$$

There is no reason to suspect the existence of collinearity.

15.20 $$R_1^2 = 0.008464, \; VIF_1 = \frac{1}{1-0.008464} = 1.009$$

$$R_2^2 = 0.008464, \; VIF_2 = \frac{1}{1-0.008464} = 1.009$$

There is no reason to suspect the existence of collinearity.

15.22   (a) $$C_p = \frac{(1-R_k^2)(n-T)}{1-R_T^2} - [n-2(k+1)] = \frac{(1-0.274)(40-7)}{1-0.653} - [40-2(2+1)]$$

$$= 35.04$$

(b) C_p overwhelmingly exceeds $k + 1 = 3$, the number of parameters (including the Y-intercept), so this model does not meet the criterion for further consideration as a best model.

15.24   Let Y = selling price, X_1 = assessed value, X_2 = time period, and X_3 = whether house was new (0 = no, 1 = yes).
Based on a full regression model involving all of the variables, all of the VIF values (1.3, 1.0, and 1.3, respectively) are less than 5. There is no reason to suspect the existence of collinearity.
Based on a best subsets regression and examination of the resulting C_p values, the best models appear to be a model with variables X_1 and X_2, which has $C_p = 2.8$, and the full regression model, which has $C_p = 4.0$. Based on a regression analysis with all original variables, variable X_3 fails to make a significant contribution to the model at the 0.05 level. Thus, the best model is the model using assessed value (X_1) and time (X_2) as the independent variables.
A residual analysis shows no strong patterns.
The final model is: $\hat{Y} = -44.9882 + 1.7506X_1 + 0.3680X_2$

15.24 $r_{Y.12}^2 = 0.9430$, $r_{adj}^2 = 0.9388$

cont.   Overall significance of the model: $F = 223.4575$, $p < 0.001$.
Each independent variable is significant at the 0.05 level.
A stepwise regression in Minitab yields the same model.

15.26   Let Y = gasoline mileage, X_1 = weight, X_2 = width, X_3 = length, and $X_4 = 1$ if SUV, 0 otherwise.
Based on a full regression model involving all of the variables:
$VIF_1 = 5.1$, $VIF_2 = 4.8$, $VIF_3 = 4.6$, $VIF_4 = 2.6$
Variable X_1 dropped from the model.
Minitab output:

Best Subsets Regression: MPG versus Width, Length, SUV1
```
Response is MPG
```

					W	L e n g t h	S U V 1
Vars	R-Sq	R-Sq(adj)	C-p	S	i d t h		
1	39.3	38.8	69.5	3.6603	X		
1	28.2	27.6	103.6	3.9806			X
1	26.6	26.0	108.5	4.0245		X	
2	61.1	60.5	4.5	2.9424		X	X
2	57.4	56.7	15.8	3.0785	X		X
2	39.3	38.3	71.5	3.6758	X	X	
3	61.9	61.0	4.0	2.9235	X	X	X

Based on regression model for remaining variables, all VIF values are less than 5. The best-subsets output reveals only one model with X_2, X_3, and X_4 has $C_p \le k + 1$. Influential analysis using hat matrix diagonal elements, residuals and Cook's distance statistic reveals that none of the observation should be removed from the regression model.

Analysis of the residual plots indicates that the homoscedasticity assumption is violated.

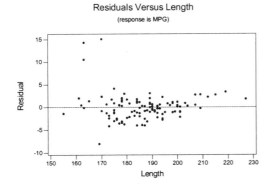

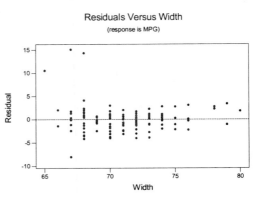

There also appears to be quadratic effect of length and width on MPG.

15.26 Minitab Output:

cont.
```
The regression equation is
MPG = 236 - 0.207 Width - 2.00 Length - 4.05 SUV1 + 0.00508 Length(SQ)
          -0.000000 Width(SQ)

Predictor          Coef       SE Coef          T          P        VIF
Constant         236.01         36.31       6.50      0.000
Width           -0.2072        0.1573      -1.32      0.190        4.4
Length          -2.0024        0.3810      -5.26      0.000      432.0
SUV1            -4.0526        0.8467      -4.79      0.000        2.4
Length(S       0.005080      0.001026       4.95      0.000      448.0
Width(SQ     -0.00000026    0.00000008      -3.20      0.002        4.2

S = 2.648      R-Sq = 69.3%      R-Sq(adj) = 68.0%

Analysis of Variance

Source            DF           SS          MS          F          P
Regression         5      1820.68      364.14      51.92      0.000
Residual Error   115       806.61        7.01
Total            120      2627.29
```

The small p-values of the squared of length and squared of width from the above regression output show that the quadratic effect of both length and width is significant at 0.05 level of significance.

The resulting model:

$$\hat{Y} = 236.01 - 0.2072X_2 - 2.0024X_3 - 4.0526X_4 - 0.00000026X_2^2 + 0.0051X_3^2$$

$$r^2 = 69.3\%, \ r_{adj}^2 = 68\%$$

Overall significance of the model: $F = 51.92$, p is essentially zero.

Residual analysis reveals that there is still problem of the lack of homoscedasticity.

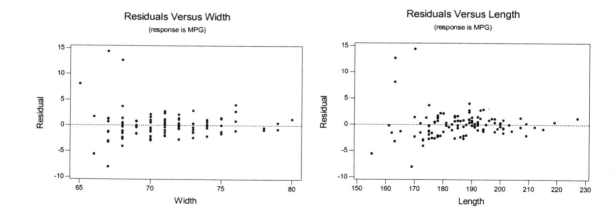

15.28 Let Y = passing rate, X_1 = % attendance, X_2 = Salary, X_3 = Spending.
Based on a full regression model involving all of the variables:
All *VIF*s are less than 5. So there is no reason to suspect collinearity between any pair of variables.
The best-subset approach yielded the following models to be considered:

Model	Variables	Cp	k	R Square	Adjusted R Square	Std. Error	Consider This Model?
1	X1	3.05	2	0.6024	0.5936	10.5787	No
2	X1X2	3.66	3	0.6145	0.5970	10.5350	No
3	X1X2X3	4.00	4	0.6288	0.6029	10.4570	Yes
4	X1X3	2.00	3	0.6288	0.6119	10.3375	Yes
5	X2	67.35	2	0.0474	0.0262	16.3755	No
6	X2X3	64.30	3	0.0910	0.0497	16.1768	No
7	X3	62.33	2	0.0907	0.0705	15.9984	No

Comparing between model 3 and model 4, the *p*-value of the *t* statistic for X_2 is 0.999.
Hence, it should be dropped.

	Coefficients	Standard Error	t Stat	P-value
Intercept	-753.4085823	99.1450557	-7.599053497	1.52907E-09
% Attendance	8.501405843	1.06451847	7.986151559	4.223E-10
Spending	0.005983693	0.003385191	1.767608559	0.084060786

From the above Excel output, the X_3 should also be dropped at 5% level of significance. The best model is the simple regression model $\hat{Y} = -771.5869 + 8.8447X_1$
The residual plot suggests that a nonlinear model on % attendance may be a better model.

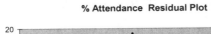

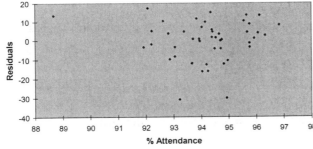

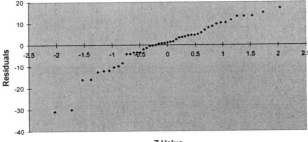

The normal probability plot indicates that with the exception of thicker left tail, the error distribution is quite normally distributed.

15.28   Residual analysis with case 19, Cincinnati (an influential point), removed yields the same
cont.   conclusion.
A quadratic regression model on % attendance yields the following:

Regression Statistics	
Multiple R	0.802758
R Square	0.644420
Adjusted R Square	0.628258
Standard Error	10.117675
Observations	47

ANOVA

	df	SS	MS	F	Significance F
Regression	2	8162.9429	4081.4714	39.8708	1.3201E-10
Residual	44	4504.1635	102.3674		
Total	46	12667.1064			

	Coefficients	Standard Error	t Stat	P-value
Intercept	6672.8367	3267.7349	2.0420	0.0472
% Attendance	-150.5694	69.9519	-2.1525	0.0369
% Attendance Squared	0.8532	0.3743	2.2792	0.0276

The p-value of the F statistic is virtually 0. There is sufficient evidence that the quadratic
regression model is significant at 5% level of significance.
The p-value of the t statistic for the quadratic term is $0.0276 < 0.05$. The quadratic term is
also significant at 5% level of significance.

The best model for the predicting passing rate is the quadratic regression regression model:
$$\hat{Y} = 6672.8367 - 150.5694X_1 + 0.8532(X_1)^2$$

15.30   Let Y = price, X_1 = text speed, X_2 = text cost, X_3 = color photo time, X_4 = color photo cost.
Based on a full regression model involving all of the variables:
All VIFs are less than 5. So there is no reason to suspect collinearity between any pair of
variables.
The best-subset approach yields the following models to be considered:
Partial PHStat output from the best-subsets selection:

Model	Cp	k	R Square	Adj. R Square	Std. Error	Consider This Model?
X1X2X3	3.063595	4	0.524353	0.394630984	59.53637	Yes
X1X2X3X4	5	5	0.527359	0.338302174	62.24466	Yes
X1X3	2.592803	3	0.452076	0.360755595	61.17948	Yes

Partial PHStat output of the full regression model:

	Coefficients	Standard Error	t Stat	P-value
Intercept	335.3080897	65.84754648	5.092188056	0.00046935
Text Speed	-23.46745075	14.06190177	-1.668867492	0.126103211
Text Cost	-6.429188147	5.698538218	-1.12821708	0.285568543
Color Photo Time	-7.470425481	4.683317933	-1.595113889	0.141770953
Color Photo Cost	13.82312558	54.81425163	0.252181233	0.806008407

15.30
cont.
Since the p-values of X_2 and X_4 are both greater than 0.05, they should be dropped from the model.

PHStat output of the model with only X_2 and X_4:

Regression Statistics	
Multiple R	0.672366138
R Square	0.452076224
Adjusted R Square	0.360755595
Standard Error	61.17947528
Observations	15

ANOVA

	df	SS	MS	F	Significance F
Regression	2	37058.19499	18529.0975	4.950428256	0.027059569
Residual	12	44915.13834	3742.928195		
Total	14	81973.33333			

	Coefficients	Standard Error	t Stat	P-value
Intercept	326.8080104	56.60295611	5.773691568	8.82928E-05
Text Speed	-23.85700143	12.91282757	-1.847542786	0.089456849
Color Photo Time	-10.23438315	3.963094482	-2.582422194	0.023990486

The most appropriate model:

$$\hat{Y} = 326.8080 - 23.8570X_1 - 10.2344X_3$$

Analysis of the residual plots does not reveal any specific pattern.

15.32   Stepwise regression attempts to find the best regression model without examining all possible regressions by adding and subtracting X variables at each step of the process. Best-subsets regression examines each possible regression model and uses the C_p statistic to determine which models can be considered to be good fitting models.

15.34   A hat matrix element h_i measures the possible influence of each X_i on the fitted regression model while a Studentized deleted residual measures the difference of an observation Y_i from the value predicted by a model that includes all other observations.

15.36   (a)   Let Y = wins, X_1 = gate receipts, X_2 = local TV and radio revenue, X_3 = other local revenue, X_4 = player compensation.
Based on a full regression model involving all of the variables:
The *VIF* for X_1, X_2, X_3, and X_4 are, respectively, 4.53, 2.50, 2.63, 3.33, and are all less than 5. So there is no reason to suspect collinearity between any pair of variables.
The best-subsets approach does not yield a clear best model with the following result:

Model	Cp	k	R Square	Adj. R Square	Std. Error	Consider This Model?
X1	0.0897	2	0.2020	0.1735	11.8243	Yes
X1X2	1.5826	3	0.2175	0.1596	11.9236	Yes
X1X2X3	3.0004	4	0.2353	0.1471	12.0117	Yes
X1X2X3X4	5.0000	5	0.2354	0.1130	12.2495	Yes
X1X2X4	3.5694	4	0.2179	0.1277	12.1476	Yes
X1X3	1.5395	3	0.2189	0.1610	11.9136	Yes
X1X3X4	3.4831	4	0.2206	0.1306	12.1271	Yes
X1X4	1.9674	3	0.2058	0.1469	12.0130	Yes
X2	1.0472	2	0.1727	0.1432	12.0393	Yes
X2X3	1.1758	3	0.2300	0.1729	11.8284	Yes
X2X3X4	3.1539	4	0.2306	0.1419	12.0485	Yes
X2X4	2.4146	3	0.1921	0.1322	12.1160	Yes
X3	0.6063	2	0.1862	0.1572	11.9407	Yes
X3X4	1.9563	3	0.2061	0.1473	12.0104	Yes
X4	1.5018	2	0.1588	0.1288	12.1400	Yes

The stepwise approach recommends that regular season gate receipts (X_1) is the only variable needed with the following result:
Stepwise
Analysis
Table of Results for General Stepwise

Regular season game receipts ($millions) entered.

	df	SS	MS	F	Significance F
Regression	1	991.10488	991.10488	7.08879	0.01271
Residual	28	3914.76178	139.81292		
Total	29	4905.86667			

	Coefficients	Standard Error	t Stat	P-value	Lower 95%
Intercept	69.0198	4.9682	13.8924	0.0000	58.8430
game receipts	0.2582	0.0970	2.6625	0.0127	0.0596

No other variables could be entered into the model. Stepwise ends.

15.36 (a)
cont.

PHStat output of the best model:					
Regression Statistics					
Multiple R	0.4495				
R Square	0.2020				
Adjusted R Square	0.1735				
Standard Error	11.8243				
Observations	30				

ANOVA					
	df	*SS*	*MS*	*F*	*Significance F*
Regression	1	991.1049	991.1049	7.0888	0.0127
Residual	28	3914.7618	139.8129		
Total	29	4905.8667			

	Coefficients	*Standard Error*	*t Stat*	*P-value*
Intercept	69.0198	4.9682	13.8924	0.0000
Regular season game receipts ($millions)	0.2582	0.0970	2.6625	0.0127

The *p*-value of game receipts is 0.013 < 0.05 and, hence, game receipts is a significant independent variable.

The residual plot does not reveal any obvious pattern. The normal probability plot shows sign of violation from the normality assumption.

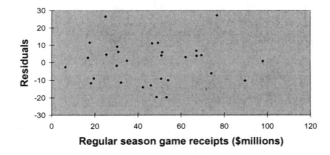

Regular season game receipts ($millions) Residual Plot

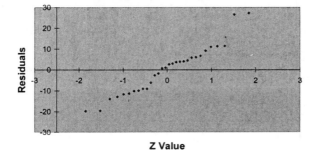

Normal Probability Plot

15.36   (b)   The r^2 in (a) is 0.2020, which is much smaller than the r^2 of 0.9430 in problem
cont.   15.35(a). The four on-field team statistics have higher explanatory power than the
                       variables used in (a).

15.38-15.40
            Let Y = appraised value, X_1 = land area, X_2 = interior size, X_3 = age, X_4 = number of rooms, X_5
            = number of bathrooms, X_6 = garage size.
            (a)
            Glen Cove:
                  Based on a full regression model involving all of the variables:
                  All *VIF*s are less than 5. So there is no reason to suspect collinearity between any
                  pair of variables.
                  The best-subset approach yielded the following models to be considered:

Model	Cp	k	R Square	Adj. R Square	Std. Error	Consider This Model?
X1X2X3	3.650863	4	0.829632	0.809974373	52.47949	Yes
X1X2X3X4	4.149255	5	0.839606	0.813942457	51.92867	Yes
X1X2X3X4X5	5.908748	6	0.841203	0.808120255	52.7349	Yes
X1X2X3X4X5X6	7	7	0.847239	0.807387908	52.83544	Yes
X1X2X3X4X6	5.115483	6	0.846472	0.814486602	51.85268	Yes

                  The stepwise regression approach reveals that the following best model:

	Coefficients	Standard Error	t Stat	P-value
Intercept	136.7940357	53.82963694	2.54124017	0.017353728
House Size(sq ft)	0.128818369	0.020923194	6.156725888	1.64543E-06
Land (acres)	276.0876372	78.19612858	3.530707239	0.001568793
Age	-1.398931849	0.475516859	-2.941918512	0.006773518

                  Combining the results of both approaches, the most appropriate multiple regression
                  model for predicting appraised value in Glen Cove is
                  $$\hat{Y} = 136.7940 + 276.0876X_1 + 0.1288X_2 - 1.3989X_3$$
            Roslyn:
                  Based on a full regression model involving all of the variables:
                  All *VIF*s are less than 5. So there is no reason to suspect collinearity between any
                  pair of variables.
                  The best-subset approach yielded the following models to be considered:

Model	Cp	k	R Square	Adj. R Square	Std. Error	Consider This Model?
X1X2X3X4X5	5.014882	6	0.860803	0.831803665	70.72967	Yes
X1X2X3X4X5X6	7	7	0.860893	0.824604266	72.22755	Yes
X1X2X3X5	4.619049	5	0.851101	0.827276952	71.67514	Yes

15.38-15.40
cont.

The stepwise regression approach reveals that the following best model:

	Coefficients	Standard Error	t Stat	P-value
Intercept	98.3024	47.5996	2.0652	0.0490
House Size(sq ft)	0.0943	0.0196	4.8230	0.0001
Land	550.1994	163.6925	3.3612	0.0024
Baths	60.6213	25.5102	2.3764	0.0251

The p-value of X_3 is greater than 0.05 in the regression model with X_1, X_2, X_3 and X_5. Combing the results of both approaches, the most appropriate multiple regression model for predicting appraised value in Roslyn is

$$\hat{Y} = 98.3024 + 550.1994X_1 + 0.0943X_2 + 60.6213X_5$$

Freeport:

Based on a full regression model involving all of the variables:
All *VIFs* are less than 5. So there is no reason to suspect collinearity between any pair of variables.
The best-subset approach yielded the following models to be considered:

Model	Cp	k	R Square	Adj. R Square	Std. Error	This Model?
X1X2X3X4	3.834689	5	0.873698	0.853489619	21.04431	Yes
X1X2X3X4X5	5.632946	6	0.874767	0.84867679	21.38716	Yes
X1X2X3X4X5X6	7	7	0.878121	0.846326523	21.55261	Yes
X1X2X3X4X6	5.028879	6	0.877968	0.85254467	21.11206	Yes
X1X2X4X5X6	5.631183	6	0.874776	0.848688081	21.38637	Yes
X1X2X4X6	3.702829	5	0.874397	0.854300154	20.98601	Yes
X1X2X5X6	4.901186	5	0.868046	0.846933926	21.50997	Yes
X1X2X6	3.084531	4	0.867075	0.851737417	21.16977	Yes
X2X3X4	2.339328	4	0.871024	0.856141953	20.85295	Yes
X2X3X4X5	4.272654	5	0.871377	0.850797473	21.23677	Yes
X2X3X4X5X6	5.626606	6	0.874801	0.848717389	21.38429	Yes
X2X3X4X6	3.626999	5	0.874799	0.854766276	20.95242	Yes
X2X3X6	3.887328	4	0.862821	0.846992473	21.50586	Yes
X2X4X5X6	4.225896	5	0.871625	0.851084891	21.21631	Yes
X2X4X6	2.232616	4	0.871589	0.85677268	20.80719	Yes
X2X5X6	3.858479	4	0.862974	0.847162986	21.49387	Yes
X2X6	1.903766	3	0.862734	0.852565858	21.11055	Yes

The stepwise regression approach reveals that the following best model:

	Coefficients	Standard Error	t Stat	P-value
Intercept	110.2676327	12.26077283	8.993530367	9.48178E-10
House Size(sq ft)	0.08210861	0.006673054	12.30450334	8.22931E-13

Combining the results of both approaches, the most appropriate multiple regression model for predicting appraised value in Freeport is

$$\hat{Y} = 110.2676 + 0.0821X_2$$

(b)   The adjusted r^2 for the best model in 15.38(a), 15.39(a), and 15.40(a) are, respectively, 0.81, 0.8117 and 0.8383. The model in 15.40(a) has the highest explanatory power after adjusting for the number of independent variables and sample size.

15.42 Let Y = appraised value, X_1 = land area, X_2 = interior size, X_3 = age, X_4 = number of rooms, X_5 = number of bathrooms, X_6 = garage size, X_7 = 1 if Glen Cove and 0 otherwise, X_8 = 1 if Roslyn and 0 otherwise.

(a) Based on a full regression model involving all of the variables:
All *VIF*s are less than 5. So there is no reason to suspect collinearity between any pair of variables.
Minitab best-subset approach yielded the following models to be considered:

Best Subsets Regression: Appraised Va versus Land (acres), House Size(s, ...
```
Response is Appraise
```

						L a n d e (a c i e s	H o u s e o R B S i a o z o t e a g S m g e h	R B a a t t C h g o s v	G l e G e R n o a C s o l v n
Vars	R-Sq	R-Sq(adj)	C-p	S					
1	51.1	50.5	285.5	132.02		X			
1	47.3	46.7	314.2	137.04					X
1	44.0	43.4	339.1	141.23			X		
2	78.3	77.8	80.8	88.425		X			X
2	71.3	70.6	134.0	101.72		X			X
2	67.5	66.8	162.5	108.15			X		X
3	84.4	83.9	36.4	75.395		X X			X
3	83.2	82.7	45.2	78.160		X		X X
3	81.5	80.8	58.7	82.178		X	X	X
4	87.0	86.4	18.4	69.148		X X		X X
4	86.9	86.3	19.5	69.516		X X	X	X
4	86.0	85.3	26.3	71.871		X X X		X
5	88.9	88.2	6.4	64.407		X X	X	X X
5	87.7	86.9	15.6	67.843		X X X		X X
5	87.6	86.9	16.0	67.976		X X	X	X X
6	**89.3**	**88.5**	**5.5**	**63.683**		**X X**	**X X**	**X X**
6	89.0	88.3	7.2	64.317		X X X	X	X X
6	89.0	88.2	7.4	64.427		X X		X X X X
7	**89.3**	**88.4**	**7.1**	**63.913**		**X X**	**X X X X**	**X X**
7	89.3	88.4	7.2	63.931		X X X X	X	X X
7	89.1	88.2	8.9	64.606		X X X	X X X X	
8	89.3	88.3	9.0	64.257		X X X X X X X X		

Following is the Minitab output of the multiple regression with all the variables included:
```
The regression equation is
Appraised Value = 20.5 + 366 Land (acres) + 0.0967 House Size(sq ft)
             - 0.143 Age - 7.52 Rooms + 40.0 Baths + 6.1 Garage + 61.6
             Glen Cove + 224 Rosyln
```

Predictor	Coef	SE Coef	T	P
Constant	20.49	41.44	0.49	0.622
Land (ac	366.00	70.66	5.18	0.000
House Si	0.09666	0.01432	6.75	0.000
Age	-0.1428	0.4029	-0.35	0.724
Rooms	-7.518	5.462	-1.38	0.172
Baths	40.02	12.38	3.23	0.002
Garage	6.05	14.64	0.41	0.680
Glen Cov	61.57	18.41	3.34	0.001
Rosyln	224.04	18.78	11.93	0.000

15.42 (a)
cont.

The individual t test for the significance of each independent variable at 5% level of significance concludes that only X_1, X_2, X_5, X_7, X_8, are significant individually. This subset, however, is not chosen using the C_p criterion.

Mintab stepwise regression analysis yields the following:
Stepwise Regression: Appraised Va versus Land (acres), House Size(s,
...

```
   Alpha-to-Enter: 0.05  Alpha-to-Remove: 0.05

   Response is Appraise on  8 predictors, with N =   90
```

Step	1	2	3	4	5
Constant	42.483	42.858	19.715	-2.732	-33.039
House Si	0.186	0.150	0.112	0.112	0.090
T-Value	9.59	11.15	8.51	9.30	7.12
P-Value	0.000	0.000	0.000	0.000	0.000
Rosyln		214	206	249	229
T-Value		10.45	11.79	13.06	12.35
P-Value		0.000	0.000	0.000	0.000
Land (ac			458	375	363
T-Value			5.80	4.99	5.19
P-Value			0.000	0.000	0.000
Glen Cov				78	68
T-Value				4.15	3.88
P-Value				0.000	0.000
Baths					43
T-Value					3.74
P-Value					0.000
S	132	88.4	75.4	69.1	64.4
R-Sq	51.08	78.30	84.41	87.04	88.89
R-Sq(adj)	50.52	77.80	83.86	86.43	88.22
C-p	285.5	80.8	36.4	18.4	6.4

Combining the stepwise regression result with the individual t test result, the most appropriate multiple regression model for predicting the appraised value is

$$\hat{Y} = -33.04 + 363.36X_1 + 0.09047X_2 + 43.04X_5 + 68.29X_7 + 229.01X_8$$

15.42   (a)   Minitab output of the most appropriate model:
cont.

Regression Analysis: Appraised Va versus House Size(s, Rosyln, ...

```
The regression equation is
Appraised Value = - 33.0 + 0.0905 House Size(sq ft) + 229 Rosyln
               + 363 Land (acres) + 68.3 Glen Cove + 43.0 Baths

Predictor          Coef      SE Coef          T        P
Constant         -33.04        22.42      -1.47    0.144
House Si        0.09047      0.01271       7.12    0.000
Rosyln           229.01        18.55      12.35    0.000
Land (ac         363.36        70.07       5.19    0.000
Glen Cov          68.29        17.62       3.88    0.000
Baths             43.04        11.51       3.74    0.000

S = 64.41       R-Sq = 88.9%      R-Sq(adj) = 88.2%

Analysis of Variance

Source            DF           SS          MS        F        P
Regression         5      2786632      557326   134.35    0.000
Residual Error    84       348450        4148
Total             89      3135083
```

(b)   The estimated average appraised value in Glen Cove is 68.29 above Freeport for two otherwise identical properties. The estimated average appraised value in Roslyn is 229.01 above Freeport for two otherwise identical properties.

15.44   Denote X_1 = weight, X_2 = width, X_3 = length, X_4 = cargo volume, X_5 = turning circle, X_6 = horsepower, and X_7 = 1 if SUV and 0 otherwise.

An analysis of the linear regression model using PHStat with all possible independent variables reveals that two of the variables, X_1 and X_3, have VIF values in excess of 5.0. Based on the procedure recommended in the text, variables were deleted one at time from the model, selecting the variable with the largest VIF value, until there were no variables with VIF > 5. Repetitions of this step resulted in the removal of weight and length from the model.

An analysis of the linear regression model with the remaining independent variables indicates that none of the remaining variables have a VIF value that is 5.0 or larger.

Renaming X_1 = width, X_2 = cargo, X_3 = turning circle, X_4 = horsepower, and X_5 = 1 if SUV and 0 otherwise.

The best-subsets approach reveals that only one model with all the 5 remaining variables is the most appropriate multiple regression model.

Influence analysis using the hat matrix elements, the Studentized deleted residuals and Cook's distance statistic does not reveal any observation that needs to be removed.

15.44
cont.

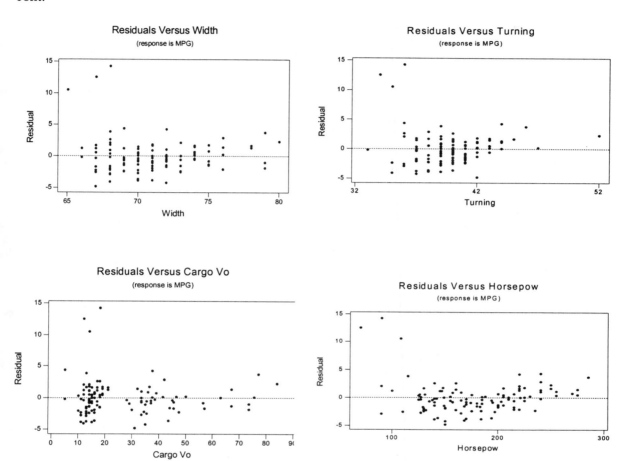

The residual plots reveal the violations of homoscedasticity assumption. Also there appears to be a quadratic relationship between MPG and horsepower. Letting $X_7 = X_4^2$, the Minitab output of the multiple regression model follows:

15.44   Regression **Analysis: MPG versus Width, Cargo Volume, ...**
cont.

```
The regression equation is
MPG = 75.7 - 0.242 Width - 0.0258 Cargo Volume - 0.304 Turning Circle
         - 0.243 Horsepower - 4.41 SUV Dummy +0.000581 Horsepower SQ

Predictor          Coef      SE Coef          T          P        VIF
Constant         75.652        6.981      10.84      0.000
Width           -0.2420       0.1106      -2.19      0.031        2.8
Cargo Vo       -0.02584      0.01556      -1.66      0.100        1.9
Turning         -0.3042       0.1067      -2.85      0.005        1.9
Horsepow       -0.24323      0.03176      -7.66      0.000       46.8
SUV Dumm        -4.4063       0.5639      -7.81      0.000        1.3
Horsepow     0.00058078   0.00008417       6.90      0.000       45.3

S = 2.355       R-Sq = 75.9%      R-Sq(adj) = 74.7%

Analysis of Variance

Source             DF           SS          MS          F          P
Regression          6      1995.26      332.54      59.98      0.000
Residual Error    114       632.03        5.54
Total             120      2627.29
```

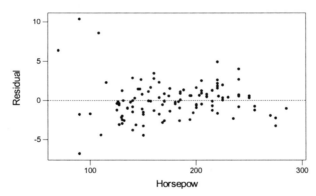

Residuals Versus Horsepow
(response is MPG)

The new residual plot for horsepower indicates that the quadratic term has captured the non-linear relationship between MPG and horsepower. The full model F test statistic has a p-value that is virtually 0. There is sufficient evidence to conclude that all the variables together significantly explain gas mileage. The individual t test statistic for each of the explanatory variables also has p-value smaller than 0.05 with the exception of cargo volume, which has a p-value of 0.0997.

15.44 The new Minitab output with cargo volume removed:
cont. **Regression Analysis: MPG versus Width, Turning Circle, ...**
```
The regression equation is
MPG = 81.3 - 0.309 Width - 0.344 Turning Circle - 0.243 Horsepower
        - 4.83 SUV Dummy +0.000586 Horsepower SQ

Predictor          Coef      SE Coef          T        P        VIF
Constant         81.254        6.158      13.20    0.000
Width           -0.3086       0.1038      -2.97    0.004        2.4
Turning         -0.3442       0.1048      -3.29    0.001        1.8
Horsepow       -0.24344      0.03201      -7.61    0.000       46.8
SUV Dumm        -4.8314       0.5062      -9.54    0.000        1.0
Horsepow     0.00058613   0.00008475       6.92    0.000       45.2

S = 2.372       R-Sq = 75.4%      R-Sq(adj) = 74.3%

Analysis of Variance

Source            DF           SS          MS        F        P
Regression         5      1979.99      396.00    70.35    0.000
Residual Error   115       647.30        5.63
Total            120      2627.29
```
The r^2 does not decrease substantially after the removal of cargo volume and the p-value of the t test for the significant of individual slope coefficient are essentially zero.
The final model is:
$$\hat{Y} = 81.254 - 0.3086 \text{ Width} - 0.3442 \text{ turning circle} - 0.2434 \text{ horsepower}$$
$$+ 5.8613 \cdot 10^{-4} \text{ horsepower}^2 - 4.8314 \text{ SUV}$$
Residual analysis on the final model still shows sign of violation of the homoscedasticity assumption.

15.46 The highest VIF value of 739.18 in the multiple regression model with solar radiation, soil temperature, vapor pressure, wind speed, relative humidity, dew point, and ambient air temperature belonged to vapor pressure. After dropping vapor pressure from the multiple regression model, the highest VIF value of 90.00 in the remaining multiple regression belonged to air temperature. After air temperature was removed from the model, soil radiation had the highest VIF of 18.84 in the remaining multiple regression. Soil radiation was dropped from the multiple regression model next. The highest VIF of 7.36 in the remaining model belonged to wind speed. Wind speed was dropped from the model next and all the VIF values in the remaining multiple regression of X_1 = soil temperature, X_2 = relative humidity, and X_3 = dew point were smaller than 5.
C_p statistic was computed for all subset and the subsets that were not recommended by the C_p statistic were simple regression with soil temperature, simple regression with relative humidity, and multiple regression with both soil temperature and relative humidity.
Using a 0.05 level of significance and performing t tests on the significance of soil temperature, dew point and relative humidity individually led to the conclusion that only dew point was significant individually. The partial F test on the significance of soil temperature and relative humidity as a group yielded a p-value of 0.627, hence, led to the conclusion that both soil temperature and relative humidity were insignificant as a group as well. The residual plot in the simple regression of radon concentration on dew point indicated some possible nonlinear relationship. A logarithmic transformation on dew point was performed. The residual plot in the linear-log model did not reveal any more nonlinear relationship and the p-value of the t test was 0.046, which was smaller than the 5% level of significance. The coefficient of determination was pretty low at 0.10. Only 10% of the variation in radon concentration could be explained by using dew point.

15.46 The normal probability plot suggests that the error distribution is very close to a normal
cont.   distribution.

15.48 (a) Let $X_1 = \text{Temp}$ $X_2 = \text{WP}$ $X_3 = \text{Promo}$ $X_4 = \text{Rival}$ $X_5 = \text{Day}$ $X_6 = \text{Weekend}$

Regression Statistics	
Multiple R	0.471852279
R Square	0.222644573
Adjusted R Square	0.158752346
Standard Error	8532.521649
Observations	80

ANOVA

	df	SS	MS	F	Significance F
Regression	6	1522194457	253699076.2	3.484689512	0.004381311
Residual	73	5314686575	72803925.69		
Total	79	6836881033			

	Coefficients	Standard Error	t Stat	P-value	Lower 95%	Upper 95%
Intercept	5377.325072	7164.386485	0.750563231	0.455328083	-8901.286284	19655.93643
Temp	163.8070086	137.2180588	1.193771506	0.236432331	-109.6683735	437.2823908
WP	4.099422123	18.07760731	0.226767959	0.821237998	-31.92922173	40.12806597
Promo	6428.248164	2998.078945	2.14412238	0.035353279	453.0813918	12403.41494
Rival	-156.0498564	2871.07393	-0.054352434	0.956802851	-5878.095826	5565.996114
Day	1317.347072	2338.694741	0.563283035	0.574968316	-3343.667986	5978.36213
Weekend	2603.405897	2249.695741	1.157225774	0.250952729	-1880.23429	7087.046084

$\widehat{Y} = 5377.325 + 163.807X_1 + 4.099X_2 + 6428.248X_3 - 156.050X_4 + 1317.347X_5 + 2603.406X_6$

(b) Intercept:

Since all the non-dummy independent variables cannot have zero values, the
intercept should be interpreted as the portion of paid attendance that varies with
factors other than those already included in the model.

Temp:

As the high temperature increases by one degree, the estimated average paid
attendance will increase by 163.807 taking into consideration all the other
independent variables included in the model.

WP:

As the winning percentage of the team improves by 1%, the estimated average paid
attendance will increase by 4.099 taking into consideration all the other independent
variables included in the model.

Promo:

The estimated average paid attendance on promotion day will be 6428.25 higher than
when there is no promotion taking into consideration all the other independent
variables included in the model.

Rival:

The estimated average paid attendance when the visiting team is considered a rival
will be 156.05 lower than when the visiting team is not considered a rival taking into
consideration all the other independent variables included in the model.

Day:

The estimated average paid attendance of a game played during the day time will be
1317.347 higher than when the game is played at night taking into consideration all
the other independent variables included in the model.

Weekend:

The estimated average paid attendance of a game played on a weekend will be
2603.406 higher than when the game is played on a weekday taking into consideration
all the other independent variables included in the model.

15.48 (c) $H_0: \beta_j = 0$ $H_1: \beta_j \neq 0$ for j = 1, 2, 3, 4, 5 or 6

cont.   At 0.05 level of significance, the independent variable that makes significance
               contribution to the regression model individually is the promotion dummy variable.

       (d)   The p values of each independent variable are reported in the EXCEL regression
               table. The p value of each independent variable measures the probability of
               observing an estimated net regression coefficient b_j which gives rise to a t test
               statistic more extreme than the one obtained from the data if the null hypothesis is
               true.

       (e) $r^2_{Y.123456} = 0.2226$. 22.26% of the total variation in paid attendance can be explained by
               the 6 independent variables.

       (f)   Adjusted $r^2 = 0.1588$.

       (g)

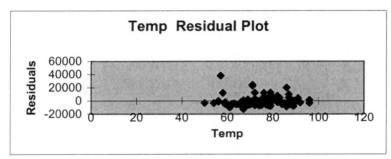

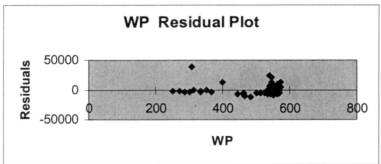

The residual plot of winning percentage reveals potential violation of the
homoscedasticity assumption as the variance of the residuals increases as the winning
percentage goes up. The normal probability plot also reveals nonnormality in the
residuals.

15.48   (h)   With all the 6 independent variables in the model:
cont. $VIF_1 = 2.31$ $VIF_2 = 2.44$ $VIF_3 = 1.79$ $VIF_4 = 1.07$ $VIF_5 = 1.47$ $VIF_6 = 1.37$
                None of the VIF is > 5.

	Cp	p+1	R Square	Adj. R Square	Std. Error	Consider This Model?
X1X2X3	2.671277	4	0.204848	0.173460041	8457.605	Yes
X1X2X3X4	4.648622	5	0.205089	0.162693622	8512.511	Yes
X1X2X3X4X5X6	7	7	0.222645	0.158752346	8532.522	Yes
X1X2X3X4X6	5.317288	6	0.219266	0.166513563	8493.071	Yes
X1X2X3X5	4.345291	5	0.208319	0.166095979	8495.198	Yes
X1X2X3X5X6	5.002954	6	0.222613	0.170086974	8474.845	Yes
X1X2X3X6	3.333519	5	0.219093	0.177444655	8437.194	Yes
X1X3	0.701547	3	0.204525	0.18386362	8404.209	Yes
X1X3X4	2.689354	4	0.204655	0.173259948	8458.629	Yes
X1X3X4X5	4.420429	5	0.207519	0.165253186	8499.49	Yes
X1X3X4X5X6	5.051424	6	0.222097	0.169535962	8477.658	Yes
X1X3X4X6	3.337455	5	0.219051	0.177400504	8437.42	Yes
X1X3X5	2.421071	4	0.207512	0.176229587	8443.423	Yes
X1X3X5X6	3.051567	5	0.222095	0.180607209	8420.959	Yes
X1X3X6	1.347375	4	0.218945	0.188114382	8382.294	Yes
X2X3	2.282487	3	0.18769	0.166591392	8492.674	Yes
X2X3X4X6	4.869121	5	0.202741	0.160220364	8525.074	Yes
X2X3X5	3.804969	4	0.192775	0.16091115	8521.567	Yes
X2X3X5X6	4.450556	5	0.207198	0.164915263	8501.21	Yes
X2X3X6	2.932984	4	0.202061	0.170563193	8472.413	Yes

Based on the smallest C_p value and the highest adjusted R-square, the two competing models are the multiple regression models using X_1, X_3 and X_6, and X_1 and X_3.

	Coefficients	Standard Error	t Stat	P-value
Intercept	6302.496667	6795.080753	0.927508722	0.356598735
Temp	184.0148363	88.9457592	2.068843281	0.04196156
Promo	7221.288697	2573.31025	2.806225443	0.006363605
Weekend	2614.297354	2207.00602	1.184544732	0.239888699

The regression result is from the multiple regression model using X_1, X_3 and X_6. Since X_6 does not make significant contribution to the regression model, the best subset model is the one using X_1 and X_3.

(a) $\hat{Y} = 6592.930 + 190.384X_1 + 8794.987X_3$

	Coefficients	Standard Error	t Stat	P-value
Intercept	6592.930345	6808.409401	0.968351043	0.335900913
Temp	190.3836008	89.01522683	2.138775663	0.035623925
Promo	8794.987426	2209.609257	3.980336069	0.000154602

15.48 (h)
cont.

(b) Intercept:

Since all the non-dummy independent variables cannot have zero values, the intercept should be interpreted as the portion of paid attendance that varies with factors other than those already included in the model.

Temp:

As the high temperature increases by one degree, the estimated average paid attendance will increase by 190.384 taking into consideration all the other independent variables included in the model.

Promo:

The estimated average paid attendance on promotion day will be 8794.99 higher than when there is no promotion taking into consideration all the other independent variables included in the model.

(c) $H_0 : \beta_j = 0$ $H_1 : \beta_j \neq 0$ for $j = 1$ or 3

At 0.05 level of significance, both the independent variables make significance contribution to the regression model individually.

(d) The p values of each independent variable are reported in the EXCEL regression table. The p value of each independent variable measures the probability of observing an estimated net regression coefficient b_j which gives rise to a t test statistic more extreme than the one obtained from the data if the null hypothesis is true.

(e) $r_{Y.13}^2 = 0.2045$. 20.45% of the total variation in paid attendance can be explained by the 2 independent variables.

(f) Adjusted $r^2 = 0.1839$.

(g)

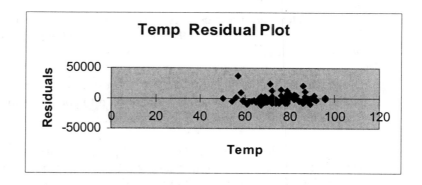

The residuals of Temp are scattered quite evenly around zero.

15.48   (j)   (a)
cont.

Let $X_1 = $ Temp $X_2 = $ WP $X_3 = $ Promo $X_4 = $ Rival $X_5 = $ Day $X_6 = $ Weekend

Regression Statistics	
Multiple R	0.435318538
R Square	0.189502229
Adjusted R Square	0.120030992
Standard Error	6251.498877
Observations	77

ANOVA

	df	SS	MS	F	Significance F
Regression	6	639630042.3	106605007.1	2.72777967	0.019370174
Residual	70	2735686675	39081238.21		
Total	76	3375316717			

	Coefficients	Standard Error	t Stat	P-value	Lower 95%	Upper 9
Intercept	13463.51856	12530.69955	1.074442692	0.286314029	-11528.1532	38455.1!
Temp	50.91778322	64.15536813	0.793663644	0.430073479	-77.03595915	178.871!
WP	0.749859186	21.34162892	0.035135987	0.972071309	-41.81464272	43.3143(
Promo	3793.84181	2220.895735	1.708248501	0.092021487	-635.5914398	8223.2;
Rival	-1477.966348	1725.058008	-0.856763275	0.394499335	-4918.483242	1962.55(
Day	485.8851931	1772.38346	0.274142252	0.784782678	-3049.019262	4020.78!
Weekend	3148.57855	1646.077842	1.912776219	0.059868274	-134.4174986	6431.57(

$$\hat{Y} = 13463.519 + 50.918X_1 + 0.750X_2 + 3793.842X_3 - 1477.966X_4 + 485.885X_5 + 3148.579X_6$$

(b) Intercept:
   Since all the non-dummy independent variables cannot have zero values, the
   intercept should be interpreted as the portion of paid attendance that varies with
   factors other than those already included in the model.

Temp:
   As the high temperature increases by one degree, the estimated average paid
   attendance will increase by 50.918 taking into consideration all the other
   independent variables included in the model.

WP:
   As the winning percentage of the team improves by 1%, the estimated average
   paid attendance will increase by 0.75 taking into consideration all the other
   independent variables included in the model.

Promo:
   The estimated average paid attendance on promotion day will be 3793.842 higher
   than when there is no promotion taking into consideration all the other
   independent variables included in the model.

Rival:
   The estimated average paid attendance when the visiting team is considered a
   rival will be 1477.97 lower than when the visiting team is not considered a rival
   taking into consideration all the other independent variables included in the
   model.

Day:
   The estimated average paid attendance of a game played during the day time will
   be 485.885 higher than when the game is played at night taking into
   consideration all the other independent variables included in the model.

Weekend:
   The estimated average paid attendance of a game played on a weekend will be
   3148.579 higher than when the game is played on a weekday taking into
   consideration all the other independent variables included in the model.

15.48 (j)   (c) $H_0 : \beta_j = 0$ $H_1 : \beta_j \neq 0$ for j = 1, 2, 3, 4, 5 or 6
cont.   At 0.05 level of significance, none of the independent variables makes a
                   significance contribution to the regression model individually.
              (d) The p values of each independent variable are reported in the EXCEL regression
                   table. The p value of each independent variable measures the probability of
                   observing an estimated net regression coefficient b_j which gives rise to a t test
                   statistic more extreme than the one obtained from the data if the null hypothesis is
                   true.
              (e) $r_{Y.123456}^2 = 0.1895$. 18.95% of the total variation in paid attendance can be
                   explained by the 6 independent variables.
              (f) Adjusted $r^2 = 0.1200$.
              (g)

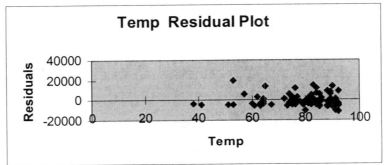

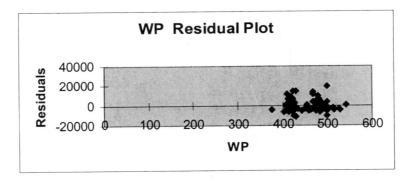

         Both residual plots have residuals quite evenly distributed across zero.

15.48   (j)   (h) With all the 6 independent variables in the model:

$VIF_1 = 1.23$ $VIF_2 = 1.25$ $VIF_3 = 1.45$ $VIF_4 = 1.01$ $VIF_5 = 1.26$ $VIF_6 = 1.32$

cont.

None of the VIF is > 5.

	Cp	p+1	R Square	Adj. R Square	Std. Error	Consider This Model?
X1X2X3X4X5X6	7	7	0.189502	0.120030992	6251.499	Yes
X1X2X3X4X6	5.075154	6	0.188632	0.131493468	6210.649	Yes
X1X2X3X5X6	5.734043	6	0.181003	0.12332724	6239.779	Yes
X1X2X3X6	3.804945	5	0.180182	0.134636703	6199.401	Yes
X1X3X4X5X6	5.001235	6	0.189488	0.132409621	6207.373	Yes
X1X3X4X6	3.075303	5	0.18863	0.143554237	6167.376	Yes
X1X3X5X6	3.738177	5	0.180955	0.135452734	6196.477	Yes
X1X3X6	1.805293	4	0.180178	0.146486803	6156.808	Yes
X2X3X4X5X6	5.629902	6	0.182209	0.124617961	6235.184	Yes
X2X3X4X6	3.657265	5	0.181892	0.13644162	6192.932	Yes
X2X3X5X6	4.284481	5	0.17463	0.128775911	6220.358	Yes
X2X3X6	2.311691	4	0.174315	0.140382496	6178.785	Yes
X3X4X5X6	3.723359	5	0.181127	0.135633832	6195.828	Yes
X3X4X6	1.765966	4	0.180633	0.146960866	6155.098	Yes
X3X5X6	2.349198	4	0.17388	0.139930365	6180.41	Yes
X3X6	0.388951	3	0.17342	0.151080206	6140.218	Yes

Based on the smallest C_p value and the highest adjusted R-square, the three competing models are the multiple regression models using X_1, X_3 and X_6, X_3, X_4 and X_6, and X_3 and X_6.

	Coefficients	Standard Err	t Stat	P-value
Intercept	14028.72	4522.418	3.10204	0.002732
Temp	44.6841	57.60299	0.775725	0.440417
Promo	4012.104	2044.739	1.962159	0.053556
Weekend	3218.274	1578.96	2.038224	0.045151

	Coefficients	Standard Err	t Stat	P-value
Intercept	17749.64	1018.023	17.4354	9.76E-28
Promo	4134.024	2035.367	2.031095	0.045887
Rival	-1356.11	1691.632	-0.80166	0.425354
Weekend	3311.231	1576.778	2.099999	0.039185

From the regression results, neither X_1 nor X_4 makes a significant contribution to the regression models. Hence, the best subset model is the one using X_3 and X_6.

(a) $\hat{Y} = 17458.392 + 4161.555X_3 + 3282.288X_6$

	Coefficients	Standard Err	t Stat	P-value
Intercept	17458.39	948.6884	18.40266	2.47E-29
Promo	4161.555	2030.158	2.049868	0.043921
Weekend	3282.288	1572.553	2.087235	0.040311

15.48 (j) (h) (b)) Intercept:
cont.

The estimated average paid attendance on a weekday with no promotion is 17458.39.

Promo:

The estimated average paid attendance on promotion day will be 4161.555 higher than when there is no promotion taking into consideration all the other independent variables included in the model.

Weekend:

The estimated average paid attendance of a game played on a weekend will be 3282.288 higher than when the game is played on a weekday taking into consideration all the other independent variables included in the model.

(c) $H_0 : \beta_j = 0$ $\qquad$ $H_1 : \beta_j \neq 0$ $\qquad$ for $j = 1$ or 3

At 0.05 level of significance, both the independent variables make a significance contribution to the regression model individually.

(d) The p values of each independent variable are reported in the EXCEL regression table. The p value of each independent variable measures the probability of observing an estimated net regression coefficient b_j which gives rise to a t test statistic more extreme than the one obtained from the data if the null hypothesis is true.

(e) $r_{Y.13}^2 = 0.1734$. 17.34% of the total variation in paid attendance can be explained by the 2 independent variables.

(f) Adjusted $r^2 = 0.1511$.

(g) Since the independent variables in the best subset regression are all dummy variables, the usual residual analysis is not meaningful here.

(k) $\qquad$ (a) Let $X_1 = $ Temp $X_2 = $ WP $X_3 = $ Promo $X_4 = $ Rival $X_5 = $ Day $X_6 = $ Weekend

Regression Statistics	
Multiple R	0.59644052
R Square	0.355741294
Adjusted R Square	0.302788524
Standard Error	6194.795829
Observations	80

ANOVA

	df	SS	MS	F	Significance F
Regression	6	1546859396	257809899.4	6.718086554	1.07962E-05
Residual	73	2801411161	38375495.36		
Total	79	4348270557			

	Coefficients	Standard Error	t Stat	P-value	Lower 95%	Upper 95%
Intercept	16771.24539	4645.04756	3.610564837	0.000557205	7513.672671	26028.8181
Temp	7.266809564	93.65591147	0.077590506	0.938366073	-179.3892794	193.9228985
WP	19.83948239	10.37259282	1.912683043	0.059711684	-0.833079299	40.51204408
Promo	3127.858202	1475.286857	2.120169503	0.037390711	187.6137427	6068.102661
Rival	-1870.720786	1560.721465	-1.198625654	0.234550231	-4981.23629	1239.794717
Day	36.02363809	1744.731248	0.020647099	0.983583501	-3441.223082	3513.270358
Weekend	5903.333891	1541.878143	3.828664357	0.000269894	2830.373099	8976.294684

$$\hat{Y} = 16771.245 + 7.267X_1 + 19.839X_2 + 3127.858X_3 - 1870.721X_4 + 36.024X_5 + 5903.334X_6$$

15.48 (k)
cont.

(b) Intercept:

Since all the non-dummy independent variables cannot have zero values, the intercept should be interpreted as the portion of paid attendance that varies with factors other than those already included in the model.

Temp:

As the high temperature increases by one degree, the estimated average paid attendance will increase by 7.267 taking into consideration all the other independent variables included in the model.

WP:

As the winning percentage of the team improves by 1%, the estimated average paid attendance will increase by 19.84 taking into consideration all the other independent variables included in the model.

Promo:

The estimated average paid attendance on promotion day will be 3127.858 higher than when there is no promotion taking into consideration all the other independent variables included in the model.

Rival:

The estimated average paid attendance when the visiting team is considered a rival will be 1870.721 lower than when the visiting team is not considered a rival taking into consideration all the other independent variables included in the model.

Day:

The estimated average paid attendance of a game played during the day time will be 36.024 higher than when the game is played at night taking into consideration all the other independent variables included in the model.

Weekend:

The estimated average paid attendance of a game played on a weekend will be 5903.334 higher than when the game is played on a weekday taking into consideration all the other independent variables included in the model.

(c) $H_0 : \beta_j = 0$ $H_1 : \beta_j \neq 0$ for $j = 1, 2, 3, 4, 5$ or 6

At 0.05 level of significance, the independent variables that make significance contribution to the regression model individually are the promotion dummy variable and the weekend dummy.

(d) The p values of each independent variable are reported in the EXCEL regression table. The p value of each independent variable measures the probability of observing an estimated net regression coefficient b_j which gives rise to a t test statistic more extreme than the one obtained from the data if the null hypothesis is true.

(e) $r^2_{Y.123456} = 0.3557$. 35.57% of the total variation in paid attendance can be explained by the 6 independent variables.

(f) Adjusted $r^2 = 0.3028$.

15.48 (k)   (g)
cont.

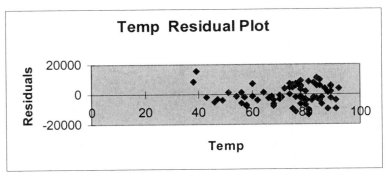

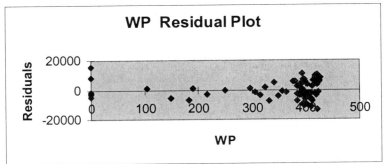

The residual plot of winning percentage reveals potential violation of the homoscedasticity assumption as the variance of the residuals increases as the winning percentage goes up.

(h) With all the 6 independent variables in the model:

$VIF_1 = 3.04$ $VIF_2 = 3.12$ $VIF_3 = 1.14$ $VIF_4 = 1.04$ $VIF_5 = 1.19$ $VIF_6 = 1.27$

None of the *VIF* is > 5.

	Cp	p+1	R Square	Adj. R Square	Std. Error	Consider This Model?
X1X2X3X4X5X6	7	7	0.355741	0.302788524	6194.796	Yes
X1X2X3X4X6	5.000426	6	0.355738	0.312206284	6152.815	Yes
X1X2X3X6	4.456634	5	0.342886	0.307839739	6172.315	Yes
X2X3X4X5X6	5.00602	6	0.355688	0.312153579	6153.05	Yes
X2X3X4X6	3.006732	5	0.355682	0.32131825	6111.922	Yes
X2X3X5X6	4.478501	5	0.342693	0.307636457	6173.221	Yes
X2X3X6	2.504038	4	0.342467	0.316512235	6133.525	Yes

Based on the smallest C_p value and the highest adjusted R-square, the two competing models are the multiple regression models using X_2, X_3 and X_6, and X_2, X_3, X_4 and X_6.

	Coefficients	Standard Err	t Stat	P-value
Intercept	17098.57	2346.003	7.288382	2.66E-10
WP	20.48423	5.87032	3.489456	0.000814
Promo	3146.767	1433.833	2.194653	0.031284
Rival	-1887.93	1522.236	-1.24024	0.218754
Weekend	5915.902	1439.383	4.110026	0.0001

15.48   (k)   (h)
cont.

cont. The regression result is from the multiple regression model using X_2, X_3, X_4 and X_6. Since X_4 does not make significant contribution to the regression model, the best subset model is the one using X_2, X_3 and X_6.

(a) $\hat{Y} = 16810.165 + 19.899X_2 + 3196.483X_3 + 5751.932X_6$

	Coefficients	Standard Err	t Stat	P-value
Intercept	16810.17	2342.701	7.175548	4.09E-10
WP	19.89863	5.871982	3.388741	0.001116
Promo	3196.483	1438.339	2.222344	0.029234
Weekend	5751.932	1438.364	3.998939	0.000146

(b) Intercept:
   The intercept should be interpreted as the portion of paid attendance that varies with factors other than those already included in the model.
WP:
   As the winning percentage of the team improves by 1%, the estimated average paid attendance will increase by 19.899 taking into consideration all the other independent variables included in the model.
Promo:
   The estimated average paid attendance on promotion day will be 3196.483 higher than when there is no promotion taking into consideration all the other independent variables included in the model.
Weekend:
   The estimated average paid attendance of a game played on a weekend will be 5751.932 higher than when the game is played on a weekday taking into consideration all the other independent variables included in the model.

(c) $H_0 : \beta_j = 0 \qquad H_1 : \beta_j \neq 0 \qquad$ for $j = 1$ or 3
   At 0.05 level of significance, all the independent variables make significance contribution to the regression model individually.

(d) The p values of each independent variable are reported in the EXCEL regression table. The p value of each independent variable measures the probability of observing an estimated net regression coefficient b_j which gives rise to a t test statistic more extreme than the one obtained from the data if the null hypothesis is true.

(e) $r^2_{Y.13} = 0.3425$. 34.25% of the total variation in paid attendance can be explained by the 2 independent variables.

(f) Adjusted $r^2 = 0.3165$.

15.48   (k) (h)   (g)
cont.

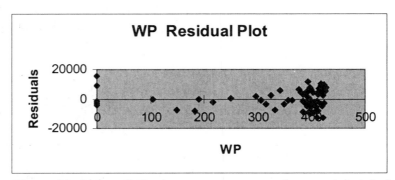

The residual plot of winning percentage reveals potential violation of the homoscedasticity assumption as the variance of the residuals increases as the winning percentage goes up.

(l)   (a) Let $X_1 = $ Temp $X_2 = $ WP $X_3 = $ Promo $X_4 = $ Rival $X_5 = $ Day $X_6 = $ Weekend

Regression Statistics	
Multiple R	0.47793149
R Square	0.228418509
Adjusted R Square	0.165000852
Standard Error	5709.178659
Observations	80

ANOVA

	df	SS	MS	F	Significance F
Regression	6	704400439.8	117400073.3	3.601812498	0.00349203
Residual	73	2379414630	32594720.95		
Total	79	3083815070			

	Coefficients	Standard Error	t Stat	P-value	Lower 95%	Upper 95%
Intercept	7945.005826	5627.986131	1.411696056	0.162287811	-3271.561963	19161.57362
Temp	43.66295279	67.56283345	0.646256981	0.520139528	-90.9896714	178.315577
WP	22.34387748	5.889108478	3.794101869	0.000303239	10.60689325	34.08086171
Promo	1644.681622	1868.021806	0.880440269	0.381510275	-2078.282993	5367.646237
Rival	1040.871005	1893.916665	0.549586486	0.584280503	-2733.702025	4815.444036
Day	-328.025123	1403.851713	-0.233660806	0.815902332	-3125.89945	2469.849204
Weekend	3166.858766	1440.803536	2.197980979	0.031121999	295.3395131	6038.378019

$$\hat{Y} = 7945.006 + 43.663X_1 + 22.344X_2 + 1644.682X_3 + 1040.871X_4 - 328.025X_5 + 3166.859X_6$$

(b) Intercept:

Since all the non-dummy independent variables cannot have zero values, the intercept should be interpreted as the portion of paid attendance that varies with factors other than those already included in the model.

Temp:

As the high temperature increases by one degree, the estimated average paid attendance will increase by 43.663 taking into consideration all the other independent variables included in the model.

WP:

As the winning percentage of the team improves by 1%, the estimated average paid attendance will increase by 22.344 taking into consideration all the other independent variables included in the model.

Promo:

The estimated average paid attendance on promotion day will be 1644.682 higher than when there is no promotion taking into consideration all the other independent variables included in the model.

15.48 (l)   (b)
cont.   Rival:
                The estimated average paid attendance when the visiting team is considered a
                rival will be 1040.871 higher than when the visiting team is not considered a
                rival taking into consideration all the other independent variables included in the
                model.
                Day:
                The estimated average paid attendance of a game played during the day time will
                be 328.025 lower than when the game is played at night taking into consideration
                all the other independent variables included in the model.
                Weekend:
                The estimated average paid attendance of a game played on a weekend will be
                3166.859 higher than when the game is played on a weekday taking into
                consideration all the other independent variables included in the model.

        (c) $H_0 : \beta_j = 0$ $H_1 : \beta_j \neq 0$ for $j = 1, 2, 3, 4, 5$ or 6

        At 0.05 level of significance, the independent variables that make significance
        contribution to the regression model individually are winning percentage and the
        weekend dummy variable.

        (d) The p values of each independent variable are reported in the EXCEL regression
        table. The p value of each independent variable measures the probability of
        observing an estimated net regression coefficient b_j which gives rise to a t test
        statistic more extreme than the one obtained from the data if the null hypothesis
        is true.

        (e) $r^2_{Y.123456} = 0.2284$. 22.84% of the total variation in paid attendance can be
        explained by the 6 independent variables.

        (f) Adjusted $r^2 = 0.1650$.

15.48   (l)   (g)
cont.

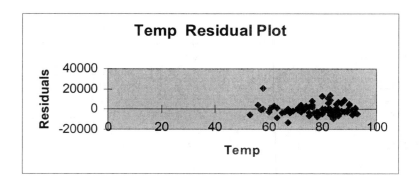

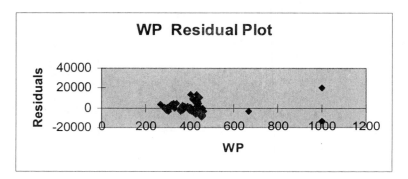

The residual plot of winning percentage reveals potential violation of the homoscedasticity assumption as the variance of the residuals increases as the winning percentage goes up. . The normal probability plot also reveals nonnormality in the residuals.

15.48   (l) (h) With all the 6 independent variables in the model:
cont.

$$VIF_1 = 1.13 \quad VIF_2 = 1.07 \quad VIF_3 = 1.17 \quad VIF_4 = 1.04 \quad VIF_5 = 1.19 \quad VIF_6 = 1.26$$
None of the VIF is > 5.

	Cp	p+1	R Square	Adj. R Square	Std. Error	Consider This Model?
X1X2X3X4X5X6	7	7	0.228419	0.165000852	5709.179	Yes
X1X2X3X4X6	5.054597	6	0.227841	0.17566856	5672.592	Yes
X1X2X3X5X6	5.302045	6	0.225226	0.172876414	5682.191	Yes
X1X2X3X6	3.366891	5	0.224541	0.183182785	5646.678	Yes
X1X2X4X5X6	5.775175	6	0.220225	0.167537725	5700.499	Yes
X1X2X4X6	3.964013	5	0.218229	0.176534829	5669.611	Yes
X1X2X5X6	4.053477	5	0.217284	0.175538792	5673.038	Yes
X1X2X6	2.258065	4	0.215121	0.184139197	5643.372	Yes
X2X3X4X5X6	5.417648	6	0.224004	0.171571978	5686.67	Yes
X2X3X4X6	3.529459	5	0.222822	0.181372856	5652.931	Yes
X2X3X5X6	3.658458	5	0.221459	0.179936675	5657.888	Yes
X2X3X6	1.778374	4	0.220191	0.189409483	5625.115	Yes
X2X4X5X6	3.938521	5	0.218499	0.176818638	5668.634	Yes
X2X4X6	2.163062	4	0.216125	0.185182974	5639.761	Yes
X2X5X6	2.181339	4	0.215932	0.184982169	5640.455	Yes
X2X6	0.417853	3	0.213432	0.193002031	5612.635	Yes

Based on the smallest C_p value and the highest adjusted R-square, the two competing models are the multiple regression models using X_2, X_3 and X_6, and X_2 and X_6.

	Coefficients	Standard Err	t Stat	P-value
Intercept	11314.11	2585.324	4.376285	3.8E-05
WP	22.33752	5.673548	3.937134	0.000181
Promo	1403.174	1728.845	0.811625	0.419542
Weekend	3266.466	1291.732	2.528749	0.01352

The regression result is from the multiple regression model using X_2, X_3 and X_6. Since X_3 does not make significant contribution to the regression model, the best subset model is the one using X_2 and X_6.

(a) $\hat{Y} = 11315.184 + 22.704X_2 + 3430.040X_6$

	Coefficients	Standard Err	t Stat	P-value
Intercept	11315.18	2579.588	4.386431	3.61E-05
WP	22.70427	5.642977	4.023456	0.000133
Weekend	3430.04	1273.082	2.69428	0.008656

(b)) Intercept:

   Since all the non-dummy independent variables cannot have zero values, the intercept should be interpreted as the portion of paid attendance that varies with factors other than those already included in the model.

WP:

   As the winning percentage of the team improves by 1%, the estimated average paid attendance will increase by 22.704 taking into consideration all the other independent variables included in the model.

Weekend:

   The estimated average paid attendance of a game played on a weekend will be 3430.04 higher than when the game is played on a weekday taking into consideration all the other independent variables included in the model.

15.48 (l)   (h)   (c) $H_0 : \beta_j = 0$ $H_1 : \beta_j \neq 0$ for $j = 2$ or 6

cont.

At 0.05 level of significance, both the independent variables make significance contribution to the regression model individually.

(d) The p values of each independent variable are reported in the EXCEL regression table. The p value of each independent variable measures the probability of observing an estimated net regression coefficient b_j which gives rise to a t test statistic more extreme than the one obtained from the data if the null hypothesis is true.

(e) $r^2_{Y.13} = 0.2134$. 21.34% of the total variation in paid attendance can be explained by the 2 independent variables.

(f) Adjusted $r^2 = 0.1930$.

(g)

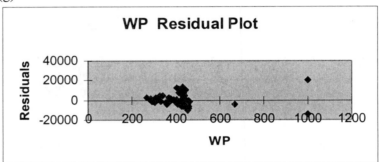

The residual plot of winning percentage reveals potential violation of the homoscedasticity assumption as the variance of the residuals increases as the winning percentage goes up.

(m)   (a) Let $X_1 = $ Temp $X_2 = $ WP $X_3 = $ Promo $X_4 = $ Rival $X_5 = $ Day $X_6 = $ Weekend

Regression Statistics	
Multiple R	0.274996342
R Square	0.075622988
Adjusted R Square	-0.002493379
Standard Error	7322.756183
Observations	78

ANOVA

	df	SS	MS	F	Significance F
Regression	6	311467110.1	51911185.01	0.968081219	0.453180881
Residual	71	3807215826	53622758.11		
Total	77	4118682936			

	Coefficients	Standard Error	t Stat	P-value	Lower 95%	Upper 95%
Intercept	8803.381879	14260.25086	0.617337098	0.538987287	-19630.76477	37237.52853
Temp	120.3238464	69.58798025	1.729089506	0.088139123	-18.43071377	259.0784066
WP	1.014493561	30.80768577	0.032929885	0.9738229	-60.41431747	62.44330459
Promo	70.48688086	2110.468161	0.033398694	0.973450367	-4137.669188	4278.64295
Rival	852.054782	2251.624406	0.378417812	0.70624938	-3637.558985	5341.668549
Day	-1128.922122	1790.602644	-0.630470488	0.530410915	-4699.284149	2441.439906
Weekend	-1138.071721	1692.127677	-0.672568469	0.503404932	-4512.080146	2235.936704

$\hat{Y} = 8803.382 + 120.324X_1 + 1.015X_2 + 70.487X_3 + 852.055X_4 - 1128.922X_5 - 1138.072X_6$

15.48 (m)
cont.

(b) Intercept:
Since all the non-dummy independent variables cannot have zero values, the intercept should be interpreted as the portion of paid attendance that varies with factors other than those already included in the model.

Temp:
As the high temperature increases by one degree, the estimated average paid attendance will increase by 120.324 taking into consideration all the other independent variables included in the model.

WP:
As the winning percentage of the team improves by 1%, the estimated average paid attendance will increase by 1.015 taking into consideration all the other independent variables included in the model.

Promo:
The estimated average paid attendance on promotion day will be 70.487 higher than when there is no promotion taking into consideration all the other independent variables included in the model.

Rival:
The estimated average paid attendance when the visiting team is considered a rival will be 852.055 higher than when the visiting team is not considered a rival taking into consideration all the other independent variables included in the model.

Day:
The estimated average paid attendance of a game played during the day time will be 1128.922 lower than when the game is played at night taking into consideration all the other independent variables included in the model.

Weekend:
The estimated average paid attendance of a game played on a weekend will be 1138.072 lower than when the game is played on a weekday taking into consideration all the other independent variables included in the model.

(c) $H_0 : \beta_j = 0$ $H_1 : \beta_j \neq 0$ for $j = 1, 2, 3, 4, 5$ or 6

At 0.05 level of significance, none of the independent variables makes significance contribution to the regression model individually.

(d) The p values of each independent variable are reported in the EXCEL regression table. The p value of each independent variable measures the probability of observing an estimated net regression coefficient b_j which gives rise to a t test statistic more extreme than the one obtained from the data if the null hypothesis is true.

(e) $r^2_{Y.123456} = 0.0756$. 7.56% of the total variation in paid attendance can be explained by the 6 independent variables.

(f) Adjusted $r^2 = -0.0025$.

15.48   (m)   (g)
cont.

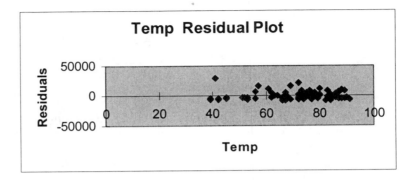

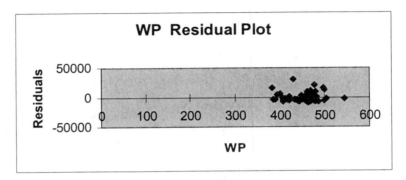

The residual plot of winning percentage reveals potential violation of the homoscedasticity assumption as the variance of the residuals increases as the winning percentage goes up.

15.48   (m)   (h) With all the 6 independent variables in the model:

cont. $VIF_1 = 1.28$ $VIF_2 = 1.15$ $VIF_3 = 1.15$ $VIF_4 = 1.15$ $VIF_5 = 1.16$ $VIF_6 = 1.04$

None of the VIF is > 5.

	Cp	p+1	R Square	Adj. R Square	Std. Error	Consider This Model?
X1	-1.85287	2	0.060688	0.048328658	7134.726	Yes
X1X2	0.121815	3	0.061018	0.035978105	7180.873	Yes
X1X2X3	2.075881	4	0.061616	0.023573066	7226.927	Yes
X1X2X3X4	3.913181	5	0.063734	0.012431678	7268.041	Yes
X1X2X3X4X5	5.452348	6	0.069734	0.005131859	7294.854	Yes
X1X2X3X4X5X6	7	7	0.075623	-0.002493379	7322.756	Yes
X1X2X3X4X6	5.397493	6	0.070448	0.005895638	7292.053	Yes
X1X2X3X5	3.621422	5	0.067532	0.016438342	7253.283	Yes
X1X2X3X5X6	5.1432	6	0.073759	0.009436291	7279.055	Yes
X1X2X3X6	3.53372	5	0.068674	0.017642733	7248.841	Yes
X1X2X4	1.941194	4	0.063369	0.025397694	7220.172	Yes
X1X2X4X5	3.456214	5	0.069683	0.018707105	7244.913	Yes
X1X2X4X5X6	5.001115	6	0.075608	0.011414609	7271.783	Yes
X1X2X4X6	3.400592	5	0.070408	0.019470944	7242.092	Yes
X1X2X5	1.633417	4	0.067376	0.029567212	7204.711	Yes
X1X2X5X6	3.143243	5	0.073758	0.023005074	7229.029	Yes
X1X2X6	1.542688	4	0.068558	0.030796333	7200.147	Yes
X1X3	0.099856	3	0.061304	0.036271627	7179.78	Yes
X1X3X4	1.913281	4	0.063733	0.025775834	7218.771	Yes
X1X3X4X5	3.452723	5	0.069729	0.018755042	7244.736	Yes
X1X3X4X5X6	5.001084	6	0.075609	0.011415042	7271.781	Yes
X1X3X4X6	3.398126	5	0.07044	0.019504808	7241.967	Yes
X1X3X5	1.649459	4	0.067167	0.029349888	7205.517	Yes
X1X3X5X6	3.172231	5	0.073381	0.022606979	7230.502	Yes
X1X3X6	1.558973	4	0.068345	0.030575716	7200.966	Yes
X1X4	-0.05876	3	0.063369	0.03839178	7171.878	Yes
X1X4X5	1.456549	4	0.069679	0.031963285	7195.811	Yes
X1X4X5X6	3.002231	5	0.075594	0.024941548	7221.861	Yes
X1X4X6	1.401182	4	0.0704	0.032713353	7193.022	Yes
X1X5	-0.3377	3	0.067	0.042120294	7157.961	Yes
X1X5X6	1.172339	4	0.073379	0.035813526	7181.486	Yes
X1X6	-0.43143	3	0.068221	0.043373084	7153.278	Yes
X2X5	2.7357	3	0.026986	0.001039407	7309.842	Yes
X3X5	2.694214	3	0.027527	0.001593931	7307.813	Yes
X4X5	2.723295	3	0.027148	0.001205218	7309.235	Yes
X5	0.905539	2	0.024775	0.011943335	7269.838	Yes
X5X6	2.581557	3	0.028993	0.003099775	7302.3	Yes

The F test on the significant of the full model at 5% level reveals that there is not enough evidence to conclude that the full regression model has any explanatory power, which rarely occurs in general. Nevertheless, based on the smallest C_p value and the highest adjusted R-square, the simple linear regression model using X_1 is the best candidate relying on the parsimonious principle.

	Coefficients	Standard Err	t Stat	P-value
Intercept	7491.469	4372.004	1.713509	0.090695
Temp	133.044	60.04016	2.215916	0.02969

15.48 (m)
cont.

(h) The regression result from the simple regression model justify the use of high temperature as the only explanatory variable. All other simple linear regressions using other independent variables fail the F test on significance of the regression model.

(a) $\hat{Y} = 7491.469 + 133.044X_1$

(b)) Intercept:
Since all the non-dummy independent variables cannot have zero values, the intercept should be interpreted as the portion of paid attendance that varies with factors other than those already included in the model.

Temp:
As the high temperature increases by one degree, the estimated average paid attendance will increase by 133.044.

(c) $H_0 : \beta_1 = 0 \qquad H_1 : \beta_1 \neq 0$
At 0.05 level of significance, the independent variable makes significance contribution to the regression model individually.

(d) The p value of the independent variable is reported in the EXCEL regression table. The p value of each independent variable measures the probability of observing an estimated slope regression coefficient b_1 which gives rise to a t test statistic more extreme than the one obtained from the data if the null hypothesis is true.

(e) $r_{Y.13}^2 = 0.0606$. Only 6.06% of the total variation in paid attendance can be explained by the independent variable.

(f) Adjusted $r^2 = 0.0483$.

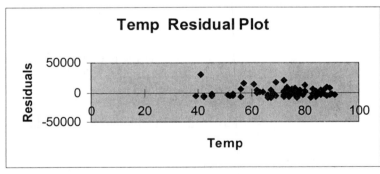

(g)

The residuals of Temp are scattered quite evenly around zero.

15.48   (n)   (a) Let $X_1 = $ Temp $X_2 = $ WP $X_3 = $ Promo $X_4 = $ Rival $X_5 = $ Day $X_6 = $ Weekend
cont.

Regression Statistics	
Multiple R	0.600933139
R Square	0.361120638
Adjusted R Square	0.309319609
Standard Error	3731.417765
Observations	81

ANOVA

	df	SS	MS	F	Significance F
Regression	6	582388672.4	97064778.73	6.971302356	6.69824E-06
Residual	74	1030337412	13923478.54		
Total	80	1612726084			

	Coefficients	Standard Error	t Stat	P-value	Lower 95%	Upper 95%
Intercept	23265.99874	6820.569934	3.411151703	0.00105123	9675.714886	36856.2826
Temp	135.4774334	36.7762813	3.683826332	0.000434563	62.19908471	208.7557821
WP	-16.28188411	12.72858082	-1.279159424	0.204837517	-41.64413801	9.080369786
Promo	1087.032124	1051.800609	1.033496382	0.304737477	-1008.726585	3182.790832
Rival	1568.675765	1086.251711	1.444118107	0.152926466	-595.7282715	3733.079801
Day	1532.808753	1030.343238	1.487668086	0.141087441	-520.1952065	3585.812713
Weekend	2360.821495	912.2867297	2.587806462	0.011619689	543.0502915	4178.592698

$$\hat{Y} = 23266.00 + 135.477X_1 - 16.282X_2 + 1087.032X_3 + 1568.676X_4 + 1532.809X_5 + 2360.822X_6$$

(b) Intercept:

Since all the non-dummy independent variables cannot have zero values, the intercept should be interpreted as the portion of paid attendance that varies with factors other than those already included in the model.

Temp:

As the high temperature increases by one degree, the estimated average paid attendance will increase by 135.477 taking into consideration all the other independent variables included in the model.

WP:

As the winning percentage of the team improves by 1%, the estimated average paid attendance will decrease by 16.282 taking into consideration all the other independent variables included in the model.

Promo:

The estimated average paid attendance on promotion day will be 1087.032 higher than when there is no promotion taking into consideration all the other independent variables included in the model.

Rival:

The estimated average paid attendance when the visiting team is considered a rival will be 1568.676 higher than when the visiting team is not considered a rival taking into consideration all the other independent variables included in the model.

Day:

The estimated average paid attendance of a game played during the day time will be 1532.809 higher than when the game is played at night taking into consideration all the other independent variables included in the model.

Weekend:

The estimated average paid attendance of a game played on a weekend will be 2360.822 higher than when the game is played on a weekday taking into consideration all the other independent variables included in the model.

15.48   (n)

cont.

(c) $H_0 : \beta_j = 0$ $H_1 : \beta_j \neq 0$ for $j = 1, 2, 3, 4, 5$ or 6

At 0.05 level of significance, the independent variables that make significance contribution to the regression model individually are high temperature and the weekend dummy variable.

(d) The p values of each independent variable are reported in the EXCEL regression table. The p value of each independent variable measures the probability of observing an estimated net regression coefficient b_j which gives rise to a t test statistic more extreme than the one obtained from the data if the null hypothesis is true.

(e) $r^2_{Y.123456} = 0.3611$. 36.11% of the total variation in paid attendance can be explained by the 6 independent variables.

(f) Adjusted $r^2 = 0.3093$.

(g)

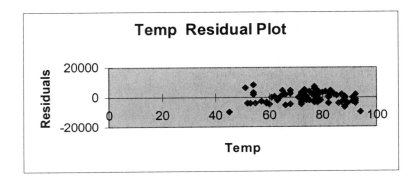

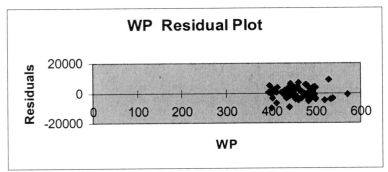

The residuals in both plots are quite evenly scattered around zero.

(h)   (a)--(g) With all the 6 independent variables in the model:

$VIF_1 = 1.08$ $VIF_2 = 1.13$ $VIF_3 = 1.07$ $VIF_4 = 1.19$ $VIF_5 = 1.22$ $VIF_6 = 1.21$

None of the VIF is > 5.

	Cp	p+1	R Square	Adj. R Square	Std. Error	Consider This Model?
X1X2X3X4X5X6	7	7	0.361121	0.309319609	3731.418	Yes

Based on the smallest C_p value and the highest adjusted R-square, the only model that satisfies $C_p \leq p + 1$ is the full model with all 6 independent variables included.

15.48   (o)
cont.

The New York Mets ran the most effective promotions in terms of increasing attendance because it has the largest estimated slope coefficient for the promotion dummy at 8794.9874. The estimated average paid attendance on promotion day will be 8794.99 higher than when there is no promotion taking into consideration all the other independent variables included in the model.

CHAPTER 16

OBJECTIVES

- To understand how and when to use moving averages and exponential smoothing to smooth a time series
- To understand how to use linear trend, quadratic trend, and exponential trend time series models
- To be able to use the Holt-Winters forecasting model
- To understand the concept of lagged variables and how to use autoregressive model
- To be able to choose the most appropriate time series forecasting model
- To be able to develop a forecasting model for seasonal data
- To understand price indexes and the difference between aggregated and unaggregated indexes

OVERVIEW AND KEY CONCEPTS

Time series: A set of numerical data obtained at a regular interval.

Component factors of the classical multiplicative time series model

- **Trend:** Overall or persistent, long-term upward or downward pattern of movement. It is usually caused by changes in technology, growth in population, wealth and value, the duration of which is several years.
- **Seasonal:** Fairly regular periodic fluctuations that occurs within each 12-month period year after year. It is caused by weather conditions, social customs, or religion customs and the duration of which is within 12 months.
- **Cyclical:** Repeating up-and-down swings or movements through four phases: from peak (prosperity) to contraction (recession) to trough (depression) to expansion (recovery or growth). It is usually caused by the interactions of numerous combinations of factors that influence the economy. Its duration is usually two to ten years.
- **Irregular:** The erratic, or "residual" fluctuations in a series that exist after taking into account all the other three components. It is usually caused by random variations in data or due to unforeseen events, such as strikes or natural disasters.
- $Y_i = T_i \times C_i \times S_i \times I_i$ where T_i, C_i, I_i are value of trend, cyclical and irregular components in time period i, and S_i is the value of the seasonal component in time period i. There is no seasonal component for annual data.

Smoothing the Annual Time Series

- **Moving averages for a chosen period of length L:**
  - A series of arithmetic means computed over time such that each mean is calculated for a sequence of observed values having that particular length L.
  - It is denoted as $MA(L)$.
  - It is easy to compute.

- **Exponential smoothing:**
  - $E_1 = Y_1$

    $E_i = WY_i + (1-W)E_{i-1}$ where

    E_i = value of the exponentially smoothed series in time period i

    E_{i-1} = value of the exponentially smoothed series already computed in time period i-1

    Y_i = observed value of the time series in period i

    W = subjectively assigned weight or smoothing coefficient $(0 < W < 1)$
  - **Forecasting with exponentially smoothed series:** $\hat{Y}_{i+1} = E_i$
  - Exponential smoothing can only be used to perform one period ahead forecast.
  - Use a W close to 0 for smoothing out unwanted cyclical and irregular component; use a W close to 1 for forecasting.

Least-Squares Trend Fitting and Forecasting

- The least-squares trend fitting is used for intermediate and long-range forecast using the trend component of a time series.
- **Linear trend model:**
  - $Y_i = \beta_0 + \beta_1 X_i + \varepsilon_i$ where X_i is the coded year with a value of 0 for the first observation, a value of 1 for the second observation, etc.
  - **Linear trend forecasting equation:** $\hat{Y}_i = b_0 + b_1 X_i$
  - b_0 is interpreted as the predicted mean value of the time series for the 1st year.
  - b_1 measures the predicted change per year in the mean value of the time series.
- **Quadratic trend model:**
  - $Y_i = \beta_0 + \beta_1 X_i + \beta_2 X_i^2 + \varepsilon_i$
  - **Quadratic trend forecasting equation:** $\hat{Y}_i = b_0 + b_1 X_i + b_2 X_i^2$
- **Exponential trend model:**
  - $Y_i = \beta_0 \beta_1^{X_i} \varepsilon_i$ or $\log Y_i = \log \beta_0 + (\log \beta_1) X_i + \log \varepsilon_i$ where $(\beta_1 - 1) \times 100\%$ is the annual compound growth rate (in %).
  - **Exponential trend forecasting equation:** $\log \hat{Y}_i = b_0 + b_1 X_i$ or

    $\hat{Y}_i = 10^{(b_0 + b_1 X_i)} = (10^{b_0})(10^{b_1})^{X_i} = \hat{\beta}_0 \hat{\beta}_1^{X_i}$ where $10^{b_0} = \hat{\beta}_0$, $10^{b_1} = \hat{\beta}_1$ and

    $(\hat{\beta}_1 - 1) \times 100\%$ is the estimated annual compound growth rate in %.
- **Selecting the appropriate least-squares trend model:**
  - Use the linear trend model if the first differences are more or less constant

    $Y_2 - Y_1 = Y_3 - Y_2 = \cdots = Y_n - Y_{n-1}$
  - Use the quadratic trend model if the second differences are more or less constant

    $\left[(Y_3 - Y_2) - (Y_2 - Y_1)\right] = \cdots = \left[(Y_n - Y_{n-1}) - (Y_{n-1} - Y_{n-2})\right]$
  - Use the exponential trend model if the percentage differences are more or less constant

    $\left(\dfrac{Y_2 - Y_1}{Y_1}\right)100\% = \left(\dfrac{Y_3 - Y_2}{Y_2}\right)100\% = \cdots = \left(\dfrac{Y_n - Y_{n-1}}{Y_{n-1}}\right)100\%$

The Holt-Winters Method

- It is an extension of the exponential smoothing and has the ability to detect future trend and overall movement.
- It can provide intermediate and/or long-term forecast.
- Level: $E_i = U\left(E_{i-1} + T_{i-1}\right) + \left(1 - U\right)Y_i$

  Trend: $T_i = VT_{i-1} + \left(1 - V\right)\left(E_i - E_{i-1}\right)$

  E_i : level of smoothed series in time period i

  E_{i-1} : level of smoothed series in time period $i - 1$

  T_i : value of trend component in time period i

  T_{i-1} : value of trend component in time period $i - 1$

  Y_i : observed value of the time series in period i

  U : smoothing constant (where $0 < U < 1$)

  V : smoothing constant (where $0 < V < 1$)

  $E_2 = Y_2$ and $T_2 = Y_2 - Y_1$

- The Holt-Winters forecast:
    - $\hat{Y}_{n+j} = E_n + j\left(T_n\right)$

      where $\hat{Y}_{n+j}$: forecasted value j years into the future

      E_n : level of smoothed series in period n

      T_n : value of trend component in period n

      j : number of years into the future

The Autoregressive Model

- The autoregressive model is appropriate for forecasting.
- It takes advantage of autocorrelation in the time series, i.e. the fact that the values of a series of data at particular points in time are highly correlated with the values that precede and succeed them.
- p^{th} **order autoregressive model:**
    - $Y_i = A_0 + A_1 Y_{i-1} + A_2 Y_{i-2} + \cdots + A_p Y_{i-p} + \delta_i$
- p^{th} **order autoregressive equation:**
    - $\hat{Y}_i = a_0 + a_1 Y_{i-1} + a_2 Y_{i-2} + \cdots + a_p Y_{i-p}$
- p^{th} **order autoregressive forecasting equation:**
    - $\hat{Y}_{n+j} = a_0 + a_1\hat{Y}_{n+j-1} + a_2\hat{Y}_{n+j-2} + \cdots + a_p\hat{Y}_{n+j-p}$

      where

      $j =$ the number of years into the future

      $\hat{Y}_{n+j-p} =$ forecast of Y_{n+j-p} from the current time period for $j - p > 0$

      $\hat{Y}_{n+j-p} =$ the observed value for Y_{n+j-p} from the current time period for $j - p \leq 0$

- *t* **test for significance of the highest-order autoregressive parameter** A_p:
  - **The hypotheses:** $H_0 : A_p = 0$ vs. $H_1 : A_p \neq 0$.

  - **Test statistic:** $t = \dfrac{a_p - A_p}{S_{a_p}}$

  - This is a two-tail test with right-tail and left-tail rejection regions.
- **Autoregressive modeling steps:**
  1. Choose *p*: Note that the degree of freedom is $(n - 2p - 1)$.
  2. Form a series of "lag predictors" variables $Y_{i-1}, Y_{i-2}, \cdots, Y_{i-p}$.
  3. Estimate the autoregressive equation.
  4. Test the significance of the highest-order autoregressive parameter A_p : If the null hypothesis is rejected, this model is selected. Otherwise, decrease *p* by 1 and repeat steps 3-4.

Selecting a Forecasting Model
- **Perform a residual analysis:**
  - Obtain the residual plots and look for pattern.

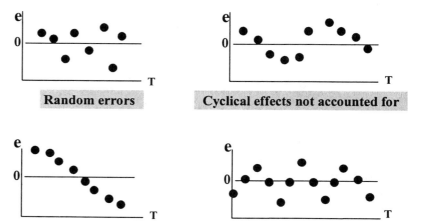

- **Measure Errors:**
  - Choose the model that gives the smallest measuring errors.

  - S_{YX} or $SSE = \sum\limits_{i=1}^{n} \left(Y_i - \hat{Y}_i \right)^2$ is sensitive to outliers

  - Mean absolute deviation $MAD = \dfrac{\sum\limits_{i=1}^{n} \left| Y_i - \hat{Y}_i \right|}{n}$ is not sensitive to extreme observations.
- **Principle of parsimony:**
  - When two or more models provide good fit to the data, select the simplest model.
  - Simplest model types: least-squares linear trend model, least-squares quadratic trend model, 1st order autoregressive model.
  - More complex types: 2nd or 3rd order autoregressive model, least-squares exponential trend model.

Forecasting with Seasonal Data

- Use categorical predictor variables with least-squares trend fitting.
- **Exponential model with quarterly data:**
  - $Y_i = \beta_0 \beta_1^{X_i} \beta_2^{Q_1} \beta_3^{Q_2} \beta_4^{Q_3} \varepsilon_i$

    where

    $X =$ coded quarter values

    $Q_1 = 1$ if first quarter, 0 otherwise

    $Q_2 = 1$ if second quarter, 0 otherwise

    $Q_3 = 1$ if third quarter, 0 otherwise

    $\beta_0 = Y$ intercept

    $(\beta_1 - 1)100\% =$ quarterly compound growth rate (in %)

    $\beta_2 =$ multiplier for first quarter relative to fourth quarter

    $\beta_3 =$ multiplier for second quarter relative to fourth quarter

    $\beta_4 =$ multiplier for third quarter relative to fourth quarter

    $\varepsilon_i =$ value of the irregular component for time period i
- **The exponential growth with quarterly data forecasting equation:**
  - $\log(\hat{Y}) = b_0 + b_1 X_i + b_2 Q_1 + b_3 Q_2 + b_4 Q_3 + b_5 Q_4$
  - $\hat{Y}_i = \hat{\beta}_0 \hat{\beta}_1^{X_i} \hat{\beta}_2^{Q_1} \hat{\beta}_3^{Q_2} \hat{\beta}_4^{Q_3}$ where $\hat{\beta}_0 = 10^{b_0}$, $\hat{\beta}_1 = 10^{b_1}$, $\hat{\beta}_2 = 10^{b_2}$, $\hat{\beta}_3 = 10^{b_3}$, and $\hat{\beta}_4 = 10^{b_4}$
- Similarly for monthly data.

Index Numbers

- **Index numbers** measure the value of an item (or group of items) at a particular point in time as a percentage of the item's (or group of items') value at another point in time.
- A **price index** reflects the percentage change in the price of a commodity (or group of commodities) in a given period of time over the price paid for that commodity (or group of commodities) at a particular point of time in the past.
- **Simple price index:** $I_i = \left(\dfrac{P_i}{P_{base}}\right)100$

  where $I_i =$ price index for year I

  $P_i =$ price for year I

  $P_{base} =$ price for the base year

- Shifting the base for a simple price index: $I_{new} = \left(\dfrac{I_{old}}{I_{new\,base}}\right)100$

  where $I_{new} =$ new price index

  $I_{old} =$ old price index

  $I_{new\,base} =$ value of the old price index for the new base year

- An **aggregate price index** reflects the percentage change in the price of a group of commodities (often referred to as a market basket) in a given period of time over the price paid for that group of commodities at a particular point of time in the past.

- An **unweighted aggregate price index** places equal weight on all the items in the market basket.
  - $$I_U^{(t)} = \left(\frac{\sum_{i=1}^{n} P_i^{(t)}}{\sum_{i=1}^{n} P_i^{(0)}} \right) 100$$

  where t = time period $(0, 1, 2, \ldots)$
  n = total number of items under consideration
  $\sum_{i=1}^{n} P_i^{(t)}$ = sum of the prices paid for each of the n commodities at time period t
  $\sum_{i=1}^{n} P_i^{(0)}$ = sum of the prices paid for each of the n commodities at time period 0
  $I_U^{(t)}$ = value of the unweighted price index at time t

- A **weighted aggregate price index** allows for the differences in the consumption levels associated with the different items comprising the market basket by attaching a weight to each item to reflect the consumption quantity of that item.

- The **Laspeyres price index** is a weighted aggregate price index that uses the consumption quantities associated with the base year in the calculation of all price indexes in the series.
  - $$I_L^{(t)} = \left(\frac{\sum_{i=1}^{n} P_i^{(t)} Q_i^{(0)}}{\sum_{i=1}^{n} P_i^{(0)} Q_i^{(0)}} \right) 100$$

  where t = time period $(0, 1, 2, \ldots)$
  n = total number of items under consideration
  $Q_i^{(0)}$ = quantity of item i at time period 0
  $I_L^{(t)}$ = value of the Laspeyres price index at time t

- The **Paasche Price Index** uses the consumption quantities experienced in the year of interest instead of using the initial quantities.
  - $$I_P^{(t)} = \left(\frac{\sum_{i=1}^{n} P_i^{(t)} Q_i^{(t)}}{\sum_{i=1}^{n} P_i^{(0)} Q_i^{(0)}} \right) 100$$

  where t = time period $(0, 1, 2, \ldots)$
  n = total number of items under consideration
  $Q_i^{(t)}$ = quantity of item i at time period t
  $I_P^{(t)}$ = value of the Paasche price index at time t

  - Is a more accurate reflection of total consumption costs at time t.
  - Accurate consumption values for current purchases are often hard to obtain.
  - If a particular product increases greatly in price compared to the other items in the market basket, consumers will avoid the high-priced item out of necessity, not because of changes in what they might prefer to purchase.

SOLUTIONS TO END OF SECTION
AND CHAPTER REVIEW EVEN PROBLEMS

16.2   (a)   Since you need data from four prior years to obtain the centered 9-year moving average for any given year and since the first recorded value is for 1955, the first centered moving average value you can calculate is for 1959.

           (b)   You would lose four years for the period 1955-1958 since you do not have enough past values to compute a centered moving average. You will also lose the final four years of recorded time series since you do not have enough later values to compute a centered moving average. Therefore, you will "lose" a total of eight years in computing a series of 9-year moving averages.

16.4   (a),(b),(c),(e)

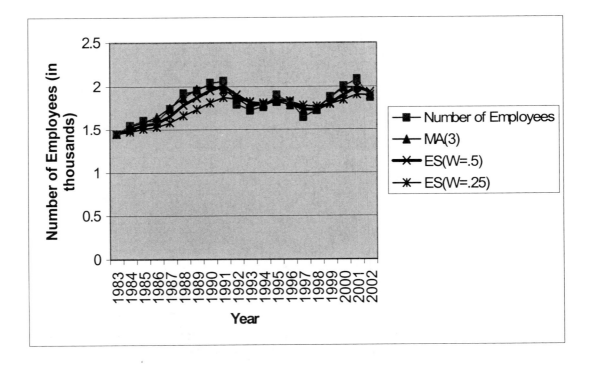

16.4   (b),(c),(e)
cont.

Year	Y_i	3-Yr Moving Total	3-Yr MA	$E_i\,(W=0.50)$	$E_i\,(W=0.25)$
1983	1.45			1.45	1.45
1984	1.55	4.61	1.54	1.50	1.48
1985	1.61	4.76	1.59	1.56	1.51
1986	1.60	4.95	1.65	1.58	1.53
1987	1.74	5.26	1.75	1.66	1.58
1988	1.92	5.61	1.87	1.79	1.67
1989	1.95	5.91	1.97	1.87	1.74
1990	2.04	6.05	2.02	1.95	1.81
1991	2.06	5.90	1.97	2.01	1.88
1992	1.80	5.59	1.86	1.90	1.86
1993	1.73	5.30	1.77	1.82	1.82
1994	1.77	5.40	1.80	1.79	1.81
1995	1.90	5.49	1.83	1.85	1.83
1996	1.82	5.37	1.79	1.83	1.83
1997	1.65	5.20	1.73	1.74	1.79
1998	1.73	5.26	1.75	1.74	1.77
1999	1.88	5.61	1.87	1.81	1.80
2000	2.00	5.96	1.99	1.90	1.85
2001	2.08	5.96	1.99	1.99	1.91
2002	1.88			1.94	1.90

(d) $\hat{Y}_{2003} = E_{2002} = 1.94$ thousand employees

(f) $\hat{Y}_{2003} = E_{2002} = 1.90$ thousand employees

(g)   The results are nearly the same.

16.6   (a),(b),(c),(e)

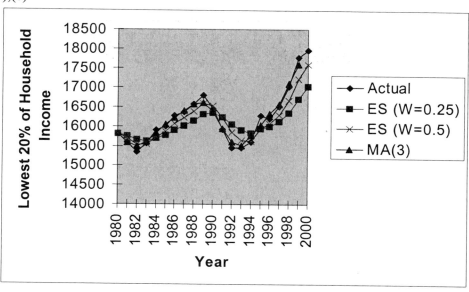

16.6   (a),(b),(c),(e)
cont.

Year	Lowest 20% of Household Income	MA(3)	ES (W=0.5)	ES (W=0.25)
1980	15810		15810	15810
1981	15595	15584	15702.5	15756.25
1982	15347	15500.67	15524.75	15653.94
1983	15560	15606	15542.38	15630.45
1984	15911	15825	15726.69	15700.59
1985	16004	16063	15865.34	15776.44
1986	16274	16216.33	16069.67	15900.83
1987	16371	16404.33	16220.34	16018.37
1988	16568	16579	16394.17	16155.78
1989	16798	16611.67	16596.08	16316.34
1990	16469	16394	16532.54	16354.5
1991	15915	15949.67	16223.77	16244.63
1992	15465	15611	15844.39	16049.72
1993	15453	15506	15648.69	15900.54
1994	15600	15774.67	15624.35	15825.4
1995	16271	16026.33	15947.67	15936.8
1996	16208	16334	16077.84	16004.6
1997	16523	16585.67	16300.42	16134.2
1998	17026	17107.67	16663.21	16357.15
1999	17774	17585	17218.6	16711.36
2000	17955		17586.8	17022.27

(d) $\hat{Y}_{2001} = E_{2000} = \$17586.8$

(f) $\hat{Y}_{2001} = E_{2000} = \$17022.27$

(g)   The exponentially smoothed forecast with W=0.5 is higher than that with W=0.25.

(h)   Actual 2001 value = $17970. The forecast in (d) is closer to the actual value.

(i)   There is a general upward trend from 1980 to 1999. There is also an obvious cyclical component with trough occurs at around 1982 and 1993.

16.8   (a),(b),(c),(e)

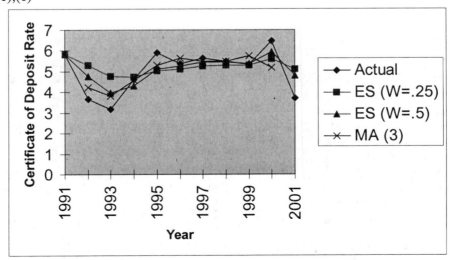

16.8   (a),(b),(c),(e)
cont.

Year	Rate	MA (3)	ES (W=.5)	ES (W=.25)
1991	5.83		5.83	5.83
1992	3.68	4.226667	4.755	5.2925
1993	3.17	3.826667	3.9625	4.761875
1994	4.63	4.573333	4.29625	4.728906
1995	5.92	5.313333	5.108125	5.02668
1996	5.39	5.643333	5.249063	5.11751
1997	5.62	5.493333	5.434531	5.243132
1998	5.47	5.473333	5.452266	5.299849
1999	5.33	5.753333	5.391133	5.307387
2000	6.46	5.166667	5.925566	5.59554
2001	3.71		4.817783	5.124155

(d) $\hat{Y}_{2002} = E_{2001} = 4.82$

(f) $\hat{Y}_{2002} = E_{2001} = 5.12$

(g)   The exponentially smoothed forecast with W = 0.5 is lower than that with W = 0.25

16.10 (a)   The Y-intercept $b_0 = 4.0$ is the fitted trend value reflecting the real total revenues (in millions of real constant 1995 dollars) during the origin or base year 1983.

(b)   The slope $b_1 = 1.5$ indicates that the real total revenues are increasing at a rate of 1.5 million dollars per year.

(c)   Year is 1987, $X = 1987 - 1983 = 4$
$\hat{Y}_5 = 4.0 + 1.5(4) = 10.0$ million dollars

(d)   Year is 2002, $X = 2002 - 1983 = 19$,
$\hat{Y}_{20} = 4.0 + 1.5(19) = 32.5$ million dollars

(e)   Year is 2005, $X = 2005 - 1983 = 22$
$\hat{Y}_{23} = 4.0 + 1.5(22) = 37.0$ million dollars

16.12 (a)

CPI

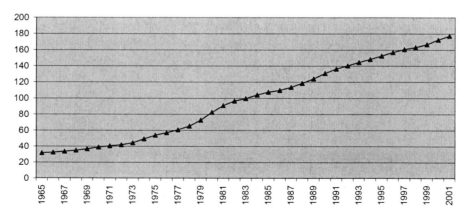

(b)   There has been an upward trend in the CPI in the United States over the 37-year period. The rate of increase became faster in the late 70's, mid 80's and late 90's but the rate of increase tapered off in the early 80's and early 90's.

16.14   (a)

Scatter Diagram

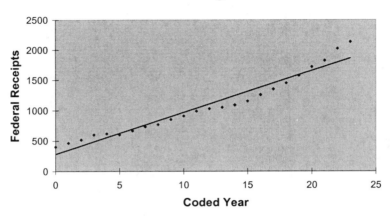

(b) $\hat{Y} = 281.1013 + 69.0691X$

(c) $\hat{Y} = 281.1013 + 69.0691X$, where X = years relative to 1978

$X = 2002 - 1978 = 24$, $\hat{Y} = 281.1013 + 69.0691(24) = \$1938.7594$ billion

$X = 2003 - 1978 = 25$, $\hat{Y} = 281.1013 + 69.0691(25) = \$2007.8285$ billion

(d)   There is an upward trend in federal receipts between 1978 and 2001. The trend appears to be non-linear. Either a quadratic trend or exponential trend model could be experimented.

16.16   (a),(b)

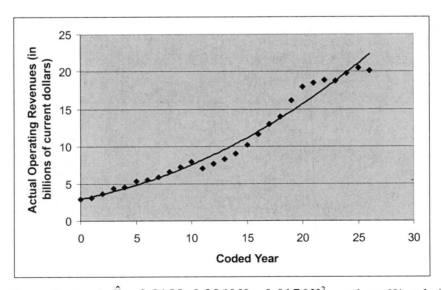

Quadratic trend: $\hat{Y} = 2.9155 + 0.2860X + 0.0176X^2$ where X is relative to 1975.

(c) $X = 2002 - 1975 = 27$; $\hat{Y} = 2.9155 + 0.2860(27) + 0.0176(27)^2 = \$23.4865$ billion

$X = 2003 - 1975 = 28$; $\hat{Y} = 2.9155 + 0.2860(28) + 0.0176(28)^2 = \$24.7419$ billion dollars

16.16   (d)
cont.

Year	Revenues	CPI	Real Revenues
1975	2.9	53.8	5.390335
1976	3.1	56.9	5.448155
1977	3.6	60.6	5.940594
1978	4.3	65.2	6.595092
1979	4.5	72.6	6.198347
1980	5.3	82.4	6.432039
1981	5.5	90.9	6.050605
1982	5.9	96.5	6.11399
1983	6.6	99.6	6.626506
1984	7.2	103.9	6.92974
1985	7.9	107.6	7.342007
1986	7	109.6	6.386861
1987	7.7	113.6	6.778169
1988	8.3	118.3	7.016061
1989	9	124	7.258065
1990	10.2	130.7	7.804132
1991	11.6	136.2	8.516887
1992	13	140.3	9.265859
1993	14	144.5	9.688581
1994	16.2	148.2	10.93117
1995	18	152.4	11.81102
1996	18.5	156.9	11.79095
1997	18.9	160.5	11.7757
1998	18.8	163	11.53374
1999	19.8	166.6	11.88475
2000	20.5	172.2	11.90476
2001	20.1	177.1	11.34952

(e),(f),(g),(h)

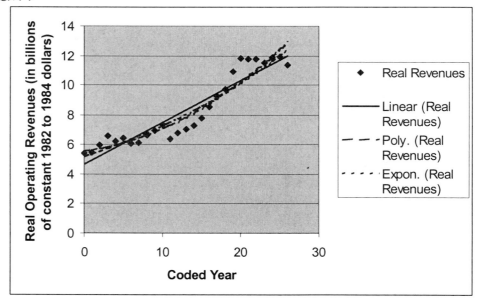

Linear trend: $\hat{Y} = 4.6459+0.2830X$ where X is relative to 1975

Quadratic trend: $\hat{Y} = 5.5401+0.0684X + 0.0083X^2$ where X is relative to 1975

Exponential trend: $\log_{10} \hat{Y} = 0.7139 + 0.0146X$ where X is relative to 1975

16.16   (i)
cont.

	Forecasts of Real Net Revenues Based on Models		
Year	Linear	Quadratic	Exponential
2002	12.2862	**13.4033**	12.8216
2003	12.5692	**13.9256**	13.2598

(j)   The forecasts of actual net revenues increase more per year than do the forecasts of real net revenues, due to the fact that the real revenues have been adjusted to remove the increase that is explained by inflation.

(k)   The actual net revenues generally increased over the period while the real net revenues experienced slight declines from 1980 to 1982, 1995 to 1998 and 2001 to 2002.

16.18   (a),(b),(c),(d)

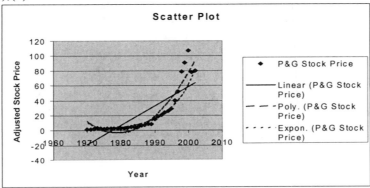

Linear trend: $\hat{Y} = -18.6780 + 2.5587X$ where X is relative to 1970

Quadratic trend: $\hat{Y} = 11.4411 - 3.2708X + 0.1822X^2$ where X is relative to 1970

Exponential trend: $\log_{10}\hat{Y} = 0.006333 + 0.05934X$ where X is relative to 1970

16.18 (e)
cont.

1st Difference	2nd Difference	% Difference
0.15		10.56338
0.6	0.45	38.21656
0.97	0.37	44.70046
-0.51	-1.48	-16.242
-0.25	0.26	-9.5057
0.28	0.53	11.76471
0.2	-0.08	7.518797
-0.15	-0.35	-5.24476
0.19	0.34	7.01107
-0.37	-0.56	-12.7586
-0.07	0.3	-2.7668
0.57	0.64	23.17073
1.65	1.08	54.45545
-0.01	-1.66	-0.21368
0.24	0.25	5.139186
1.38	1.14	28.10591
0.86	-0.52	13.6725
1.09	0.23	15.24476
0.46	-0.63	5.582524
5.81	5.35	66.78161
3.82	-1.99	26.32667
2.02	-1.8	11.02019
3.41	1.39	16.75676
2.09	-1.32	8.796296
2.93	0.84	11.33462
10.86	7.93	37.73454
12.39	1.53	31.25631
26.27	13.88	50.4901
12.44	-13.83	15.88761
16.45	4.01	18.12872
-29.13	-45.58	-27.176
1.94	31.07	2.485268

Investigating the 1st, 2nd and percentage differences does not suggest any particular tren model is more appropriate than the other. The exponential trend does seem to be fittin the data better especially in the early years.

(f)   Using the exponential trend model, $\hat{Y}_{2003} = 10^{(0.006333+0.05934(2003-1970))} = \$92.18$

16.20 (a)   For Time Series I, the graph of Y vs. X appears to be more linear than the graph of log Y vs. X, so a linear model appears to be more appropriate. For Time Series II, the graph of log Y vs. X appears to be more linear than the graph of Y vs. X, so an exponential model appears to be more appropriate.

(b)   Time Series I: $\hat{Y} = 100.082 + 14.9752X$, X = years relative to 1993

Time Series II: $\hat{Y} = 99.704(1.1501)^{X}$, X = years relative to 1993

(c)   Time Series I: $\hat{Y} = 100.082 + 14.9752(10) = 249.834$

Time Series II: $\hat{Y} = 99.704(1.1501)^{10} = 403.709$

16.22 (a)

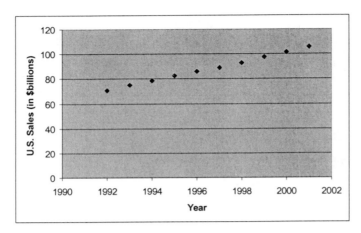

(b)

Year	Sales	Adjusted Salses	CPI
1992	70.6	50.32	140.3
1993	74.9	51.83	144.5
1994	78.5	52.97	148.2
1995	82.5	54.13	152.4
1996	85.9	54.75	156.9
1997	88.8	55.33	160.5
1998	92.5	56.75	163
1999	97.5	58.52	166.6
2000	101.4	58.89	172.2
2001	105.5	59.57	177.1

(c), (d), (e), (f)

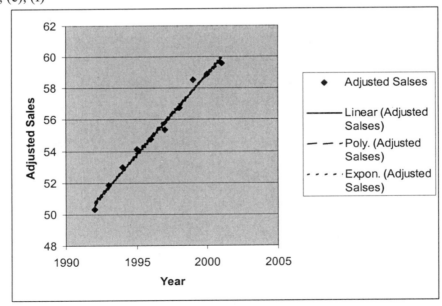

Linear trend: $\hat{Y} = 70.6964 + 3.8030X$ where X is relative to 1992

Quadratic trend: $\hat{Y} = 50.5363 + 1.1476X - 0.0138X^2$ where X is relative to 1992

Exponential trend: $\log_{10} \hat{Y} = 1.7059 + 0.0081X$ where X is relative to 1992

16.22   (g)
cont.

	Year	Forecasts of adjusted sales Based on Models		
		Linear	Quadratic	Exponential
	2002	60.9329	60.6284	61.1614
	2003	61.9559	61.4854	62.3071

16.24 $E_{15} = 25.30$, $T_{15} = 2.13$

$$\hat{Y}_{16} = E_{15} + T_{15} = 25.30 + 2.13 = 25.30$$

$$\hat{Y}_{17} = E_{15} + 2T_{15} = 25.30 + (2)2.13 = 27.43$$

$$\hat{Y}_{18} = E_{15} + 3T_{15} = 25.30 + (3)2.13 = 29.57$$

$$\hat{Y}_{19} = E_{15} + 4T_{15} = 25.30 + (4)2.13 = 31.70$$

$$\hat{Y}_{20} = E_{15} + 5T_{15} = 25.30 + (5)2.13 = 33.83$$

16.26   (a)

Year	GDP	E	T	Year	GDP	E	T
1975	4084.4			1989	6591.8	6590.825	227.1329
1976	4311.7	4311.7	227.3	1990	6707.9	6740.917	173.2046
1977	4511.8	4519.96	213.972	1991	6676.4	6747.717	56.72086
1978	4760.6	4752.6	227.0393	1992	6880.0	6857.331	93.74652
1979	4912.1	4932.362	193.9452	1993	7062.6	7029.143	148.3924
1980	4900.9	4968.522	83.49586	1994	7347.7	7296.651	231.7729
1981	5021.0	5030.305	68.29707	1995	7543.8	7539.187	239.3073
1982	4919.3	4973.091	-19.5611	1996	7813.2	7802.788	256.3131
1983	5132.3	5078.669	68.03636	1997	8159.5	8129.38	305.5084
1984	5505.2	5397.652	243.6988	1998	8515.7	8491.457	345.1059
1985	5717.1	5694.375	280.8161	1999	8875.8	8864.029	364.3322
1986	5912.4	5931.237	250.0484	2000	9224.0	9225.308	362.1954
1987	6113.3	6133.696	216.7354	2001	9214.5	9326.401	179.4236
1988	6368.4	6363.009	225.5401	**U = 0.30**	**V = 0.30**		

$\hat{Y}_{2002} = E_{2001} + 1T_{2001} = 9326.4011 + (1)(179.4236) = 9505.82$ billions of constant 1996 dollars.

$\hat{Y}_{2003} = E_{2001} + 2T_{2001} = 9326.4011 + (2)(179.4236) = 9685.25$ billions of constant 1996 dollars.

16.26 (b)
cont.

Year	GDP	E	T
1975	4084.4		
1976	4311.7	4311.7	227.3
1977	4511.8	4530.84	224.852
1978	4760.6	4757.164	225.2937
1979	4912.1	4961.351	218.9615
1980	4900.9	5096.489	193.8144
1981	5021.0	5209.512	169.5771
1982	4919.3	5241.152	128.1961
1983	5132.3	5298.234	106.8617
1984	5505.2	5435.127	115.8711
1985	5717.1	5600.829	130.8203
1986	5912.4	5785.874	147.0879
1987	6113.3	5987.064	163.3183
1988	6368.4	6215.787	182.9399

Year	GDP	E	T
1989	6591.8	6456.649	200.3165
1990	6707.9	6672.246	204.9006
1991	6676.4	6816.923	186.8334
1992	6880.0	6966.629	175.6954
1993	7062.6	7118.407	168.5202
1994	7347.7	7305.159	173.9897
1995	7543.8	7498.544	179.8083
1996	7813.2	7718.807	191.9446
1997	8159.5	7985.376	214.332
1998	8515.7	8294.506	242.7713
1999	8875.8	8638.834	273.2383
2000	9224.0	9005.65	301.3119
2001	9214.5	9279.224	292.9902
U = 0.70	V = 0.70		

$$\hat{Y}_{2002} = E_{2001} + 1T_{2001} = 9279.2236 + (1)(292.9902) = 9572.21 \text{ billions of constant}$$
1996 dollars.

$$\hat{Y}_{2003} = E_{2001} + 2T_{2001} = 9279.2236 + (2)(292.9902) = 9865.20 \text{ billions of}$$
constant 1996 dollars.

(c)

Year	GDP	E	T
1975	4084.4		
1976	4311.7	4311.7	227.3
1977	4511.8	4519.96	221.588
1978	4760.6	4754.884	225.5889
1979	4912.1	4932.612	211.2305
1980	4900.9	4973.783	160.2126
1981	5021.0	5054.899	136.4836
1982	4919.3	5000.925	79.34631
1983	5132.3	5116.691	90.27241
1984	5505.2	5415.729	152.902
1985	5717.1	5672.559	184.0805
1986	5912.4	5895.672	195.7901
1987	6113.3	6106.749	200.3761
1988	6368.4	6350.017	213.2439

Year	GDP	E	T
1989	6591.8	6583.238	219.237
1990	6707.9	6736.273	199.3762
1991	6676.4	6754.175	144.9339
1992	6880.0	6885.733	140.9211
1993	7062.6	7051.816	148.4699
1994	7347.7	7303.476	179.4268
1995	7543.8	7525.531	192.2153
1996	7813.2	7784.564	212.2606
1997	8159.5	8110.697	246.4225
1998	8515.7	8468.126	279.7243
1999	8875.8	8837.415	306.5938
2000	9224.0	9200.003	323.3919
2001	9214.5	9307.168	258.524
U = 0.30	V = 0.70		

$$\hat{Y}_{2002} = E_{2001} + 1T_{2001} = 9307.1684 + (1)(258.5240) = 9565.69 \text{ billions of constant}$$
1996 dollars.

$$\hat{Y}_{2003} = E_{2001} + 2T_{2001} = 9307.1684 + (2)(258.5240) = 9824.22 \text{ billions of}$$
constant 1996 dollars.

(d) Given the historical movement of the time series, which suggests that there is a cyclical component in addition to the upward trend, a better projection model will be to give more weight to the more recent levels and trends. As a result, any recent changes in the level or trend of the time series that are caused by the cyclical component will be readily picked up in the projection. Hence, the projection in model (a) will be a better choice.

16.26   (e)   The forecasts in (a)-(c) are higher than those of Problem 16.13 (c). The GDP has
cont.   been on the expansionary path since 1992. This is being captured and reflected in the
                Holt-Winters method with U = 0.3 and V = 0.3, which gives more weight to recent
                levels and trends of the time series, but not in the linear trend, which is very much
                constrained by the model specification. The linear trend model will be more
                appropriate if the forecasts are longer-run than the immediate short-run forecasts.

16.28   (a)

Year	Real Operating Revenues	E	T	Year	Real Operating Revenues	E	T
1975	5.3903			1989	7.2581	7.1735	0.2256
1976	5.4482	5.4482	0.0578	1990	7.8041	7.6826	0.4241
1977	5.9406	5.8102	0.2708	1991	8.5169	8.3938	0.6251
1978	6.5951	6.4409	0.5227	1992	9.2659	9.1918	0.7461
1979	6.1983	6.4279	0.1477	1993	9.6886	9.7634	0.6239
1980	6.4320	6.4751	0.0774	1994	10.9312	10.7680	0.8904
1981	6.0506	6.2012	-0.1686	1995	11.8110	11.7653	0.9652
1982	6.1140	6.0896	-0.1287	1996	11.7909	12.0728	0.5048
1983	6.6265	6.4268	0.1975	1997	11.7757	12.0163	0.1119
1984	6.9297	6.8381	0.3471	1998	11.5337	11.7121	-0.1794
1985	7.3420	7.2950	0.4240	1999	11.8848	11.7791	-0.0069
1986	6.3869	6.7865	-0.2288	2000	11.9048	11.8650	0.0581
1987	6.7782	6.7120	-0.1207	2001	11.3495	11.5216	-0.2230
1988	7.0161	6.8886	0.0874 U = 0.3		V = 0.3		

$$\hat{Y}_{2002} = E_{2001} + 1T_{2001} = 11.5216 + (1)(-0.223) = 11.2986 \text{ billions of dollars.}$$

$$\hat{Y}_{2003} = E_{2001} + 2T_{2001} = 11.5216 + (2)(-0.223) = 11.0756 \text{ billions of dollars.}$$

(b)

Year	Real Operating Revenues	E	T	Year	Real Operating Revenues	E	T
1975	5.3903			1989	7.2581	7.1582	0.0888
1976	5.4482	5.4482	0.0578	1990	7.8041	7.4141	0.1389
1977	5.9406	5.6364	0.0969	1991	8.5169	7.8422	0.2257
1978	6.5951	5.9918	0.1745	1992	9.2659	8.4272	0.3335
1979	6.1983	6.1759	0.1774	1993	9.6886	9.0391	0.4170
1980	6.4320	6.3769	0.1845	1994	10.9312	9.8986	0.5498
1981	6.0506	6.4082	0.1385	1995	11.8110	10.8572	0.6724
1982	6.1140	6.4169	0.0996	1996	11.7909	11.6080	0.6959
1983	6.6265	6.5494	0.1095	1997	11.7757	12.1454	0.6484
1984	6.9297	6.7402	0.1338	1998	11.5337	12.4158	0.5350
1985	7.3420	7.0144	0.1760	1999	11.8848	12.6310	0.4390
1986	6.3869	6.9493	0.1036	2000	11.9048	12.7204	0.3342
1987	6.7782	6.9705	0.0789	2001	11.3495	12.5431	0.1807
1988	7.0161	7.0394	0.0759 U = 0.70		V = 0.70		

$$\hat{Y}_{2002} = E_{2001} + 1T_{2001} = 12.5431 + (1)(0.1807) = 12.7238 \text{ billions of dollars.}$$

$$\hat{Y}_{2003} = E_{2001} + 2T_{2001} = 12.5431 + (2)(0.1807) = 12.9045 \text{ billions of dollars.}$$

16.28 (c)
cont.

Year	Real Operating Revenues	E	T	Year	Real Operating Revenues	E	T
1975	5.3903			1989	7.2581	7.1869	0.1225
1976	5.4482	5.4482	0.0578	1990	7.8041	7.6557	0.2264
1977	5.9406	5.8102	0.1491	1991	8.5169	8.3265	0.3597
1978	6.5951	6.4044	0.2826	1992	9.2659	9.0919	0.4814
1979	6.1983	6.3449	0.1800	1993	9.6886	9.6540	0.5056
1980	6.4320	6.4599	0.1605	1994	10.9312	10.6997	0.6676
1981	6.0506	6.2215	0.0408	1995	11.8110	11.6779	0.7608
1982	6.1140	6.1585	0.0097	1996	11.7909	11.9853	0.6248
1983	6.6265	6.4890	0.1059	1997	11.7757	12.0260	0.4496
1984	6.9297	6.8293	0.1762	1998	11.5337	11.8163	0.2518
1985	7.3420	7.2411	0.2469	1999	11.8848	11.9397	0.2133
1986	6.3869	6.7172	0.0157	2000	11.9048	11.9792	0.1611
1987	6.7782	6.7646	0.0252	2001	11.3495	11.5868	-0.0049
1988	7.0161	6.9482	0.0727	U = 0.3	V = 0.7		

$$\hat{Y}_{2002} = E_{2001} + 1T_{2001} = 11.5868 + (1)(-0.0049) = 11.5818 \text{ billions of dollars.}$$

$$\hat{Y}_{2003} = E_{2001} + 2T_{2001} = 11.5868 + (2)(-0.0049) = 11.5769 \text{ billions of dollars.}$$

(d)   Given the historical movement of the time series, which suggests that there is a cyclical component in addition to the upward trend, a better projection model will be to give more weight to the more recent levels and trends. As a result, any recent changes in the level or trend of the time series that are caused by the cyclical component will be readily picked up in the projection. Hence, the projection in model (a) will be a better choice.

(e)

Year	Linear	Quadratic	Exponential	HW (U = 0.3, V = 0.3)	HW (U= 0.7, V = 0.7)	HW (U = 0.3, V = 0.7)
2002	12.2862	**13.4033**	12.8216	11.2986	12.7238	11.5818
2003	12.5692	**13.9256**	13.2598	11.0756	12.9045	11.5769

The real operating revenue of Coca Cola has experienced contraction since 1996 with a slight sign of recovery in 1999. This is being captured and reflected in the Holt-Winters method with U = 0.3 and V = 0.3, which gives more weight to recent levels and trends of the time series, but not in the 3 trend models in Problem 16.15(i), which are very much constrained by the model specifications. The Holt-Winters method with U = 0.7 and V = 0.7, and U = 0.3 and V = 0.7, which gives more weight to past trends behaves more like the trend models.

16.30   (a)

Year	P&G Stock Price	E	T	Year	P&G Stock Price	E	T
1970	1.42			1987	7.15	7.06	0.94
1971	1.57	1.57	0.15	1988	8.24	8.17	1.05
1972	2.17	2.04	0.37	1989	8.70	8.86	0.80
1973	3.14	2.92	0.73	1990	14.51	13.05	3.18
1974	2.63	2.94	0.23	1991	18.33	17.70	4.21
1975	2.38	2.62	-0.15	1992	20.35	20.82	3.44
1976	2.66	2.60	-0.06	1993	23.76	23.91	3.20
1977	2.86	2.76	0.10	1994	25.85	26.23	2.58
1978	2.71	2.76	0.02	1995	28.78	28.79	2.57
1979	2.90	2.86	0.08	1996	39.64	37.15	6.63
1980	2.53	2.65	-0.12	1997	52.03	49.56	10.67
1981	2.46	2.48	-0.16	1998	78.30	72.88	19.53
1982	3.03	2.82	0.19	1999	90.74	91.24	18.71
1983	4.68	4.18	1.01	2000	107.19	108.02	17.36
1984	4.67	4.82	0.76	2001	78.06	92.25	-5.83
1985	4.91	5.11	0.43	2002	80	81.93	-8.98
1986	6.29	6.06	0.80	**U = 0.3**		**V = 0.3**	

$$\hat{Y}_{2003} = E_{2002} + (2003 - 2002)\, T_{2002} = 81.9285 + (1)(-8.9764) = 72.95$$

(b)

Year	P&G Stock Price	E	T	Year	P&G Stock Price	E	T
1970	1.42			1987	7.15	6.11	0.60
1971	1.57	1.57	0.15	1988	8.24	7.17	0.74
1972	2.17	1.86	0.19	1989	8.70	8.14	0.81
1973	3.14	2.37	0.29	1990	14.51	10.62	1.31
1974	2.63	2.65	0.29	1991	18.33	13.85	1.88
1975	2.38	2.77	0.24	1992	20.35	17.12	2.30
1976	2.66	2.90	0.20	1993	23.76	20.72	2.69
1977	2.86	3.03	0.18	1994	25.85	24.14	2.91
1978	2.71	3.06	0.14	1995	28.78	27.57	3.07
1979	2.90	3.11	0.11	1996	39.64	33.34	3.88
1980	2.53	3.01	0.05	1997	52.03	41.66	5.21
1981	2.46	2.88	-0.01	1998	78.30	56.30	8.04
1982	3.03	2.92	0.01	1999	90.74	72.26	10.41
1983	4.68	3.45	0.17	2000	107.19	90.03	12.62
1984	4.67	3.93	0.26	2001	78.06	95.27	10.41
1985	4.91	4.41	0.32	2002	80	97.98	8.10
1986	6.29	5.20	0.46			**U = 0.7**	**V = 0.7**

$$\hat{Y}_{2003} = E_{2002} + (2003 - 2002)\, T_{2002} = 97.9764 + (1)(8.0971) = 106.07$$

16.30 (c)
cont.

Year	P&G Stock Price	E	T		Year	P&G Stock Price	E	T
1970	1.42				1987	7.15	6.99	0.72
1971	1.57	1.57	0.15		1988	8.24	8.08	0.83
1972	2.17	2.04	0.24		1989	8.70	8.76	0.78
1973	3.14	2.88	0.43		1990	14.51	13.02	1.83
1974	2.63	2.83	0.28		1991	18.33	17.29	2.56
1975	2.38	2.60	0.13		1992	20.35	20.20	2.66
1976	2.66	2.68	0.11		1993	23.76	23.49	2.85
1977	2.86	2.84	0.13		1994	25.85	26.00	2.75
1978	2.71	2.79	0.07		1995	28.78	28.77	2.76
1979	2.90	2.89	0.08		1996	39.64	37.21	4.46
1980	2.53	2.66	-0.01		1997	52.03	48.92	6.64
1981	2.46	2.52	-0.05		1998	78.30	71.48	11.41
1982	3.03	2.86	0.07		1999	90.74	88.38	13.06
1983	4.68	4.15	0.44		2000	107.19	105.47	14.27
1984	4.67	4.65	0.45		2001	78.06	90.56	5.52
1985	4.91	4.97	0.41		2002	80	84.82	2.14
1986	6.29	6.02	0.60			**U = 0.7**	**V = 0.7**	

$$\hat{Y}_{2003} = E_{2002} + (2003 - 2002)T_{2002} = 84.8234 + (1)(2.1394) = 86.96$$

(d) Given the historical movement of the time series, which suggests that the stock price had been gaining values at an increasing rate up until 1999 and had since experienced a decline in values, a better projection model will be to give more weight to the more recent levels and trends. If there is a very strong prior opinion on a likely recovery back to the level prior to the decline in 1999, then a Holt-Winters method with U = 0.7 and V = 0.7 that assigns more weight to the past values and trends should be used. Otherwise, the projection in model (a) will be a better choice, especially since the projection is for the immediate short-run forecast in year 2003.

(e) The forecasts in (a) and (c) are lower and the forecast in (b) is higher than that in the exponential trend model of Problem 16.18 (f) reflecting the fact that the exponential trend model is very much restricted by its model specification while the Holt-Winters method with U = 0.3 and V = 0.3 is more capable of capturing the more recent drop in price and downward adjustment in trend.

16.32 $t = \dfrac{a_3}{S_{a_2}} = \dfrac{0.24}{0.10} = 2.4 > t_{10,0.025} = 2.2281$. Reject H_0. There is sufficient evidence that the third-order regression parameter is significantly different than zero. A third-order autoregressive model is appropriate.

16.34 (a) $t = \dfrac{a_3}{S_{a_2}} = \dfrac{0.24}{0.15} = 1.6 < t_{10,0.025} = 2.2281$. Do not reject H_0. . There is not sufficient evidence that the third-order regression parameter is significantly different than zero. A third-order autoregressive model is not appropriate.

(b) Fit a second-order autoregressive model and test to see if it is appropriate.

16.36   (a)

	Coefficients	Standard Error	t Stat	P-value
Intercept	0.426983234	0.408126756	1.046202504	0.307947743
YLag1	1.175726093	0.23125408	5.084131237	5.66619E-05
YLag2	-0.082638804	0.350892147	-0.235510555	0.816207253
YLag3	-0.127775896	0.24012012	-0.532133234	0.600495879

Since p-value = 0.60 > 0.05, do not reject H_0 that $A_3 = 0$. Third-order term can be deleted.

(b)

	Coefficients	Standard Error	t Stat	P-value
Intercept	0.450510113	0.373128703	1.207385305	0.240104897
YLag1	1.185670101	0.219538008	5.400750922	2.00777E-05
YLag2	-0.218278619	0.224677467	-0.97151985	0.341850619

Since p-value = 0.34 > 0.05, do not reject H_0 that $A_2 = 0$. Second-order term can be deleted.

(c)

	Coefficients	Standard Error	t Stat	P-value
Intercept	0.380859356	0.350928317	1.085291034	0.288574421
X Variable 1	0.981523446	0.041142135	23.85689136	3.16321E-18

Since p-value is essentially zero, reject H_0 that $A_1 = 0$. A first-order autoregressive model is appropriate.

(d) $\hat{Y}_i = 0.3809 + 0.9815 Y_{i-1}$

Year	Forecasts
2002	11.52067938
2003	11.68867627

16.38   (a)

	Coefficients	Standard Error	t Stat	P-value
Intercept	3.156146171	1.743216204	1.810530537	0.081785757
Ylag1	0.957419882	0.176027589	5.439033087	1.05893E-05
Ylag2	1.451194465	0.533385437	2.720723825	0.011461407
Ylag3	-1.754992778	0.546919932	-3.208866009	0.003524403

Since the p value = 0.0035 < 0.05 level of significance, the 3rd order term is significant.

(b)

	Coefficients	Standard Error	t Stat	P-value
Intercept	2.157453863	1.912472595	1.128096616	0.26885298
Ylag1	1.164767566	0.186579268	6.242749143	9.54755E-07
Ylag2	-0.166638695	0.198662284	-0.838803883	0.40868367

Since the p value = 0.41 > 0.05 level of significance, the 2nd order term is not significant.

(c)

	Coefficients	Standard Error	t Stat	P-value
Intercept	2.121375862	1.828612588	1.160101312	0.255157048
Ylag1	1.016338709	0.051959093	19.56036272	1.2556E-18

Since the p value is essentially zero, the 1st order term is significant.

(d)   The 3rd order autoregressive model should be used for forecasting.

$\hat{Y}_i = 3.1561 + 0.9574 Y_{i-1} + 1.4512 Y_{i-2} - 1.7550 Y_{i-3}$

Year	Forecasts
2003	4.9123

16.40 (a) $S_{YX} = \sqrt{\dfrac{\sum_{i=1}^{n}(Y_i - \hat{Y}_i)^2}{n-p-1}} = \sqrt{\dfrac{45}{12-1-1}} = 2.121$. The standard error of the estimate is 2.121 billion constant 1995 dollars.

(b) $MAD = \dfrac{\sum_{i=1}^{n}\left|Y_i - \hat{Y}_i\right|}{n} = \dfrac{18}{12} = 1.5$. The mean absolute deviation is 1.5 billion constant 1995 dollars.

16.42 (a)

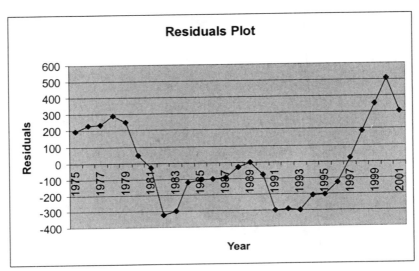

(b) Excel output:

Regression Statistics	
Multiple R	0.988517544
R Square	0.977166935
Adjusted R Square	0.976253613
Standard Error	238.738489
Observations	27

$S_{YX} = 238.7385$

(c) $MAD = 5242.6761/27 = 194.1732$

(d) The residuals in the linear trend model show strings of consecutive positive and negative values. An autoregressive model will probably do better.

16.44 (a)

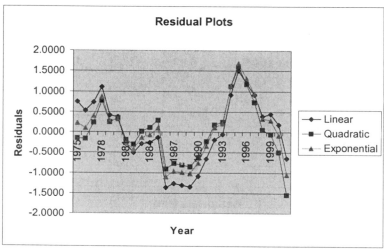

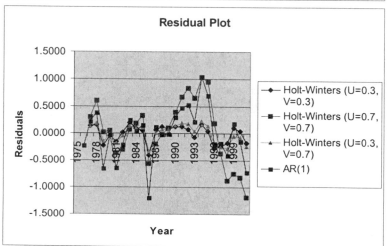

(b), (c)

	Linear	Quadratic	Exponential	Holt-Winters (U=0.3, V=0.3)	Holt-Winters (U=0.7, V=0.7)	Holt-Winters (U=0.3, V=0.7)	AR(1
S_{YX}	0.8537	0.7310	0.7586	NA	NA	NA	0.486
MAD	0.6976	0.5270	0.5751	0.1348	0.4739	0.1415	0.354

(d)   The residuals in the three trend models show strings of consecutive positive and negative values. The Holt-Winters method with $U = 0.7$, $V = 0.7$ and $U = 0.3$, $V = 0.7$ also shows strings of consecutive positive and negative values, in particular in the right tail. The Holt-Winters method with $U = 0.3$, $V = 0.3$ and the autoregressive model perform well for the historical data and has a fairly random pattern of residuals. The Holt-Winters method with $U = 0.3$, $V = 0.3$ also has the smallest values in MAD. Based on the principle of parsimony, the Holt-Winters method with $U = 0.3$, $V = 0.3$ would probably be the best model for forecasting.

16.46   (a)

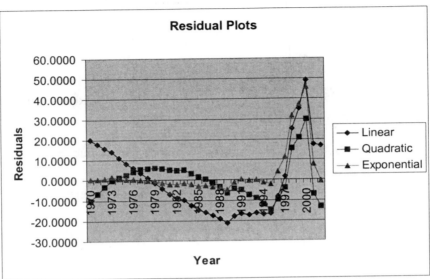

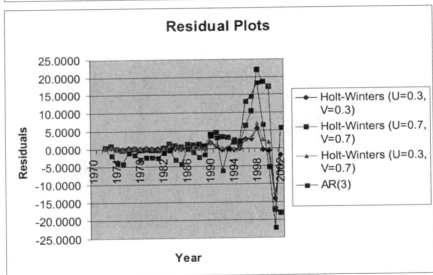

(b), (c)

	Linear	Quadratic	Exponential	Holt-Winters (U=0.3, V=0.3)	Holt-Winters (U=0.7, V=0.7)	Holt-Winters (U=0.3, V=0.7)	AR(3)
S_{YX}	18.04	9.85	12.48	NA	NA	NA	7.27
MAD	14.73	7.13	5.36	1.09	4.41	1.27	4.66

(d)   The residuals in the three trend models show strings of consecutive positive and negative values. The Holt-Winters method with $U = 0.7$, $V = 0.7$ also shows strings of consecutive positive and negative values, in particular in the right tail. The Holt-Winters method with $U = 0.3$ and $V = 0.3$, $U = 0.3$ and $V = 0.7$, and the autoregressive model perform well for the historical data and has a fairly random pattern of residuals. The Holt-Winters method with $U = 0.3$, $V = 0.3$ also has the smallest values in MAD and SSE. Based on the principle of parsimony, the Holt-Winters method with $U = 0.3$, $V = 0.3$ would probably be the best model for forecasting.

16.48   (a) $\log b_0 = 2$. $b_0 = 10^2 = 100$. This is the fitted value for January 1998 prior to adjustment by the January multiplier.

   (b) $\log b_1 = 0.01$. $b_1 = 10^{0.01} = 1.0233$. The estimated monthly compound growth rate is $(b_1 - 1)100\% = 2.33\%$.

   (c) $\log b_2 = 0.1$. $b_2 = 10^{0.1} = 1.2589$. The January values in the time series are estimated to require a 25.89% increase above the value determined based on the monthly compound growth rate.

16.50   (a) $\log b_0 = 3.0$. $b_0 = 10^{3.0} = 1,000$. This is the fitted value for January 1998 prior to adjustment by the quarterly multiplier.

   (b) $\log b_1 = 0.1$. $b_1 = 10^{0.1} = 1.2589$. The estimated quarterly compound growth rate is $(b_1 - 1)100\% = 25.89\%$.

   (c) $\log b_3 = 0.2$. $b_3 = 10^{0.2} = 1.5849$. The second quarter values in the time series are estimated to require a 58.49% increase above the value determined based on the quarterly compound growth rate.

16.52   (a)

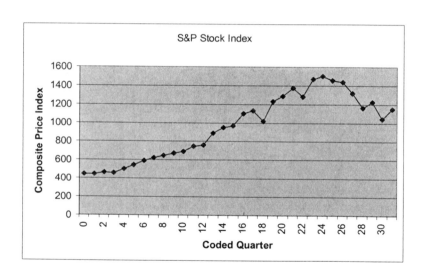

16.52   (b)
cont.

Regression Analysis

Regression Statistics	
Multiple R	0.875781469
R Square	0.766993182
Adjusted R Square	0.73485431
Standard Error	0.088772986
Observations	34

ANOVA

	df	SS	MS	F	Significance F
Regression	4	0.752285221	0.188071305	23.8650	8.13576E-09
Residual	29	0.228538649	0.007880643		
Total	33	0.980823871			

	Coefficients	Standard Error	t Stat	P-value
Intercept	2.71074	0.04102	66.07946	0.00000
Coded Quarter	0.01514	0.00155	9.74644	0.00000
Q1	-0.00981	0.04316	-0.22735	0.82174
Q2	-0.01312	0.04314	-0.30424	0.76311
Q3	-0.01108	0.04441	-0.24940	0.80481

$$\log_{10}\hat{Y} = 2.7107 + 0.01514X - 0.00981Q_1 - 0.01312Q_2 - 0.01108Q_3$$

(c) $\hat{Y}_{33} = 1533.0348$ (d) $\hat{Y}_{34} = 1575.3824$

(e)   2002: $\hat{Y}_{35} = 1638.9942$ $\hat{Y}_{36} = 1740.9994$

2003: $\hat{Y}_{37} = 1762.5019$ $\hat{Y}_{38} = 1811.1881$ $\hat{Y}_{39} = 1884.3214$ $\hat{Y}_{40} = 2001.5949$

(f) $\log_{10} b_1 = 0.01514$. $b_1 = 10^{0.01514} = 1.0355$. The estimated quarterly compound growth rate is $(b_1 - 1)\,100\% = 3.55\%$.

(g) $\log_{10} b_3 = -0.01312$. $b_3 = 10^{-0.01312} = 0.9702$. The second quarter values in the time series are estimated to be on average 2.98% below the fourth quarter values.

16.54   (a)

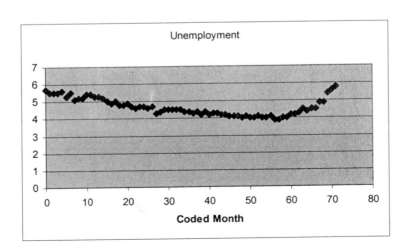

16.54 (b)
cont.

Regression Statistics	
Multiple R	0.5922628
R Square	0.3507753
Adjusted R Square	0.2187296
Standard Error	0.0430142
Observations	72

ANOVA

	df	SS	MS	F	Significance F
Regression	12	0.0589808	0.0049151	2.6564687	0.0064784
Residual	59	0.1091633	0.0018502		
Total	71	0.1681441			

	Coefficients	Standard Error	t Stat	P-value	Lower 95%	Upper 95%
Intercept	0.7278497	0.0202786	35.8924675	0.0000000	0.6872722	0.7684272
Coded Month	-0.0013857	0.0002474	-5.6020573	0.0000006	-0.0018807	-0.0008907
M1	-0.0177743	0.0249829	-0.7114598	0.4796029	-0.0677650	0.0322164
M2	-0.0170793	0.0249572	-0.6843450	0.4964368	-0.0670185	0.0328599
M3	-0.0189670	0.0249339	-0.7606940	0.4498693	-0.0688597	0.0309256
M4	-0.0202006	0.0249130	-0.8108441	0.4207140	-0.0700514	0.0296503
M5	-0.0205155	0.0248946	-0.8240945	0.4132050	-0.0703295	0.0292985
M6	-0.0184837	0.0248786	-0.7429543	0.4604574	-0.0682657	0.0312983
M7	-0.0173716	0.0248651	-0.6986356	0.4875246	-0.0671266	0.0323833
M8	-0.0152033	0.0248540	-0.6117044	0.5430834	-0.0649361	0.0345295
M9	-0.0145395	0.0248454	-0.5851982	0.5606460	-0.0642550	0.0351761
M10	-0.0108814	0.0248392	-0.4380747	0.6629319	-0.0605846	0.0388218
M11	-0.0054824	0.0248355	-0.2207469	0.8260516	-0.0551782	0.0442134

$$\log \hat{Y} = 0.7278 - 0.001386X - 0.01777M_1 - 0.01708M_2 - 0.01897M_3$$
$$- 0.02020M_4 - 0.02052M_5 - 0.01848M_6 - 0.01737M_7$$
$$- 0.01520M_8 - 0.01454M_9 - 0.01088M_{10} - 0.005482M_{11}$$

(c) $\hat{Y}_{71} = 4.2205\,\%$

(d) $\hat{Y}_{72} = 4.261\,\%$

(e)   Forecasts for 2002: $\hat{Y}_{73} = 4.0767\,\%$, $\hat{Y}_{74} = 4.0702\,\%$, $\hat{Y}_{75} = 4.0396\,\%$,

$\hat{Y}_{76} = 4.0153\,\%$, $\hat{Y}_{77} = 3.9996\,\%$, $\hat{Y}_{78} = 4.0056\,\%$, $\hat{Y}_{79} = 4.0031\,\%$,

$\hat{Y}_{80} = 4.0103\,\%$, $\hat{Y}_{81} = 4.0036\,\%$, $\hat{Y}_{82} = 4.0246\,\%$, $\hat{Y}_{83} = 4.0620\,\%$, $\hat{Y}_{84} = 4.1005\,\%$

(f) $\log b_1 = -0.0013857$. $b_1 = 10^{-0.0013857} = 0.9968$. The estimated monthly compound growth rate is $(b_1 - 1)\,100\% = -0.3186\%$.

(g) $\log b_8 = -0.0173716$. $b_8 = 10^{-0.0173716} = 0.9608$. The July values in the time series are estimated to be on average 3.92% below the December values.

16.56 (a)   The retail industry is heavily subject to seasonal variation due to the holiday seasons and so are the revenues for Toys R Us.

(b)

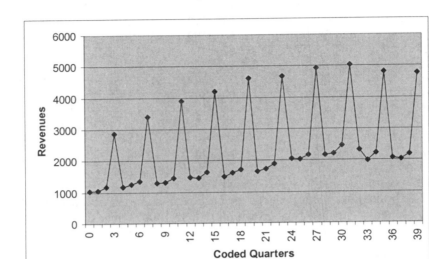

There is obvious seasonal effect in the time series.

(c) $\hat{Y}_i = 2882.9903(1.0187)^{X_i}(0.4003)^{Q_1}(0.3960)^{Q_2}(0.4256)^{Q_3}$

(d) $\log b_1 = 0.008043$. $b_1 = 10^{0.008043} = 1.0187$. The estimated quarterly compound growth rate is $(b_1 - 1)100\% = 1.87\%$

(e) $\log b_2 = -0.3976$. $b_2 = 10^{-0.3976} = 0.4003$. The 1st quarter values in the time series are estimated to be on average 59.97% below the 4th quarter values.
$\log b_3 = -0.4024$. $b_3 = 10^{-0.4024} = 0.3960$. The 2nd quarter values in the time series are estimated to be on average 60.40% below the 4th quarter values.
$\log b_4 = -0.3710$. $b_4 = 10^{-0.3710} = 0.4256$. The 3nd quarter values in the time series are estimated to be on average 57.44% below the 4th quarter values.

(f)   Forecasts for 2002: $\hat{Y}_{41} = 2420.78$, $\hat{Y}_{42} = 2439.26$, $\hat{Y}_{43} = 2670.97$,
$\hat{Y}_{44} = 6392.92$

(g)   Forecasts for 2003: $\hat{Y}_{45} = 2606.92$, $\hat{Y}_{46} = 2626.82$, $\hat{Y}_{47} = 2876.35$,
$\hat{Y}_{48} = 6884.49$

16.58   The price of the commodity in 2002 was 75% higher than that in 1995.

16.60 (a) $I_U^{2002} = \dfrac{\sum_{i=1}^{3} P_i^{2002}}{\sum_{i=1}^{3} P_i^{1995}}(100) = \dfrac{43}{23}(100) = 186.96$

(b) $I_L^{2002} = \dfrac{\sum_{i=1}^{3} P_i^{2002} Q_i^{1995}}{\sum_{i=1}^{3} P_i^{1995} Q_i^{1995}}(100) = \dfrac{240}{148}(100) = 162.16$

(c) $I_P^{2002} = \dfrac{\sum_{i=1}^{3} P_i^{2002} Q_i^{2002}}{\sum_{i=1}^{3} P_i^{1995} Q_i^{1995}}(100) = \dfrac{227}{148}(100) = 153.38$

16.62 (a), (b)

Year	DJIA	Price Index (base = 1979)	Price Index (base = 1990)	Year	DJIA	Price Index (base = 1979)	Price Index (base = 1990)
1979	838.7	100.00	31.84	1991	3168.8	377.82	120.32
1980	964	114.94	36.60	1992	3301.1	393.60	125.34
1981	875	104.33	33.22	1993	3754.1	447.61	142.54
1982	1046.5	124.78	39.73	1994	3834.4	457.18	145.59
1983	1258.6	150.07	47.79	1995	5117.1	610.12	194.29
1984	1211.6	144.46	46.00	1996	6448.3	768.84	244.84
1985	1546.7	184.42	58.73	1997	7908.3	942.92	300.27
1986	1896	226.06	71.99	1998	9181.4	1094.72	348.61
1987	1938.8	231.17	73.62	1999	11497.1	1370.82	436.54
1988	2168.6	258.57	82.34	2000	10788	1286.28	409.61
1989	2753.2	328.27	104.54	2001	10021.5	1194.88	380.51
1990	2633.7	314.02	100.00				

(c) The price index using 1990 as the base year is more useful because it is closer to the present and the DJIA has grown more than 1000% over the 23-year period.

16.64 (a), (b)

Year	CPI	Price Index (base = 1990)	Price Index (base = 2001)
1990	129.9	100.00	74.91
1991	135.7	104.46	78.26
1992	139.2	107.16	80.28
1993	141.9	109.24	81.83
1994	146	112.39	84.20
1995	150.7	116.01	86.91
1996	154.4	118.86	89.04
1997	160	123.17	92.27
1998	164.4	126.56	94.81
1999	167.3	128.79	96.48
2000	172.2	132.56	99.31
2001	173.4	133.49	100.00

(c) Both price indices are useful. The one using 1990 as the base year conveys a picture of how the CPI has grown since 1990 as a percentage of that in year 1990. The one using 2001 as the base year reveals what the CPI in prior years was as a percentage of the current level. Since the price index is usually used to compare the growth of price from some base year in the past, the price using 1990 as the base is more useful.

(d) The CPI in UK has grown 33.49% from 1990 to 2001 compared to the 6.5% growth in Japan over the same period.

16.66 (a), (c)

Year	Price	Price Index (base=1980)	Price Index (base=1990)	Year	Price	Price Index (base=1980)	Price Index (base=1990)
1980	0.703	100.00	40.52	1992	0.936	133.14	53.95
1981	0.792	112.66	45.65	1993	1.141	162.30	65.76
1982	0.763	108.53	43.98	1994	1.604	228.17	92.45
1983	0.726	103.27	41.84	1995	1.323	188.19	76.25
1984	0.854	121.48	49.22	1996	1.103	156.90	63.57
1985	0.697	99.15	40.17	1997	1.213	172.55	69.91
1986	1.104	157.04	63.63	1998	1.452	206.54	83.69
1987	0.943	134.14	54.35	1999	1.904	270.84	109.74
1988	0.871	123.90	50.20	2000	1.443	205.26	83.17
1989	0.797	113.37	45.94	2001	1.414	201.14	81.50
1990	1.735	246.80	100.00	2002	1.451	206.40	83.63

16.66 (b)   The average price per pound of fresh tomatoes in 2002 in the U.S. is 106.40% higher
cont.   than that in 1980.
       (d)   The average price per pound of fresh tomatoes in 2002 in the U.S. is 16.37% lower
              than that in 1990.
       (e)

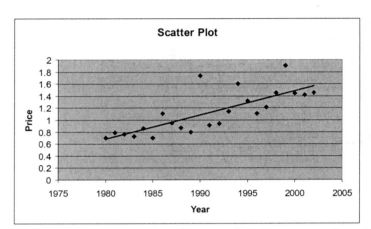

There is an upward trend in the cost of fresh tomatoes from 1980 to 2002.

16.68 Forecasting methodology is important as a tool for planning for the future.

16.70 Trend is the overall long-term tendency or impression of upward or downward movements.
       The cyclical component depicts the up-and-down swings or movements through the series.
       Any observed data that do not follow the trend curve modified by the cyclical component are
       indicative of the irregular or random component. When data are recorded monthly or
       quarterly, an additional component called the seasonal factor is considered.

16.72 The exponential trend model is appropriate when the percentage difference from observation
       to observation is constant.

16.74 Autoregressive models have independent variables that are the dependent variable lagged by
       a given number of time periods.

16.76 The standard error of the estimate relies on the squared sum of the deviations, which gives
       increased weight to large difference. The mean absolute deviation is the average of the
       absolute value of the deviations.

16.78 An index number provides a measure of the value of an item (or group of items) at a
       particular point in time as a percentage of the item's (or group of items') value at another
       point in time.

16.80 Both the Laspeyres price index and Paasche price index are weight aggregate price index.
       The Laspeyres price index uses the consumption quantities associated with the base year as
       the weights while the Paasche price index uses the consumption quantities in the year of
       interest as the weights.

16.82   (a),(b)

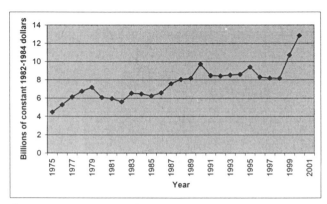

(c) $\hat{Y} = 4.8359 + 0.2324X$, where X = years relative to 1975

(d) $\hat{Y} = 5.7201 + 0.0202X + 0.0082X^2$, where X = years relative to 1975

(e) $\hat{Y} = 5.2207(1.0293)^X$, where X = years relative to 1975

(f) $\hat{Y}_i = 0.1245 + 1.2061Y_{i-1} - 0.1322Y_{i-2} - 0.0225Y_{i-3}$

        Test of A_3: p-value = $0.93 > 0.05$. Do not reject H_0 that $A_3 = 0$. Third-order term can be deleted.

(g) $\hat{Y}_i = 0.0928 + 1.2213Y_{i-1} - 0.1961Y_{i-2}$

        Test of A_2: p-value = $0.43 > 0.05$. Do not reject H_0 that $A_2 = 0$. Second-order term can be deleted.

(h) $\hat{Y}_i = -0.004784 + 1.0494Y_{i-1}$

        Test of A_1: p-value is virtually $0 < 0.05$. Reject H_0 that $A_1 = 0$. A first-order autoregressive model is appropriate.

(i)-(k)

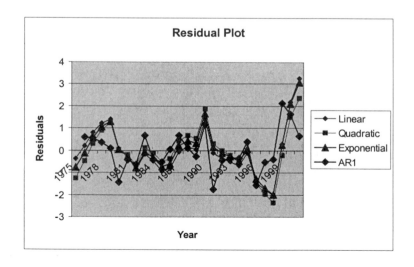

16.82   (i)-(k)
cont.

	Linear	Quadratic	Exponential	AR1
SSE	34.44513	29.17023133	31.10697	20.37813
Syx	1.173799	1.102463743	1.115472	0.92146
MAD	0.815541	0.761041968	0.765284	0.696345

(l), (m) The residuals in the first three models show strings of consecutive positive and negative values. The autoregressive model performs well for the historical data and has a fairly random pattern of residuals. It also has the smallest values in MAD and standard error of estimate. Based on the principle of parsimony, the autoregressive model will be a good model for forecasting. We will use the 1st order autoregressive model to perform forecast.

For 2002: $\hat{Y}_{2002} = -0.004784 + 1.0494 Y_{2001} = \$14.8087$ billions.

For 2003: $\hat{Y}_{2003} = -0.004784 + 1.0494 \hat{Y}_{2002} = \$15.5352$ billions.

16.84   (a),(b)

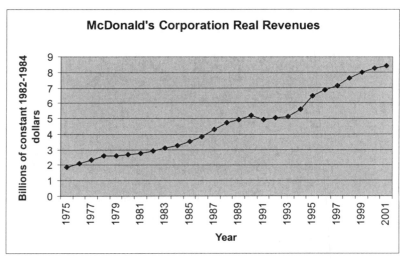

(c) $\hat{Y} = 1.4026 + 0.2512X$ where $X =$ years relative to 1975

(d) $\hat{Y} = 2.0299 + 0.1007X + 0.005791X^2$, where $X =$ years relative to 1975

(e) $\hat{Y} = 2.0335(1.0582)^X$, where $X =$ years relative to 1975

(f) $\hat{Y}_i = 0.09838 + 1.3533 Y_{i-1} - 0.3921 Y_{i-2} + 0.05667 Y_{i-3}$

   Test of A_3: p-value $= 0.8158 > 0.05$. Do not reject H_0 that $A_3 = 0$. Third-order term can be deleted.

(g) $\hat{Y}_i = 0.09721 + 1.3378 Y_{i-1} - 0.3221 Y_{i-2}$

   Test of A_2: p-value $= 0.1508$. Do not reject H_0 that $A_2 = 0$. Second-order term can be deleted.

(h) $\hat{Y}_i = 0.1232 + 1.0285 Y_{i-1}$

   Test of A_1: p-value is virtually 0. Reject H_0 that $A_1 = 0$. A first-order autoregressive model is appropriate.

16.84   (i)
cont.

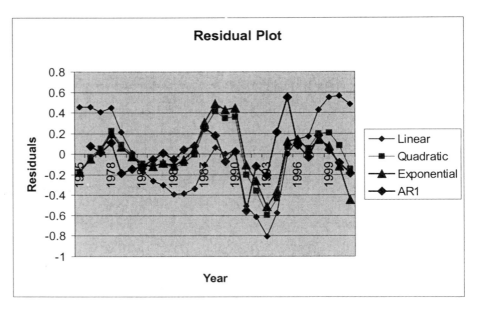

(j), (k)

	Linear	**Quadratic**	**Exponential**	**AR1**
SSE	4.124639	1.469777	1.588282	0.993597
Syx	0.406184	0.247469	0.252054	0.20347
MAD	0.327783	0.182647	0.187285	0.140235

(l)   The residuals in the first three models show strings of consecutive positive and negative values. The autoregressive model performs well for the historical data and has a fairly random pattern of residuals. It also has the smallest values in the standard error of the estimate, MAD and SSE. Based on the principle of parsimony, the autoregressive model would probably be the best model for forecasting.

(m) $\hat{Y}_{2002} = 0.1232 + 1.0285Y_{2001} = \$8.7763\,\text{billions}$

$\hat{Y}_{2003} = 0.1232 + 1.0285Y_{2002} = \$9.1495\,\text{billions}$

16.86 **Variable A:**

(a)

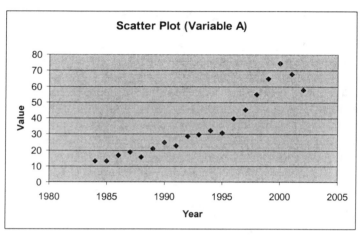

(b) $\hat{Y} = 5.6797 + 3.2920X$, where X = years relative to 1984

(c) $\hat{Y} = 12.8291 + 0.7687X + 0.1402X^2$, where X = years relative to 1984

(d) $\hat{Y} = 12.5725(1.1032)^X$, where X = years relative to 1984

(e) $\hat{Y}_i = 4.8765 + 1.4115Y_{i-1} - 0.3383Y_{i-2} - 0.2083Y_{i-3}$

Test of A_3: p-value = 0.72 > 0.05. Do not reject H_0 that $A_3 = 0$. Third-order term can be deleted.

(f) $\hat{Y}_i = 4.4775 + 1.4003Y_{i-1} - 0.4981Y_{i-2}$

Test of A_2: p-value = 0.13. Do not reject H_0 that $A_2 = 0$. Second-order term can be deleted.

(g) $\hat{Y}_i = 3.8565 + 0.9595Y_{i-1}$

Test of A_1: p-value is virtually 0. Reject H_0 that $A_1 = 0$. A first-order autoregressive model is appropriate.

(h)

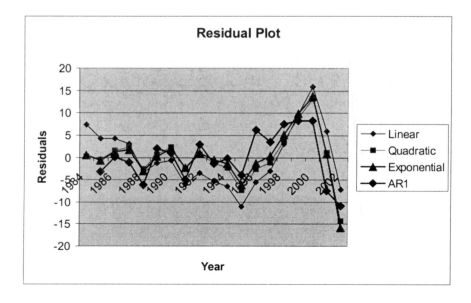

16.86   (i), (j)
cont.

	Linear	Quadratic	Exponential	AR1
SSE	838.8739	572.2798	635.7085	524.1271
Syx	7.024637	5.980593	6.115114	5.723456
MAD	5.641802	3.649209	3.589535	4.39278

(k)   The residuals in the linear trend model shows strings of consecutive positive and negative values. The quadratic trend, exponential trend and the autoregressive models perform well for the historical data and has a fairly random pattern of residuals. The autoregressive model AR(1) has the smallest values in the standard error of the estimate while the exponential trend model has the smallest MAD. Based on the principle of parsimony, the autoregressive model would probably be the best model for forecasting.

(l) $\hat{Y}_{2003} = 3.8565 + 0.9595 Y_{2002} = 59.2295$

   $\hat{Y}_{2004} = 3.8565 + 0.9595 \hat{Y}_{2003} = 60.6885$

Variable B:
(a)

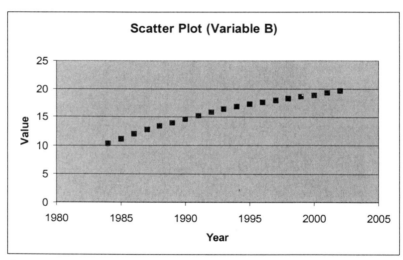

(b) $\hat{Y} = 11.2161 + 0.5108X$, where X = years relative to 1984

(c) $\hat{Y} = 10.3218 + 0.8264X - 0.01754X^2$, where X = years relative to 1984

(d) $\hat{Y} = 11.4503(1.0345)^X$, where X = years relative to 1984

(e) $\hat{Y}_i = 0.8114 + 1.7603 Y_{i-1} - 1.1678 Y_{i-2} + 0.3745 Y_{i-3}$

   Test of A_3: p-value = 0.09 > 0.05. Do not reject H_0 that $A_3 = 0$. Third-order term can be deleted.

(f) $\hat{Y}_i = 0.8792 + 1.3871 Y_{i-1} - 0.4247 Y_{i-2}$

   Test of A_2: p-value = 0.06 > 0.05. Do not reject H_0 that $A_2 = 0$. Second-order term can be deleted.

(g) $\hat{Y}_i = 1.4527 + 0.9401 Y_{i-1}$

   Test of A_1: p-value is virtually 0. Reject H_0 that $A_1 = 0$. A first-order autoregressive model is appropriate.

16.86 (h)
cont.

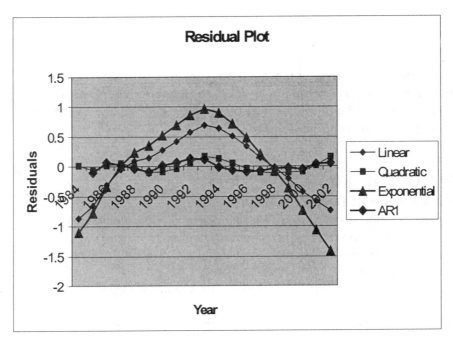

(i), (j)

	Linear	Quadratic	Exponential	AR1
SSE	4.320581	0.148825	9.964195	0.086353
Syx	0.504135	0.096445	0.765591	0.073465
MAD	0.406717	0.074911	0.622331	0.060005

(k)   The residuals in the linear trend and exponential models show strings of consecutive positive and negative values. The quadratic trend and the autoregressive models perform well for the historical data and has a fairly random pattern of residuals. The autoregressive model AR(1) has the smallest values in the standard error of the estimate and MAD. Based on the principle of parsimony, the autoregressive model would probably be the best model for forecasting.

(l) $\hat{Y}_{2003} = 1.4527 + 0.9401 Y_{2002} = 19.9473$

$\hat{Y}_{2004} = 1.4527 + 0.9401 \hat{Y}_{2003} = 20.2052$

CHAPTER 17

OBJECTIVES
- To be able to use the payoff table and decision trees to evaluate alternative courses of action
- To be able to use several criteria to select an alternative course of action
- To be able to use Bayes' theorem to revise probabilities in the light of sample information
- To understand the concept of utility

OVERVIEW AND KEY CONCEPTS

Some Basic Features of Decision Making
- **Alternative courses of action:** The decision maker must have two or more possible choices to evaluate prior to selecting one course of action.
- **Events or states of the world:** The decision maker must list the events that can occur and consider each event's possibility of action.
- **Payoffs:** The decision maker must associate a monetary value or payoff with the result of each event.
- **Decision criteria:** The decision maker must determine how the best course of action is to be selected.

Payoff Table
- A payoff table contains each possible event that can occur for each alternative course of action.

Consider a food vendor determining
whether to sell soft drinks or hot dogs.

Event (E_i)	Course of Action (A_j)	
	Sell Soft Drinks (A_1)	Sell Hot Dogs (A_2)
Cool Weather (E_1)	$x_{11} = \$50$	$x_{12} = \$100$
Warm Weather (E_2)	$x_{21} = \$200$	$x_{22} = \$125$

x_{ij} = payoff (profit) for event i and action j

Decision Tree

- A decision tree pictorially represents the events and courses of action through a set of branches and nodes.

Food Vendor Profit Tree Diagram

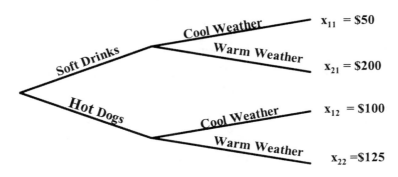

Opportunity Loss

- The opportunity loss is the difference between the highest possible profit (payoff or monetary value) for an event and the actual profit obtained for an action taken.
- **The opportunity loss table:**

Event	Optimal Action	Profit of Optimal Action	Alternative Course of Action	
			Sell Soft Drinks	**Sell Hot Dogs**
Cool Weather	Hot Dogs	100	100 - 50 = 50	100 - 100 = 0
Warm Weather	Soft Drinks	200	200 - 200 = 0	200 - 125 = 75

Some Decision Criteria

- **Expected monetary value (*EMV*):**
  - The expected profit (payoff or monetary value) for taking an action.
  - $$EMV(j) = \sum_{i=1}^{N} x_{ij} P_i$$

    where

    $EMV(j) =$ expected monetary value of action j

    $x_{ij} =$ payoff that occurs when action j is taken and event i occurs

    $P_i =$ probability of occurence of event i

- **Expected opportunity loss (*EOL*):**
  - $$EOL(j) = \sum_{i=1}^{N} l_{ij} P_i$$
    where

    $EOL(j) =$ expected opportunity loss of action j

    $l_{ij} =$ opportunity loss that occurs when action j is taken and event i occurs

    $P_i =$ probability of occurence of event i
- **Expected profit under certainty (*EPUC*):** The expected profit one could make if one has perfect information about which event will occur.
- **Expected value of perfect information:**
  - The expected value of perfect information is the expected opportunity loss from the best decision, i.e. the minimum *EOL* among all the courses of action.
  - It also represents the maximum amount one would pay to obtain perfect information.
  - The difference between expected profit under certainty and the expected monetary value from he best action.
  - $$EVPI = EPUC - \max_j EMV(j) = \min_j EOL(j)$$
- **Return to risk ratio:**
  - Expressed the relationship between the return (expected payoff) and the risk (standard deviation).
  - $$RRR(j) = \frac{EMV(j)}{\sigma_j}$$
- **Coefficient of variation:**
  - Coefficient of variation is the inverse of return to risk ratio.
  - $$CV(j) = \frac{\sigma_j}{EMV(j)} = \frac{1}{RRR(j)}$$

Decision Making with Sample Information

- Decision maker chooses the best course of action A_j using some prior probabilities of events $P(E_i)$. When new information becomes available in the form of conditional probabilities of an action given a specific event, $P(A_j \mid E_i)$, one can update the probabilities of the events using the Bayes's theorem to obtain the posterior probabilities of events, $P(E_i \mid A_j)$, and re-evaluate all the decision criteria.

Utility

- Each incremental amount of profit or loss does not have the same value to every individual.
    - A **risk adverse** person, once reaching a goal, assigns less value to each incremental amount of profit.
    - A **risk seeker** assigns more value to each incremental amount of profit.
    - A **risk neutral** person assigns the same value to each incremental amount of profit.

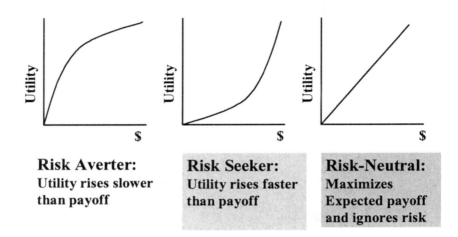

Risk Averter:
Utility rises slower than payoff

Risk Seeker:
Utility rises faster than payoff

Risk-Neutral:
Maximizes Expected payoff and ignores risk

SOLUTIONS TO END OF SECTION
AND CHAPTER REVIEW EVEN PROBLEMS

17.2 (a) Opportunity loss table:

		Profit of	Alternative Courses of Action	
Event	Optimum Action	Optimum Action	A	B
1	A	50	50 – 50 = 0	50 – 10 = 40
2	A	300	300 – 300 = 0	300 – 100 = 200
3	A	500	500 – 500 = 0	500 – 200 = 300

(b)

17.4 (a)-(b) Payoff table:

		Action		
Event	Company A		Company B	
1	$10,000 + $2•1,000 =	$12,000	$2,000 + $4•1,000 =	$6,000
2	$10,000 + $2•2,000 =	$14,000	$2,000 + $4•2,000 =	$10,000
3	$10,000 + $2•5,000 =	$20,000	$2,000 + $4•5,000 =	$22,000
4	$10,000 + $2•10,000 =	$30,000	$2,000 + $4•10,000 =	$42,000
5	$10,000 + $2•50,000 =	$110,000	$2,000 + $4•50,000 =	$202,000

(d) Opportunity loss table:

		Profit of	Alternative Courses of Action	
Event	Optimum Action	Optimum Action	A	B
1	A	12,000	0	6,000
2	A	14,000	0	4,000
3	B	22,000	2,000	0
4	B	42,000	12,000	0
5	B	202,000	92,000	0

17.6 (a) $EMV_A = 50(0.5) + 200(0.5) = 125$ $EMV_B = 100(0.5) + 125(0.5) = 112.50$

(b) $EOL_A = 50(0.5) + 0(0.5) = 25$ $EOL_B = 0(0.5) + 75(0.5) = 37.50$

(c) Perfect information would correctly forecast which event, 1 or 2, will occur. The value of perfect information is the increase in the expected value if you knew which of the events 1 or 2 would occur prior to making a decision between actions. It allows us to select the optimum action given a correct forecast.

EMV with perfect information = 100 (0.5) + 200 (0.5) = 150

$EVPI = EMV$ with perfect information – EMV_A = 150 – 125 = 25

(d) Based on (a) and (b) above, select action A because it has a higher expected monetary value (a) and a lower opportunity loss (b) than action B.

17.6   (e) $\sigma_A^2 = (50 - 125)^2 (0.5) + (200 - 125)^2 (0.5) = 5625$ $\sigma_A = 75$
cont.
$CV_A = \dfrac{75}{125} \cdot 100\% = 60\%$

$\sigma_B^2 = (100 - 112.5)^2 (0.5) + (125 - 112.5)^2 (0.5) = 156.25$ $\sigma_B = 12.5$

$CV_B = \dfrac{12.5}{112.5} \cdot 100\% = 11.11\%$

(f)   Return to risk ratio for $A = \dfrac{125}{75} = 1.667$

Return to risk ratio for $B = \dfrac{112.5}{12.5} = 9.0$

(g)   Based on (e) and (f), select action B because it has a lower coefficient of variation and a higher return to risk ratio.

(h)   The best decision depends on the decision criteria. In this case, expected monetary value leads to a different decision than the return to risk ratio.

17.8   (a)   Rate of return $= \dfrac{\$100}{\$1,000} \cdot 100\% = 10\%$

(b) $CV = \dfrac{\$25}{\$100} \cdot 100\% = 25\%$

(c)   Return to risk ratio $= \dfrac{\$100}{\$25} = 4.0$

17.10   Select portfolio A because it has a higher expected monetary value while it has the same standard deviation as portfolio B.

17.12   (a) EMV(Soft drinks) $= 50(0.4) + 60(0.6) = 56$
EMV(Ice cream) $= 30(0.4) + 90(0.6) = 66$

(b) EOL(Soft drinks) $= 18$
EOL(Ice cream) $= 8$

(c) $EVPI$ is the maximum amount of money the vendor is willing to pay for the information about which event will occur.

(d)   Based on (a) and (b), choose to sell ice cream because you will earn a higher expected monetary value and incur a lower opportunity cost than choosing to sell soft drinks.

(e) CV(Soft drinks) $= \dfrac{4.899}{56} \cdot 100\% = 8.748\%$

CV(Ice cream) $= \dfrac{29.394}{66} \cdot 100\% = 44.536\%$

(f)   Return to risk ratio for soft drinks $= 11.431$
Return to risk ratio for ice cream $= 2.245$

17.14   (a) $EMV_A = 500(0.3) + 1,000(0.5) + 2,000(0.2) = 1,050$
$EMV_B = -2,000(0.3) + 2,000(0.5) + 5,000(0.2) = 1,400$
$EMV_C = -7,000(0.3) - 1,000(0.5) + 20,000(0.2) = 1,400$

(b) $\sigma_A^2 = (500 - 1,050)^2 (0.3) + (1,000 - 1,050)^2 (0.5) + (2,000 - 1,050)^2 (0.2)$ $=$ 272,500

$\sigma_A = 522.02$

$\sigma_B^2 = (-2,000 - 1,400)^2 (0.3) + (2,000 - 1,400)^2 (0.5) + (5,000 - 1,400)^2 (0.2)$ $=$ 6,240,000

$\sigma_B = 2,498.00$

$\sigma_C^2 = (-7,000 - 1,400)^2(0.3) + (-1,000 - 1,400)^2(0.5)$
$+ (20,000 - 1,400)^2(0.2) = 93,240,000$

$\sigma_C = 9656.09$

17.14   (c)   Opportunity loss table:

		Profit of	Alternative Courses of Action		
Event	Optimum Action	Optimum Action	A	B	C
1	A	500	0	2,500	7,500
2	B	2,000	1,000	0	3,000
3	C	20,000	18,000	15,000	0

$EOL_A = 0(0.3) + 1,000(0.5) + 18,000(0.2) = 4,100$
$EOL_B = 2,500(0.3) + 0(0.5) + 15,000(0.2) = 3,750$
$EOL_C = 7,500(0.3) + 3,000(0.5) + 0(0.2) = 3,750$

   (d) EMV with perfect information $= 500(0.3) + 2,000(0.5) + 20,000(0.2)$
$$= 5,150$$

$EVPI = EMV$ with perfect information $- EMV_{B \ or \ C} = 5,150 - 1,400 = 3,750$
The investor should not be willing to pay more than \$3,750 for a perfect forecast.

   (e) $CV_A = \dfrac{522.02}{1050} \cdot 100\% = 49.72\%$ $CV_B = \dfrac{2498.00}{1400} \cdot 100\% = 178.43\%$

$CV_C = \dfrac{9656.09}{1400} \cdot 100\% = 689.72\%$

   (f)   Return to risk ratio for $A = \dfrac{1050}{522.02} = 2.01$

Return to risk ratio for $B = \dfrac{1400}{2498} = 0.56$

Return to risk ratio for $B = \dfrac{1400}{9656.09} = 0.14$

(g)-(h) Actions B and C optimize the expected monetary value, but action A minimizes the coefficient of variation and maximizes the investor's return to risk.

   (i)

	(1) 0.1, 0.6, 0.3	(2) 0.1, 0.3, 0.6	(3) 0.4, 0.4, 0.2	(4) 0.6, 0.3, 0.1
(a) Max EMV	C: 4,700	C: 11,000	A or B: 800	A: 800
(b) σ Max EMV	σ_C: 10,169	σ_C: 11,145	σ_A: 548 σ_B: 2,683	σ_A: 458
(c) Min EOL & (d) $EVPI$	C: 2,550	C: 1,650	A: 4,000 or B: 4,000	A: 2,100
(e) Min CV	A: 40.99%	A: 36.64%	A: 54.77%	A: 57.28%
(f) Max Return to risk	A: 2.4398	A: 2.7294	A: 1.8257	A: 1.7457
(g) Choice on (e), (f)	Choose A	Choose A	Choose A	Choose A
(h) Compare (a) and (g)	Different: (a) C (g) A	Different: (a) C (g) A	Different: (a) A or B (g) A	Same: A

17.16 (a) $EMV_A = 12,000(0.45) + 14,000(0.2) + 20,000(0.15) + 30,000(0.1)$
$+ 110,000(0.1) = 25,200$
$EMV_B = 6,000(0.45) + 10,000(0.2) + 22,000(0.15) + 42,000(0.1)$
$+ 202,000(0.1) = 32,400$

(b) $EOL_A = 0(0.45) + 0(0.2) + 2,000(0.15) + 12,000(0.1) + 92,000(0.1)$
$= 10,700$
$EOL_B = 6,000(0.45) + 4,000(0.2) + 0(0.15) + 0(0.1) + 0(0.1)$
$= 3,500$

(c) EMV with perfect information $= 12,000(0.45) + 14,000(0.2) + 22,000(0.15)$
$+ 42,000(0.1) + 202,000(0.1) = 35,900$
$EVPI = EMV$, perfect information $- EMV_B = 35,900 - 32,400 = 3,500$
The author should not be willing to pay more than \$3,500 for a perfect forecast.

(d) Sign with company B to maximize the expected monetary value (\$32,400) and minimize the expected opportunity loss (\$3,500).

(e) $CV_A = \dfrac{28,792}{25,200} \cdot 100\% = 114.25\%$ 　　　　　　 $CV_B = \dfrac{57,583}{32,400} \cdot 100\% = 177.73\%$

(f) Return to risk ratio for $A = \dfrac{25,200}{28,792} = 0.8752$
Return to risk ratio for $B = \dfrac{32,400}{57,583} = 0.5627$

(g) Signing with company A will minimize the author's risk and yield the higher return to risk.

(h) Company B has a higher EMV than A, but choosing company B also entails more risk and has a lower return to risk ratio than A.

(i) Payoff table:

	Pr	A	B
Event 1	0.3	12,000	6,000
Event 2	0.2	14,000	10,000
Event 3	0.2	20,000	22,000
Event 4	0.1	30,000	42,000
Event 5	0.2	110,000	202,000
	EMV	35,400	52,800
	σ	37,673	75,346
	CV	106.42%	142.70%
	Return to risk	0.9397	0.7008

Opportunity loss table:

	Pr	A	B
Event 1	0.3	0	6,000
Event 2	0.2	0	4,000
Event 3	0.2	2,000	0
Event 4	0.1	12,000	0
Event 5	0.2	92,000	0
	EOL	20,000	2,600

The author's decision is not affected by the changed probabilities.

17.18 (a) $P(E_1 \mid F) = \dfrac{P(F \mid E_1) \cdot P(E_1)}{P(F \mid E_1) \cdot P(E_1) + P(F \mid E_2) \cdot P(E_2)} = \dfrac{0.6(0.5)}{0.6(0.5) + 0.4(0.5)} = 0.6$

$P(E_2 \mid F) = 1 - P(E_1 \mid F) = 1 - 0.6 = 0.4$

(b) $EMV_A = (0.6)(50) + (0.4)(200) = 110$
$EMV_B = (0.6)(100) + (0.4)(125) = 110$

(c) $EOL_A = (0.6)(50) + (0.4)(0) = 30$
$EOL_B = (0.6)(0) + (0.4)(75) = 30$

(d) $EVPI = (0.6)(100) + (0.4)(200) = 30$

(e)   Both have the same EMV.

(f) $\sigma_A^2 = (0.6)(60)^2 + (0.4)(90)^2 = 5400$ $\qquad \sigma_A = 73.4847$
$\sigma_B^2 = (0.6)(10)^2 + (0.4)(15)^2 = 150$ $\qquad \sigma_B = 12.2474$
$CV_A = \dfrac{73.4847}{110} \cdot 100\% = 66.8\%$ $\qquad CV_B = \dfrac{12.2474}{110} \cdot 100\% = 11.1\%$

(g)   Return to risk ratio for $A = \dfrac{110}{73.4847} = 1.497$

Return to risk ratio for $B = \dfrac{110}{12.2474} = 8.981$

(h)   Action B has a better return to risk ratio.
(i)   Both have the same EMV, but action B has a better return to risk ratio.

17.20 $P(\text{forecast cool} \mid \text{cool weather}) = 0.80$
$P(\text{forecast warm} \mid \text{warm weather}) = 0.70$

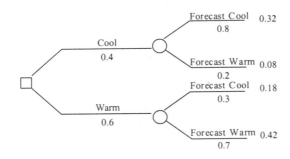

	Forecast Cool	Forecast Warm	Totals
Cool	0.32	0.08	0.4
Warm	0.18	0.42	0.6
Totals	0.5	0.5	

(a)   Revised probabilities: $P(\text{cool} \mid \text{forecast cool}) = \dfrac{0.32}{0.5} = 0.64$

$P(\text{warm} \mid \text{forecast cool}) = \dfrac{0.18}{0.5} = 0.36$

17.20 (a)
cont.

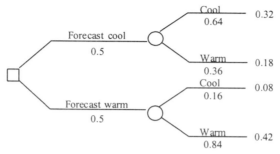

(b) EMV(Soft drinks) = 50(0.64) + 60(0.36) = 53.6
EMV(Ice cream) = 30(0.64) + 90(0.36) = 51.6
EOL(Soft drinks) = 10.8 EOL(Ice cream) = 12.8
EMV with perfect information = 50(0.64) + 90(0.36) = 64.4
$EVPI = EMV$, perfect information $- EMV_A = 64.4 - 53.6 = 10.8$
The vendor should not be willing to pay more than $10.80 for a perfect forecast of the weather.
The vendor should sell soft drinks to maximize value and minimize loss.
CV(Soft drinks) = $\frac{4.8}{53.6} \cdot 100\% = 8.96\%$
CV(Ice cream) = $\frac{28.8}{51.6} \cdot 100\% = 55.81\%$
Return to risk ratio for soft drinks = 11.1667
Return to risk ratio for ice cream = 1.7917
Based on these revised probabilities, the vendor's decision changes because of the increased likelihood of cool weather given a forecast for cool. Under these conditions, she should sell soft drinks to maximize the expected monetary value and minimize her expected opportunity loss.

17.22 (a) P(favorable | 1,000) = 0.01 P(favorable | 2,000) = 0.01
P(favorable | 5,000) = 0.25 P(favorable | 10,000) = 0.60
P(favorable | 50,000) = 0.99

P(favorable *and* 1,000)   = 0.01(0.45) = 0.0045
P(favorable *and* 2,000)   = 0.01(0.20) = 0.0020
P(favorable *and* 5,000)   = 0.25(0.15) = 0.0375
P(favorable *and* 10,000)   = 0.60(0.10) = 0.0600
P(favorable *and* 50,000)   = 0.99(0.10) = 0.0990

Joint probability table:

	Favorable	Unfavorable	Totals
1,000	0.0045	0.4455	0.45
2,000	0.0020	0.1980	0.20
5,000	0.0375	0.1125	0.15
10,000	0.0600	0.0400	0.10
50,000	0.0990	0.0010	0.10
Totals	0.2030	0.7970	

17.22 (a) Given an unfavorable review, the revised conditional probabilities are:
cont.

$P(1,000 \mid \text{unfavorable})$ = 0.4455/0.7970 = 0.5590
$P(2,000 \mid \text{unfavorable})$ = 0.1980/0.7970 = 0.2484
$P(5,000 \mid \text{unfavorable})$ = 0.1125/0.7970 = 0.1412
$P(10,000 \mid \text{unfavorable})$ = 0.0400/0.7970 = 0.0502
$P(50,000 \mid \text{unfavorable})$ = 0.0010/0.7970 = 0.0013

(b) Payoff table, given unfavorable review:

	Pr	A	B
1,000	0.5590	12,000	6,000
2,000	0.2484	14,000	10,000
5,000	0.1412	20,000	22,000
10,000	0.0502	30,000	42,000
50,000	0.0013	110,000	202,000
	EMV	14,658.60	11,315.4
	σ^2	31,719,333.50	126877326.67
	σ	5,631.99	11263.98
	CV	38.42%	99.55%
	Return to risk	2.6027	1.0046

Opportunity loss table:

	Pr	A	B
Event 1	0.5590	0	6,000
Event 2	0.2484	0	4,000
Event 3	0.1412	2,000	0
Event 4	0.0502	12,000	0
Event 5	0.0013	92,000	0
	EOL	1,004.40	4,347.60

(c) The author's decision is affected by the changed probabilities. Under the new circumstances, signing with company A maximizes the expected monetary value ($14,658.60), minimizes the expected opportunity loss ($1,004.40), minimizes risk with a smaller coefficient of variation and yields a higher return to risk than choosing company B.

17.26 A payoff table presents the alternatives in a tabular format, while the decision tree organizes the alternatives and events visually.

17.28 Since it is the difference between the *highest* possible profit for an event and the actual profit obtained for an action taken. It can never be negative.

17.30 The expected value of perfect information represents the maximum amount you would pay to obtain perfect information. It represents the alternative course of action with the smallest expected opportunity loss. It is also equal to the expected profit under certainty minus the expected monetary value of the best alternative course of action.

17.32   Expected monetary value measures the average return or profit of an alternative course of action over the long run without regard for the variability in the payoffs under different events. The return to risk ratio considers the variability in the payoffs in evaluating which alternative course of action should be chosen.

17.34   A risk averter attempts to reduce risk, while a risk seeker looks for situations which are riskier.

17.36   (a), (c), (g), (h)   Payoff table:

	Pr	A: Buy 6,000	B: Buy 8,000	C: Buy 10,000	D: Buy 12,000
Sell 6,000	0.1	2,100	1,400	700	0
Sell 8,000	0.5	2,100	2,800	2,100	1,400
Sell 10,000	0.3	2,100	2,800	3,500	2,800
Sell 12,000	0.1	2,100	2,800	3,500	4,200
	EMV	2,100	2,660	2,520	1,960
	σ	0	420	896	1,120
	CV	0	15.79%	35.57%	57.14%
	Return to risk	undefined	6.3333	2.8111	1.7500

(d)   Opportunity loss table:

	Pr	A: Buy 6,000	B: Buy 8,000	C: Buy 10,000	D: Buy 12,000
Sell 6,000	0.1	0	700	1,400	2,100
Sell 8,000	0.5	700	0	700	1,400
Sell 10,000	0.3	1,400	700	0	700
Sell 12,000	0.1	2,100	1,400	700	0
	EOL	980	420	560	1,120

(e) $EVPI = \$420$. The management of Shop-Quick Supermarkets should not be willing to pay more than $420 for a perfect forecast.

(f)   To maximize the expected monetary value and minimize expected opportunity loss, the management should buy 8,000 loaves.

(i)   Action B (buying 8,000 loaves) maximizes the return to risk and, while buying 6,000 loaves reduces the coefficient of variation to zero, action B has a smaller coefficient of variation than C or D.

17.36 (k)
cont.

Payoff table:

	Pr	A: Buy 6,000	B: Buy 8,000	C: Buy 10,000	D: Buy 12,000
Sell 6,000	0.3	2,100	1,400	700	0
Sell 8,000	0.4	2,100	2,800	2,100	1,400
Sell 10,000	0.2	2,100	2,800	3,500	2,800
Sell 12,000	0.1	2,100	2,800	3,500	4,200
	EMV	2,100	2,380	2,100	1,540
	σ	0	642	1,084	1,321
	CV	0	26.96%	51.64%	85.76%
	Return to risk	undefined	3.7097	1.9365	1.1660

Opportunity loss table:

	Pr	A: Buy 6,000	B: Buy 8,000	C: Buy 10,000	D: Buy 12,000
Sell 6,000	0.3	0	700	1,400	2,100
Sell 8,000	0.4	700	0	700	1,400
Sell 10,000	0.2	1,400	700	0	700
Sell 12,000	0.1	2,100	1,400	700	0
	EOL	700	490	770	1,330

The management's decision is not affected by the changed probabilities.

17.38 (c), (f) Payoff table:

	Pr	New	Old
Weak	0.3	− 4,000,000	0
Moderate	0.6	1,000,000	0
Strong	0.1	5,000,000	0
EMV		− 100,000	0
σ		2,808,914	0
CV		− 2,808.94%	undefined
Return to risk		− 0.0356	undefined

(b), (d), (e) Opportunity loss table:

	Pr	New	Old
Weak	0.3	4,000,000	0
Moderate	0.6	0	1,000,000
Strong	0.1	0	5,000,000
	EOL	1,200,000	1,100,000

$EVPI = \$1,100,000$. The product manager should not be willing to pay more than $\$1,100,000$ for a perfect forecast.

(g) The product manager should continue to use the old packaging to maximize expected monetary value and to minimize expected opportunity loss and risk.

17.38 (h) cont.

(c), (f)   Payoff table:

	Pr	New	Old
Weak	0.6	– 4,000,000	0
Moderate	0.3	1,000,000	0
Strong	0.1	5,000,000	0
EMV		– 1,600,000	0
σ		3,136,877	0
CV		– 196.05%	undefined
Return to risk		– 0.5101	undefined

(b), (d), (e) Opportunity loss table:

	Pr	New	Old
Weak	0.6	4,000,000	0
Moderate	0.3	0	1,000,000
Strong	0.1	0	5,000,000
EOL		2,400,000	800,000

$EVPI = \$800,000$. The product manager should not be willing to pay more than $800,000 for a perfect forecast.

(g)   The product manager should continue to use the old packaging to maximize expected monetary value and to minimize expected opportunity loss and risk.

(i)   (c), (f)   Payoff table:

	Pr	New	Old
Weak	0.1	– 4,000,000	0
Moderate	0.3	1,000,000	0
Strong	0.6	5,000,000	0
EMV		2,900,000	0
σ		2,913,760.457	0
CV		100.47%	undefined
Return to risk		0.9953	undefined

(b), (d), (e) Opportunity loss table:

	Pr	New	Old
Weak	0.1	4,000,000	0
Moderate	0.3	0	1,000,000
Strong	0.6	0	5,000,000
EOL		400,000	3,300,000

The product manager should use the new packaging to maximize expected monetary value and to minimize expected opportunity loss and risk.

17.38   (j) P(Sales decreased | weak response) = 0.6
cont. P(Sales stayed same | weak response) = 0.3
              P(Sales increased | weak response) = 0.1
              P(Sales decreased | moderate response) = 0.2
              P(Sales stayed same | moderate response) = 0.4
              P(Sales increased | moderate response) = 0.4
              P(Sales decreased | strong response) = 0.05
              P(Sales stayed same | strong response) = 0.35
              P(Sales increased | strong response) = 0.6

              P(Sales decreased *and* weak response) = 0.6(0.3) = 0.18
              P(Sales stayed same *and* weak response) = 0.3(0.3) = 0.09
              P(Sales increased *and* weak response) = 0.1(0.3) = 0.03
              P(Sales decreased *and* moderate response) = 0.2(0.6) = 0.12
              P(Sales stayed same *and* moderate response) = 0.4(0.6) = 0.24
              P(Sales increased *and* moderate response) = 0.4(0.6) = 0.24
              P(Sales decreased *and* strong response) = 0.05(0.1) = 0.005
              P(Sales stayed same *and* strong response) = 0.35(0.1) = 0.035
              P(Sales increased *and* strong response) = 0.6(0.1) = 0.06

Joint probability table:

	Pr	Sales Decrease	Sales Stay Same	Sales Increase
Weak	0.3	0.180	0.090	0.030
Moderate	0.6	0.120	0.240	0.240
Strong	0.1	0.005	0.035	0.060
	Total	0.305	0.365	0.330

(j)   Given the sales stayed the same, the revised conditional probabilities are:

$$P(\text{weak response} \mid \text{sales stayed same}) = \frac{.09}{.365} = 0.2466$$

$$P(\text{moderate response} \mid \text{sales stayed same}) = \frac{.24}{.365} = 0.6575$$

$$P(\text{strong response} \mid \text{sales stayed same}) = \frac{.035}{.365} = 0.0959$$

(k)   (c), (f)   Payoff table:

	Pr	New	Old
Weak	0.2466	– 4,000,000	0
Moderate	0.6575	1,000,000	0
Strong	0.0959	5,000,000	0
EMV		150,600	0
σ		2,641,575.219	0
CV		1,754.03%	undefined
Return to risk		0.0570	undefined

17.38 (k)
cont.

(b), (d), (e)   Opportunity loss table:

	Pr	New	Old
Weak	0.2466	4,000,000	0
Moderate	0.6575	0	1,000,000
Strong	0.0959	0	5,000,000
	EOL	986,400	1,137,000

$EVPI$ = $986,400. The product manager should not be willing to pay more than $986,400 for a perfect forecast.
The product manager should use the new packaging to maximize expected monetary value and to minimize expected opportunity loss and risk.

(l)   Given the sales decreased, the revised conditional probabilities are:

$$P(\text{weak response} \mid \text{sales decreased}) = \frac{.18}{.305} = 0.5902$$

$$P(\text{moderate response} \mid \text{sales decreased}) = \frac{.12}{.305} = 0.3934$$

$$P(\text{strong response} \mid \text{sales decreased}) = \frac{.005}{.305} = 0.0164$$

(m)

(c), (f)   Payoff table:

	Pr	New	Old
Weak	0.5902	− 4,000,000	0
Moderate	0.3934	1,000,000	0
Strong	0.0164	5,000,000	0
	EMV	− 1,885,400	0
	σ	2,586,864.287	0
	CV	− 137.21%	undefined
	Return to risk	− 0.7288	undefined

(b), (d), (e)   Opportunity loss table:

	Pr	New	Old
Weak	0.5902	4,000,000	0
Moderate	0.3934	0	1,000,000
Strong	0.0164	0	5,000,000
	EOL	2,360,800	475,400

$EVPI$ = $475,400. The product manager should not be willing to pay more than $475,400 for a perfect forecast.
The product manager should continue to use the old packaging to maximize expected monetary value.

17.40   (c), (e), (f)   Payoff table:*

	Pr	A: Do Not Call Mechanic	B: Call Mechanic
Very low	0.25	20	100
Low	0.25	100	100
Moderate	0.25	200	100
High	0.25	400	100
	EMV	180	100
	σ	142	0
	CV	78.96%	0
	Return to risk	1.2665	undefined

Note: The payoff here is cost and not profit. The opportunity cost is therefore calculated as the difference between the payoff and the minimum in the same row.

(b), (d)   Opportunity loss table:

	Pr	A: Do Not Call Mechanic	B: Call Mechanic
Very low	0.25	80	0
Low	0.25	0	0
Moderate	0.25	0	100
High	0.25	0	300
	EOL	20	100

(g)   We want to minimize the expected monetary value because it is a cost. To minimize the expected monetary value, call the mechanic.

(h)   Given 2 successes out of 15, the binomial probabilities and their related revised conditional probabilities are:

	Pr	Binomial Probabilities	Revised Conditional Probabilities
Very low	0.01	0.0092	0.0092/0.6418 = 0.0143
Low	0.05	0.1348	0.1348/0.6418 = 0.2100
Moderate	0.10	0.2669	0.2669/0.6418 = 0.4159
High	0.20	0.2309	0.2309/0.6418 = 0.3598
		0.6418	

17.40   (i)
cont.

Payoff table:

	Pr	A: Do Not Call Mechanic	B: Call Mechanic
Very low	0.0144	20	100
Low	0.2100	100	100
Moderate	0.4159	200	100
High	0.3598	400	100
	EMV	248	100
	σ	121	0
	CV	48.68%	0
	Return to risk	2.0544	undefined

Opportunity loss table:

	Pr	A: Do Not Call Mechanic	B: Call Mechanic
Very low	0.0144	80	0
Low	0.2100	0	0
Moderate	0.4159	0	100
High	0.3598	0	300
	EOL	1.15	149.53

We want to minimize the expected monetary value because it is a cost. To minimize the expected monetary value, call the mechanic.

CHAPTER 18

OBJECTIVES
- To understand the basic themes of quality management and Deming's 14 points
- To understand the basic aspects of the Six Sigma Management approach
- To be able to construct various control charts
- To know which control chart to use for a particular type of data
- To be able to measure the capability of a process

OVERVIEW AND KEY CONCEPTS
Themes of Quality Management
1. The primary focus is on process improvement.
2. Most of the variation in a process is due to the system and not the individual.
3. Teamwork is an integral part of a quality management organization.
4. Customer satisfaction is a primary organizational goal.
5. Organizational transformation must occur in order to implement quality management.
6. Fear must be removed from organizations.
7. Higher quality costs less not more but it requires an investment in training.

Deming's 14 Points for Management
1. Create constancy of purpose for improvement of product and service.

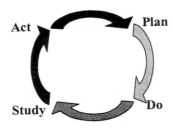

The Shewhart-Deming Cycle
Focuses on Constant Improvement

2. Adopt the new philosophy.
3. Cease dependence on inspection to achieve quality.
4. End the practice of awarding business on the basis of price tag alone. Instead, minimize total cost by working with a single supplier.
5. Improve constantly and forever every process for planning, production and service.
6. Institute training on the job.
7. Adopt and institute leadership.
8. Drive out fear.
9. Break down barriers between staff areas.
10. Eliminate slogans, exhortations, and targets for the workforce.
11. Eliminate numerical quotas for the workforce and numerical goals for management.
12. Remove barriers that rob people of pride of workmanship. Eliminate the annual rating or merit system.
13. Institute a vigorous program of education and self-improvement for everyone.
14. Put everyone in the company to work to accomplish the transformation.

Six Sigma Management

- A method for breaking processes into a series of steps in order to eliminate defects and produce near perfect results.
- Has a clear focus on obtaining bottom-line results in a relatively short three to six-month period of time.
- **The Six Sigma DMAIC model:**
  - **Define:** The problem to be solved needs to be defined along with the costs, benefits of the project, and the impact on the customer.
  - **Measure:** Operational definitions for each Critical-To-Quality (CTQ) characteristic must be developed. In addition, the measurement procedure must be verified so that it is consistent over repeated measurements.
  - **Analyze:** The root causes of why defects can occur need to be determined along with the variables in the process that cause these defects to occur. Data are collected to determine the underlying value for each process variable often using control charts.
  - **Improve:** The importance of each process variable on the CTQ characteristic is studied using designed experiments. The objective is to determine the best level for each variable that can be maintained in the long term.
  - **Control:** The objective is to maintain the gains that have been made with a revised process in the long term by avoiding potential problems that can occur when a process is changed.
- Its implementation requires a data-oriented approach using statistical tools such as control charts and designed experiments.
- Involves training everyone in the company in the DMAIC model.

Control Charts

- The **control chart** is a means of monitoring variation in the characteristic of a product or services by focusing on the time dimension in which the process produces products or services and studying the nature of the variability in the process.
- **Special (assignable) causes of variation:** Large fluctuations or patterns in the data that are not inherent to a process. They are often caused by changes in the process that represents either problems to be fixed or opportunities to exploit.
- **Chance (common) causes of variation:** The inherent variability that exists in a process. These consist of the numerous small causes of variability that operate randomly or by chance.
- An **out-of-control process** contains both common causes of variation and assignable causes of variation. Because assignable causes of variation are not part of the process design, an out-of-control process is unpredictable.
- An **in-control process** contains only common causes of variation. Because theses causes of variation are inherent to the process, an in-control process is predictable. An in-control-process is sometimes said to be in a **state of statistical control**.

- **Control limits:**
  - o Statistical measure of interest $\pm$ 3 standard deviations
- **Identifying pattern in control charts:**

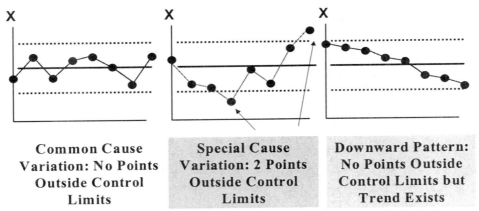

| Common Cause Variation: No Points Outside Control Limits | Special Cause Variation: 2 Points Outside Control Limits | Downward Pattern: No Points Outside Control Limits but Trend Exists |

  - o A trend exists if there are 8 consecutive points above (or below) the centerline or 8 consecutive points that are increasing (or decreasing).
- **The first type of control error:** The belief that observed value represents special cause when in fact it is due to common cause.
- **The second type of control error:** Treating special cause variation as if it is common cause variation.
- When a process is out-of-control, the assignable causes of variation must be identified. If the assignable causes of variation are detrimental to the quality of the product or service, a plan to eliminate this source of variation must be implemented. If an assignable cause of variation increases quality, the process should be change so that it is incorporated into the process design and becomes a common cause source of variation and the process is improved.
- When a process is in control, it must be determined whether the amount of common cause variation in the process is small enough to satisfy the customers of the products or services. If it is small enough to consistently satisfy the customers, the control charts can be used to monitor the process on a continuous basis to make sure that it does not go out-of-control. If it is too large, the process should be altered.

Control Chart for the Proportion of Nonconforming Item (the p Chart)

- It is an attribute chart, which is used when sampled items are classified according to whether they conform or do not conform to operationally defined requirement.
- When used with unequal sample sizes over time, the unequal sample sizes should not differ by more than 25% from average sample size.

- $LCL_p = \max\left(0, \bar{p} - 3\sqrt{\dfrac{\bar{p}(1-\bar{p})}{\bar{n}}}\right)$, $UCL_p = \bar{p} + 3\sqrt{\dfrac{\bar{p}(1-\bar{p})}{\bar{n}}}$

  where

  X_i = number of nonforming items in sample i

  n_i = sample size for sample i

  $p_i = X_i / n_i$ = proportion of nonconforming items in sample i

  $$\bar{n} = \dfrac{\displaystyle\sum_{i=1}^{k} n_i}{k}$$

  $$\bar{p} = \dfrac{\displaystyle\sum_{i=1}^{k} X_i}{\displaystyle\sum_{i=1}^{k} n_i}$$

  k = number of samples

Morals of the Red Bead Example
- Variation is an inherent part of any process.
- The system is primarily responsible for worker performance.
- Only management can change the system.
- Some workers will always be above average and some will be below.

The c Chart
- It is an attribute chart and a control chart for the number of nonconformities (or occurrences) in a unit (called an area of opportunity).
- $LCL_c = \bar{c} - 3\sqrt{\bar{c}}$, $UCL_c = \bar{c} + 3\sqrt{\bar{c}}$

  where

  $$\bar{c} = \dfrac{\displaystyle\sum_{i=1}^{k} c_i}{k}$$

  $\bar{c}$ = average number of occurrences

  k = number of units sampled

  c_i = number of occurrences in unit i

Control Chart for the Range (R) and Mean $(\bar{X})$
- They are variable control charts.
- They are more sensitive in detecting special-cause variation than the p chart.
- They are typically used in pairs
- The R chart monitors the variation in the process while the $\bar{X}$ chart monitors the process average.
- The R chart should be examined first because if it indicates the process is out-of-control, the interpretation of the $\bar{X}$ chart will be misleading.

- **Control chart for the range:**
    - $LCL_R = D_3\bar{R}$, $UCL_R = D_4\bar{R}$
      where

$$\bar{R} = \frac{\sum_{i=1}^{k} R_i}{k}$$

D_3 and D_4 are to obtained from a table.
- **Control chart for the mean:**
    - $LCL_{\bar{X}} = \bar{\bar{X}} - A_2\bar{R}$, $UCL_{\bar{X}} = \bar{\bar{X}} + A_2\bar{R}$
      where

$$\bar{\bar{X}} = \frac{\sum_{i=1}^{k} \bar{X}_i}{k}$$

$$\bar{R} = \frac{\sum_{i=1}^{k} R_i}{k}$$

$\bar{X}$ = the sample mean of n observations at time i

R_i = the range of n observations at time i

k = number of subgroups

and A_2 is to be obtained from a table.

Process Capability
- **Process capability** is the ability of a process to consistently meet specified customer-driven requirement.
- **Specification limits** are technical requirements set by management in response to customer's expectations.
- The **upper specification limit** (*USL*) is the largest value a characteristic of interest can have and still conform to customer's expectation.
- The **lower specification limit** (*LSL*) is the smallest value that is still conforming.

Estimating Process Capability:
- Must have an in-control process first before being able to estimate process capability.
- Estimate process capability by estimating the percentage of product or service within specification.
- **For a characteristic with an *LSL* and a *USL*:**
  P(an outcome will be within specification)

  $= P(LSL < X < USL)$

  $= P\left(\dfrac{LSL - \bar{\bar{X}}}{\bar{R}/d_2} < Z < \dfrac{USL - \bar{\bar{X}}}{\bar{R}/d_2} \right)$

  where Z is the standardized normal random variable.

- **For a characteristic with only an *LSL*:**

  P(an outcome will be within specification)

  $= \text{P}(LSL < X)$

  $= \text{P}\left(\dfrac{LSL - \overline{\overline{X}}}{\overline{R}/d_2} < Z\right)$

- **For a characteristic with only a *USL*:**

  P(an outcome will be within specification)

  $= \text{P}(X < USL)$

  $= \text{P}\left(Z < \dfrac{USL - \overline{\overline{X}}}{\overline{R}/d_2}\right)$

- A **Capability Index** is an aggregate measure of a process' ability to meet specification limits. The larger the value of a capability index, the more capable a process is of meeting customer requirement.

- **To measure a process' potential:**

  - **The C_p index:** $C_p = \dfrac{USL - LSL}{6\left(\overline{R}/d_2\right)} = \dfrac{\text{specification spread}}{\text{process spread}}$

  - C_p is a measure of process potential, not of actual performance, because it does not consider the current process average.

  - $C_p > 1$ indicates that if the process average can be centered, then more than 99.73% of the observations will be inside the specification limits.

  - $C_p < 1$ indicates that the process is not very capable of meeting requirement for even if the process average can be centered, less than 99.73% of the observations will be inside the specification limits.

- **To measure a process' actual performance:**

  - For one-sided specification limits:

    $CPL = \dfrac{\overline{\overline{X}} - LSL}{3\left(\overline{R}/d_2\right)}$

    $CPU = \dfrac{USL - \overline{\overline{X}}}{3\left(\overline{R}/d_2\right)}$

    CPL (*CPU*) >1 implies that the process mean is more than 3 standard deviation away from the lower (upper) specification limit.

  - For two-sided specification limits:

    $C_{pk} = \min\left(CPL, CPU\right)$

    $C_{pk} = 1$ indicates that the process average is 3 standard deviations away from the closest specification limit.

    Larger C_{pk} indicates larger capability of meeting the requirements.

SOLUTIONS TO END OF SECTION
AND CHAPTER REVIEW EVEN PROBLEMS

18.2   (a)   Proportion of nonconformances largest on Day 4, smallest on Day 3.

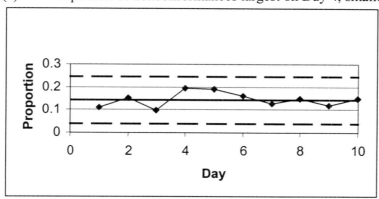

(b) $\overline{n}$ = 1036/10 = 103.6, $\overline{p}$ = 148/1036 = 0.142857,

$$LCL = \overline{p} - 3\sqrt{\frac{\overline{p}(1-\overline{p})}{\overline{n}}} = 0.142857 - 3\sqrt{\frac{0.142857(1-0.142857)}{103.6}} = 0.039719$$

$$UCL = \overline{p} + 3\sqrt{\frac{\overline{p}(1-\overline{p})}{\overline{n}}} = 0.142857 + 3\sqrt{\frac{0.142857(1-0.142857)}{103.6}} = 0.245995$$

(c)   Proportions are within control limits, so there do not appear to be any special causes of variation.

18.4   (a)

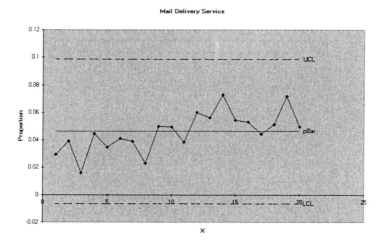

(b)   Although none of the points are outside the control limits, there is evidence of a pattern over time, since the first eight points are all below the center line and most of the later points are above the center line. Thus, the special causes that might be contributing to this pattern should be investigated before any change in the system of operation is contemplated.

18.6   (a) $\bar{n} = 113345/22 = 5152.0455$, $\bar{p} = 1460/113345 = 0.01288$,

$$LCL = \bar{p} - 3\sqrt{\frac{\bar{p}(1-\bar{p})}{\bar{n}}} = 0.01288 - 3\sqrt{\frac{0.01288(1-0.01288)}{5152.0455}} = 0.00817$$

$$UCL = \bar{p} + 3\sqrt{\frac{\bar{p}(1-\bar{p})}{\bar{n}}} = 0.01288 - 3\sqrt{\frac{0.01288(1-0.01288)}{5152.0455}} = 0.01759$$

SPSS output:

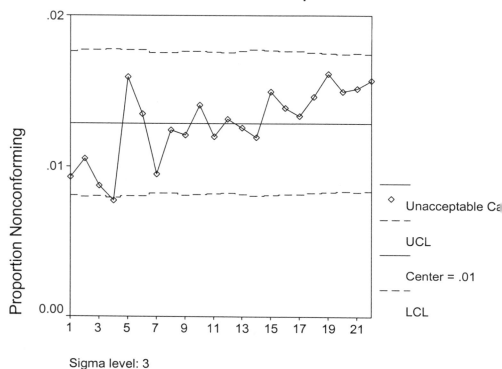

Note: The UCL and LCL are represented by jagged lines. SPSS calculates separate control limits for each day depending on the sample size of that day.
The proportion of unacceptable cans is below the LCL on Day 4. There is evidence of a pattern over time, since the last eight points are all above the mean and most of the earlier points are below the mean. Thus, the special causes that might be contributing to this pattern should be investigated before any change in the system of operation is contemplated.

(b)   Once special causes have been eliminated and the process is stable, Deming's fourteen points should be implemented to improve the system. They might also look at day 4 to see if they could identify and exploit the special cause that led to such a low proportion of defects on that day.

18.8   (a) $\bar{p} = 0.1091$, $LCL = 0.0751$, $UCL = 0.1431$. Points 9, 26, and 30 are above the UCL.

    (b)   First, the reasons for the special cause variation would need to be determined and local corrective action taken. Once special causes have been eliminated and the process is stable, Deming's fourteen points should be implemented to improve the system.

18.12   (a) $\bar{c} = 115/10 = 11.5$, $LCL = \bar{c} - 3\sqrt{\bar{c}} = 11.5 - 3\sqrt{11.5} = 1.32651$
               $UCL = \bar{c} + 3\sqrt{\bar{c}} = 11.5 + 3\sqrt{11.5} = 21.67349$

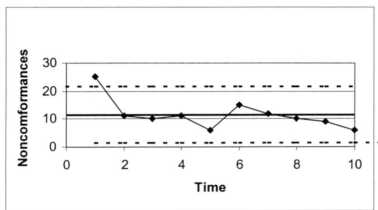

    (b)   Yes, the number of nonconformances per unit for Time Period 1 is above the upper control limit.

18.14   (a)   The twelve errors committed by Gina appear to be much higher than all others, and Gina would need to explain her performance.

    (b) $\bar{c} = 5.5$, $UCL = 12.56$, LCL does not exist. The number of errors is in a state of statistical control since none of the tellers are outside the UCL.

    (c)   Since Gina is within the control limits, she is operating within the system, and should not be singled out for further scrutiny.

    (d)   The process needs to be studied and potentially changed using principles of Six Sigma® management and/or Deming management.

18.16   (a) $\bar{C} = 3.057$

18.16   (b)   Minitab output:
cont.

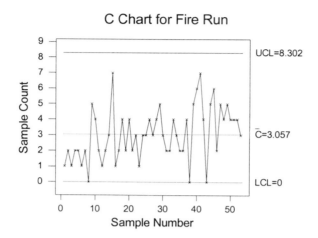

C Chart for Fire Run

(c)   There is evidence of a pattern over time, since the first eight points are all below the
mean. Thus, the special causes that might be contributing to this pattern should be
investigated before any change in the system of operation is contemplated.

(d)   Even though weeks 15 and 41 experienced seven fire runs each, they are both below
the upper control limit. They can, therefore, be explained by chance causes.

(e)   After having identified the special causes that might have contributed to the first
eight points that are below the average, the fire department can use the c-chart to
monitor the process in future weeks in real-time and identify any potential special
causes of variation that might have arisen and could be attributed to increased arson,
severe drought or holiday-related activities.

18.18   (a) $d_2 = 2.059$ (d) $D_4 = 2.282$
         (b) $d_3 = 0.88$ (e) $A_2 = 0.729$
         (c) $D_3 = 0$

18.20   (a) $\overline{R} = 3.34$, $\overline{\overline{X}} = 5.916$. R chart: $UCL = 7.6219$; LCL does not exist.
         $\overline{X}$ chart: $UCL = 8.3511$; $LCL = 3.4814$

18.20   (b)
cont.

SPSS output:

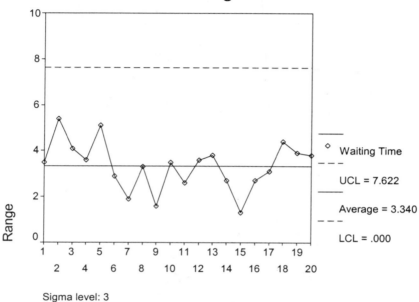

Sigma level: 3

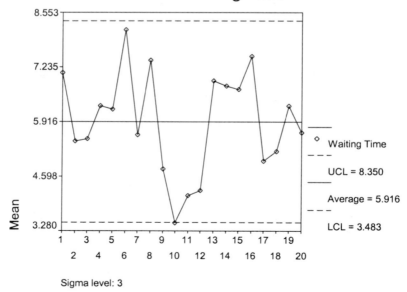

Sigma level: 3

The $\overline{X}$ of sample 10 is slightly below the *LCL*. The process is out-of-control.

18.22   (a) $\overline{R}$ = 0.8794, *R* chart: *UCL* = 2.0068; *LCL* does not exist

R Chart

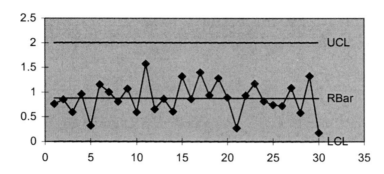

(b) $\overline{\overline{X}}$ = 20.1065, $\overline{X}$ chart: *UCL* = 20.7476; *LCL* = 19.4654

XBar Chart

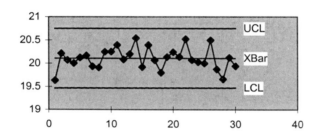

(c)   The process appears to be in control since there are no points outside the lower and upper control limits of both the R-chart and Xbar-chart, and there is no pattern in the results over time.

18.24   (a) $\overline{R}$ = 8.145, $\overline{\overline{X}}$ = 18.12.

R chart: $LCL = D_3 \overline{R} = 0\,(8.145) = 0$. *LCL* does not exist.

$UCL = D_4 \overline{R} = (2.282)\,(8.145) = 18.58689$.

For $\overline{X}$ chart: $LCL = \overline{\overline{X}} - A_2 \overline{R} = 18.12 - (0.729)\,(8.145) = 12.1823$

$UCL = \overline{\overline{X}} + A_2 \overline{R} = 18.12 + (0.729)\,(8.145) = 24.0577$

(b)   There are no sample ranges outside the control limits and there does not appear to be a pattern in the range chart. The sample mean on Day 15 is above the *UCL* and the sample mean on Day 16 is below the *LCL*, which is an indication there is evidence of special cause variation in the sample means.

18.26   (a) $\overline{R} = 0.3022$, R chart: $UCL = 0.6389$; LCL does not exist

$\overline{\overline{X}} = 90.1317$, $\overline{X}$ chart: $UCL = 90.3060$; $LCL = 89.9573$

R Chart

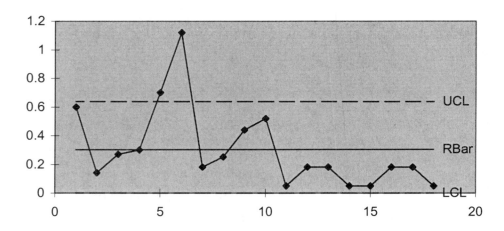

XBar Chart

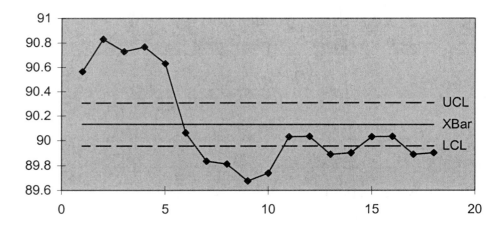

(b)   The R-chart is out-of-control because the 5th and 6th data points fall above the upper
control limit. There is also a downward trend in the right tail of the R-chart, which
signifies that special causes of variation must be identified and corrected. Even
though the X-bar chart also appears to be out-of-control because majority of the data
point fall above or below the control limit, any interpretation will be misleading
because the R-chart has indicated the presence of out-of-control conditions. There is
also a downward trend in the control chart. Special causes of variation should be
investigated and eliminated.

18.28   (a)   Estimate of the population mean = $\overline{\overline{X}} = 100$

Estimate of population standard deviation = $\overline{R}/d_2 = \dfrac{3.386}{1.693} = 2$

$$P(98 < X < 102) = P\left(\frac{98-100}{2} < Z < \frac{102-100}{2}\right) = 0.6827$$

(b) $P(93 < X < 107.5) = P\left(\dfrac{93-100}{2} < Z < \dfrac{107.5-100}{2}\right) = .9997$

(c) $P(X > 93.8) = P\left(Z > \dfrac{93.8-100}{2}\right) = .9990$

(d) $P(X < 110) = P\left(Z < \dfrac{110-100}{2}\right) \cong 1$

18.30   (a) $P(18 < X < 22) = P\left(\dfrac{18-20.1065}{0.8794/2.059} < Z < \dfrac{22-20.1065}{0.8794/2.059}\right)$

$= P(-4.932 < Z < 4.4335) = 0.9999$

(b) $C_p = \dfrac{(USL - LSL)}{6\left(\overline{R}/d_2\right)} = \dfrac{(22-18)}{6(0.8794/2.059)} = 1.56$

$CPL = \dfrac{\left(\overline{\overline{X}} - LSL\right)}{3\left(\overline{R}/d_2\right)} = \dfrac{(20.1065-18)}{3(0.8704/2.059)} = 1.644$

$CPU = \dfrac{\left(USL - \overline{\overline{X}}\right)}{3\left(\overline{R}/d_2\right)} = \dfrac{(22-20.1065)}{3(0.8704/2.059)} = 1.4778$

$C_{pk} = \min(CPL, CPU) = 1.4778$

18.32   (a)

$$P(5.2 < X < 5.8) = P\left(\frac{5.2-5.509}{0.2248/2.059} < Z < \frac{5.8-5.509}{0.2248/2.059}\right)$$

$$= P(-2.830 < Z < 2.665) = 0.9938$$

(b)   According to the estimate in (a), only 99.38% of the tea bags will have weight fall between 5.2 grams and 5.8 grams. The process is, therefore, incapable of meeting the 99.7% goal.

18.34   Chance or common causes of variation represent the inherent variability that exists in a system. These consist of the numerous small causes of variability that operate randomly or by chance. Special or assignable causes of variation represent large fluctuations or patterns in the data that are not inherent to a process. These fluctuations are often caused by changes in a system that represent either problems to be fixed or opportunities to exploit.

18.36   When only common causes of variation are present, it is up to management to change the system.

18.38   Attribute control charts are used for categorical data such as the proportion of
        nonconformances. Variables control charts are used for numerical variables and are based on
        statistics such as the mean and standard deviation.

18.40   From the red bead experiment we learned that variation is an inherent part of any process,
        that workers work within a system over which they have little control, that it is the system
        that primarily determines their performance, and that only management can change the
        system.

18.42   Process potential measures the potential of a process in satisfying production specification
        limits or customer satisfaction but does not take into account the actual performance of the
        process while process performance refers to the actual performance of the process in
        satisfying production specification limits.

18.44   Capability analysis is not performed on out-of-control processes because out-of-control
        processes do not allow one to predict their capability. They are considered incapable of
        meeting specifications and, therefore, incapable of satisfying the production requirement.

18.46   (a)

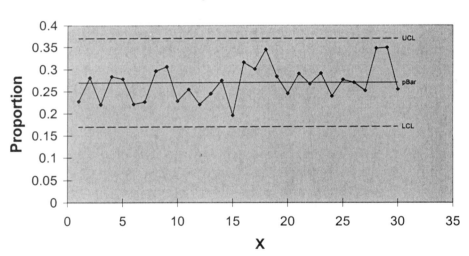

        (b)   Yes, RudyBird's market share is in control before the start of the in-store promotion
                since all sample proportions fall within the control limits.

18.46   (c)
cont.

p Chart

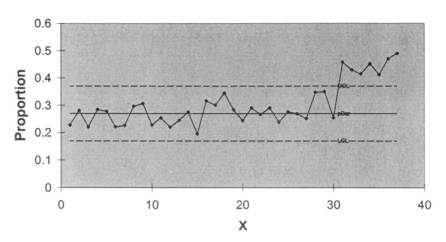

After including the data for days 31-37, there is an apparent upward trend in the p Chart during the promotion period and all the market share proportions in that period are above the upper control limit. The process became out-of-control. This assignable cause variation can be attributed to the in-store promotion. The promotion was successful in increasing the market share of RudyBird.

18.48   (a) $\bar{p} = 0.75175$, $LCL = 0.62215$, $UCL = 0.88135$. Although none of the points are outside either the LCL or UCL, there is a clear pattern over time with lower values occurring in the first half of the sequence and higher values occurring toward the end of the sequence.

(b)   This would explain the pattern in the results over time.

(c)   Had this information been known, separate control charts could have been developed for the two halves of the sequence.

18.50   (a) $\bar{p} = 0.1198$, $LCL = 0.0205$, $UCL = 0.2191$.

(b)   The process is out of statistical control. The proportion of trades that are undesirable is below the LCL on Day 24 and are above the UCL on Day 4.

(c)   Special causes of variation should be investigated and eliminated. Next, process knowledge should be improved to decrease the proportion of trades that are undesirable.